EDWARD ROBINSON SQUIBB

DOCTOR SQUIBB

the life and times
of a
rugged idealist

by

Lawrence G. Blochman

SIMON AND SCHUSTER · NEW YORK · 1958

LIBRARY OF CONGRESS CATALOG CARD NUMBER: 58-11805
MANUFACTURED IN THE UNITED STATES OF AMERICA
BY AMERICAN BOOK—STRATFORD PRESS, INC., NEW YORK

Contents

Acknowledgments

I T WOULD HAVE BEEN impossible to write the story of Dr. Squibb without reading his private journals. The author is therefore grateful to Mr. George S. Squibb, his great-grandson, for access to the half-forgotten journals and other family papers. He would also like to express his thanks to Miss Winifred Sewell, librarian, and Miss Genevieve Ford, archivist of the Library of the Squibb Institute for Medical Research, for their valuable aid in the collection of data; to Mr. Ferdinand W. Nitardy, retired vice-president of E. R. Squibb & Sons, for his diligent accumulation of historical material while some of the principals of the old firm were still alive; to Professor A. B. Nichols of the U. S. Pharmacopoeia for documentation on Dr. Squibb's long association with various revision committees; to Mr. W. R. McHargue, vice-president, and Mr. James V. Shannon, public-relations director, for giving the author free access to company files; to Mr. Joseph Barnes of Simon and Schuster for his editorial advice; and to many others who contributed to the planning and writing of this book.

L.G.B.

Preface

PERHAPS THE MOST remarkable commentary on the remarkable life story of Dr. Edward Robinson Squibb is the fact that it is almost unknown today. His name, of course, is a household word from Maine to Madagascar, but the man who made it so has been until now only a vague shadow to this generation.

Free-association tests today would find most people equating "Squibb" and "toothpaste," even though the firm that bears the Squibb name did not start making toothpaste until twenty-one years after the founder's death.

A hundred years ago "Squibb" meant "ether" to the physicians and apothecaries of the United States. Dr. Squibb was a true pioneer in anesthesia. He received his M.D. degree in 1845, the year before Dr. W. T. G. Morton gave his first public demonstration of the use of ether to eliminate pain in surgery. Thus Dr. Squibb's medical career not only paralleled the birth and growth of the era of anesthetics; at times the two were indistinguishable.

As an assistant surgeon in the United States Navy, Dr. Squibb saw ether used and misused. He noted that its effect varied greatly, and that it was not always successful in producing deep anesthesia. Finding that the variations were a direct result of impurities and of uneven strength, he was the first to devise a method of making pure ether of uniform potency. He also invented a process of distilling ether with live steam, thus eliminating the danger of an open flame to so volatile a liquid.

Once he had standardized the manufacture of ether, he followed his product into the operating room to perfect the techniques of its administration and to study effective dosage. To this end he invented a mask to replace the inhaler of Dr. Morton.

Uniformity and purity became a lifetime passion with Dr. Squibb, a crusade which was to embrace all pharmacy. During his four years aboard the sailing ships of the Brazil and Mediterranean squadrons, he was appalled by the proportion of filthy, adulterated, and mislabeled drugs he was issued for use in the sick bay. Assigned to shore duty, he demonstrated to the Navy that pure drugs could be manufactured for less money than was being paid for inferior and adulterated pharmaceuticals.

Although he left the Navy after ten years, he never left the service of his country—or of humanity. He refused to patent his inventions and discoveries; they belonged to anyone who could benefit by them. He fought desperately to translate his ideals into action, and although frequently defeated, sometimes because of his own uncompromising bluntness, he always came back for more. His battle to revise and universalize the United States Pharmacopoeia—the bible, the vade mecum, and the basic code of ethical American pharmacy— began before the Civil War. During the Lincoln Administration, he rallied the medical societies of the country to demand enforcement of the Act of 1848 prohibiting the import of adulterated drugs. The Squibb-written petition to the President and the Secretary of the Treasury asked the appointment of honest inspectors with some scientific background. When political appointments continued, he attacked the problem on a state level—he wrote a pure-food-and-drug act which became law in New York State in 1880 and in New Jersey shortly thereafter. His efforts to secure similar Federal legislation were hamstrung during his lifetime by one of the first Congressional lobbies in United States history.

When the American Medical Association in 1877 rejected Dr. Squibb's plan to have the physicians take over the Pharmacopoeia—a plan proposed because (according to Squibb) the Pharmaceutical Society had been infiltrated by quacks, mountebanks, and patent-medicine fakers—the physicians also rejected the Squibb proposal to issue a periodical supplement to the Pharmacopoeia which would keep the profession abreast of progress in the medical sciences. Dr. Squibb then founded his own publication, called *An Ephemeris,* written almost entirely by himself, describing and evaluating new medicines, apparatus, and techniques, and swatting charlatans and quack nostrums whenever one raised a greedy head. The A.M.A. *Journal* did not come along until a year later.

When a vocal, organized minority of the New York State Medical Society voted to vitiate its own code of ethics and let down the bars to quacks, Dr. Squibb recorded the vote of each delegate in his *An Ephemeris* and sponsored a new society composed of physicians who favored an ethical code.

He never stopped fighting for nationwide regulation of food and drugs to insure their purity and conformance to label. Although the political atmosphere in Washington was hostile to the realization of his dream during his lifetime, his ideals survived him. A young Indiana chemist, a fellow member of the American Chemical Society, carried on where he had left off. Thirty years after their first meeting and six years after Dr. Squibb's death, Dr. Harvey W. Wiley, with the blessing of President Theodore Roosevelt, won Congressional approval for a Federal pure-food-and-drug law.

The story of Dr. Squibb the crusader is recorded in the proceedings of the many medical and scientific societies to which he belonged, and upon the statute books.

The story of Dr. Squibb the manufacturing pharmacist to the medical profession is told in the many thousands of pages of his own *An Ephemeris,* in the papers he read before scientific groups or contributed to professional journals (he wrote more than a hundred papers for the *American Journal of Pharmacy* and the Pharmaceutical Association alone), and in the imprint he left upon the United States Pharmacopoeia.

The story of Dr. Squibb the man, however, has until very recently been gathering dust in the attic of the suburban New York home of Mr. George S. Squibb, his great-grandson. That story was recorded by Dr. Squibb in detail and in his own hand. Dr. Squibb left a private journal which, because it was intended for the eyes of no one but himself, has remained strictly a family document until now.

Dr. Squibb was a diarist of great energy and peculiar ability. He wrote down everything he did or thought during his adult life, filling a dozen thick thirteen-by-eight-inch ledgers with thousands of pages of his clear, bold, copperplate script. His journals sweep through more than half a century (Pepys gave up after nine years), from the end of the Mexican War to a few days before his death in the last year of the nineteenth century. Only a year or so are blank, because the volumes recording them were evidently burned in the fire which destroyed Dr. Squibb's Brooklyn laboratory a hundred years ago. Two of the volumes graciously made available to this biographer by Mr. George Squibb are badly burned along the edges, a reminder that Dr. Squibb nearly lost his life in saving them.

The Squibb journals have an amazing scope. The doctor's interests were multiple, his curiosity sharp, his tastes catholic. His indignant record of health and routine in the wooden ships of the nineteenth-century Navy shares space with his reflections on European political trends, Italian opera, and the mores of American sailors. His notes of lectures during his refresher course at Jefferson Medical College are interspersed with vignettes of his professors, a fire buff's view of Philadelphia's most spectacular conflagrations, comment on the joys of eating oysters, and a philosophic treatise on woman's role in marriage. Detailed descriptions of his early experiments with ether and chloroform (with costs figured to the last penny) are mingled with his thoughts on religion and the limitations of its ministers, drama criticism, the problems of parenthood, and his heartbreaking, nerve-wracking concern over his wife's health. The pages of the journals are interlarded with pressed flowers from the ruins of Pompeii, theater programs, summonses to jury duty, hotel bills from a Vermont summer resort, newspaper clippings, invitations to the dedication of the Statue of Liberty and the opening of the Brooklyn Bridge, snatches of verse (clipped from the *Journal of Commerce*), and letters from his children and grandchildren. The whole constitutes a personal and sharply observed panorama of nineteenth-century Philadelphia, New York, and Brooklyn, a critical appraisal of the state of American medicine a century ago, and a vivid self-portrait of Dr. Squibb the man.

From his own words Dr. Squibb emerges as a rugged idealist who was constantly at war with a materialistic world, a man of great integrity who could not abide sham or dishonesty, not even as a means to a worthy end; a perfectionist aware of his own imperfections yet intolerant of weakness in others. Though inherently a kindly man, he urged the retention of flogging in the Navy and whipped his own children soundly when they deviated from the truth. A Godfearing man, he was often at odds with the men of God. An impolitic person, he never hesitated to charge head down into a political situation on behalf of a principle. Very much in love with his young bride, he was unhappy to discover, after the honeymoon was over, that he had not married the paragon he had always imagined he was waiting for. But though he grumbled to his diary, he spent sleepless nights watching over her and humored her slightest whim. When he laid down the law as lord and master of the manor, she merely smiled and did what she wanted. His children also listened obediently to paternal advice and did the contrary. His high-mindedness was not contagious at short range.

It is a very human story that emerges from the voluminous, frank, and intimate Squibb journals. Uncut, they would fill at least twenty volumes like this one. They have been edited for space, of course, and for pertinence. They have been para-phrased when economy so dictated. They have been counter-balanced by quotes and facts from other contemporary sources. But the author has, as far as practical, let Dr. Squibb tell his own story in his own words, with all his idiosyncrasies and his personal syntax, his prayers and his gripes, his tri-umphs and his sorrows. It is a story well worth the telling.

LAWRENCE G. BLOCHMAN

New York City,
February 17, 1958

one

SEAGOING QUAKER

I

THE YOUNG PHYSICIAN had a hard time making up his mind. The country was at war. The streets of Philadelphia were gay with naval uniforms. The river front at the Navy Yard was a forest of tall masts rising from a haze of rigging where the frigates and sloops of war were moored, refitting for sea. The exciting, big-bosomed silhouette of a full-rigged ship of the line, swelling with pride as she caught the wind that blew to combat, had become a familiar sight on the Delaware.

Young Dr. Squibb was just as vague as other Philadelphians about the justice or causes of the Mexican War. He had no opinion on the Texas boundary dispute and little interest in the future of distant California. Neither did many of his hundred and fifty classmates, the fledgling M.D.s of the class of 1845, Jefferson Medical College. Yet dozens of them had joined the Navy as assistant surgeons, drawn by the call of high adventure, the magic spell of far places, and the comfortable prospect of being fed and clothed and sheltered while gaining priceless professional experience.

The practical and medical aspects of a naval career were not particularly attractive to Dr. Squibb. He already had a large if unremunerative practice among his numerous relatives, as well as a small but growing number of paying patients. He had a living from his alma mater, for Jefferson Medical College had retained him after graduation as clerk of clinics, assistant demonstrator of anatomy, and curator of the college medical museum. With his friend and classmate, Dr. Samuel G. White, he was also running a tutoring course which netted $30 a student for lectures and sample examinations given five nights a week and Saturday mornings. But Squibb longed to go to sea with his classmates. He, too, dreamed of the romance of strange lands, the vastness of the seven seas, the beauty and grace of a ship under full sail. There was only one thing that held him back: Edward Robinson Squibb was a Quaker.

Quakers do not make war.

Quakers do not take oaths.

Dr. Squibb could not remain a member of the Society of Friends if he joined the armed forces and took an oath to defend the Constitution of the United States against all enemies.

The decision that he would have to make would of course affect his conscience, his career, his whole life. It was also destined to influence an important aspect of the life of the nation.

II

EDWARD ROBINSON SQUIBB was not just any Quaker. His ancestors had crossed the Atlantic with William Penn, and the Squibbs, charter members of the Society of Friends in America, were consequently of the Quaker aristocracy.

The earliest known English Squibb is believed to have been made a yeoman by Edward IV in the fifteenth century. His grandson was Great John the Yeoman of Dorsetshire. Great John's grandson, Nathaniel Squibb, came to Pennsylvania early in the eighteenth century, settled in Chester County, and founded a populous family which during the following century intermarried with other early settlers like the Robinsons (Francis and Elizabeth Robinson came from England to

Pennsylvania at about the same time as Nathaniel Squibb)
and the Hamiltons, who came from Derby, England, to
Darby, Pennsylvania. Rachel Robinson Hamilton, for example, was the grandmother of Dr. Squibb's father, James
Robinson Squibb.

James Squibb for some reason broke away from the Squibb
country around Philadelphia and migrated downstream to
Wilmington, Delaware, where son Edward was born.

Edward Robinson Squibb was probably born during the
night of July 4–5, 1819. He himself always claimed the Fourth
of July as his birthday, although the records of both the Wilmington Meeting of Friends and the Pennsylvania Genealogi-
cal Society show his birth date as July 5. He was a first child.

His mother, Catherine Harrison Bonsall, was the fourth
generation of the family of Samuel Bunting, who came from
Derbyshire, England, to Darby, Pennsylvania, in 1722. Catherine Squibb gave birth to two sons and three daughters and
died shortly after the death of all three girls in one year, 1831.

After their mother's death, the two surviving Squibb children, Edward, then twelve, and his younger brother Robert,
accompanied their father to the Philadelphia region, which
was densely populated by relatives. Grandmother Squibb,
who was living in Cherry Street, in Philadelphia proper, took
her son James and grandson Robert to live with her while
another son, Jacob Squibb, found work for James. Edward
was sent to live with Grandmother Bonsall in suburban
Darby. Both grandmothers were to have great influence on
Edward's life. Since his father a few years later suffered a
stroke which left him an ineffectual invalid for the rest of his
days, Grandmother Squibb and Grandmother Bonsall were
to serve as both mother and father to him.

At the time the Wilmington Squibbs moved to the Philadelphia region, the American Society of Friends was divided into
two camps: the Orthodox, which was similar in doctrine to
most evangelical Christian churches, with strong emphasis
on the personal presence of Jesus and even more reliance on
the guidance of the Holy Spirit; and the Hicksites, followers

of Elias Hicks, a Long Islander who turned the Quaker custom of "every man his own preacher" into the leadership of a sect with views closer to those of the Unitarians. Although Edward Squibb was an alert and intelligent boy, it is highly improbable that he was aware of the difference between the Orthodox and Hicksite approaches to Quakerism. If he was, at the age of twelve he was neutral.

When a Friend changed his residence, it was customary for him to carry a letter attesting to his good standing in the local meeting so that the meeting in his new home might welcome him as a member. Playing no favorites, when Edward Squibb went to live with Grandmother Bonsall he carried letters from both groups. On September 26, 1831, the Orthodox Wilmington Monthly Meeting addressed the Orthodox Meeting in Darby as follows:

DEAR FRIENDS:
Request has been made for a certificate for Edward Squibb, a minor, who has removed from ours to reside within the limits of your meeting. We accordingly recommend him a member of our Society to your Christian care and regard, and are your Friends.

Signed in, and by direction
of Wilmington Monthly Meeting
of Friends held 9mo 26th 1831.

JOHN W. TATUM, Clk.

A few months later a similar certificate was addressed by the Hicksite Meeting of Wilmington to the Hicksite Meeting of Darby.

Apparently four years of growing up while attending both meetings swung the balance in favor of the schismatic group, for when eighteen-year-old Edward Squibb took up residence in Philadelphia proper in September 1835, it was the Darby Hicksite Meeting he asked to certify him to the Cherry Street Meeting in Philadelphia. Only two years later did he ask the Darby Orthodox Friends to certify him to the Orthodox Meeting in town.

This was in 1837, an important year in Edward Squibb's

life, although he may not have realized it at the time. In 1837 he took a part-time job to defray his current school expenses and to provide tuition for the medical education he had decided should be his. He was first apprenticed to Warder Morris, a Philadelphia pharmacist, and when he had learned the art of grinding crude drugs, mixing elixirs and compounding powders, he went to work for the pharmaceutical house of J. H. Sprague.

He entered Jefferson Medical College in 1842, as he had planned, and three years later, at the age of twenty-six, received his M.D. degree. But his five years learning the drug business from Messrs. Morris and Sprague not only were to give a new direction to his life, but would also affect the future of the pharmaceutical industry in the United States.

III

EDWARD ROBINSON SQUIBB's Quaker boyhood and formative years in Wilmington endowed him with a Gothic sense of justice, a passionate love of truth, a reverence for the Almighty which included a literal acceptance of His word and an intolerant puritanical scale of moral values, and a Victorian attitude toward women which did not quite match the liberal, equal-rights views of the Society of Friends.

Boyhood on the Delaware estuary also left him with a nostalgic fondness for the smell of tidewater, a great liking for terrapin in any form, and what amounted almost to a passion for Chesapeake Bay oysters. It was partly to indulge his taste for oysters and terrapin (plus a more recent appreciation of Aunt Mary Bonsall's mince pies) and partly to debate the question of the Society of Friends vs. the United States Navy with Grandmother Bonsall and her various descendants and collateral relatives that Dr. Squibb went to Darby on Christmas Day, 1846.

A bitter wind was sweeping dust clouds through the cold, unpaved streets of Philadelphia that Christmas morning as Edward Squibb left the lodgings at 294 Chestnut Street, above

Eleventh Street, which he shared with his classmate Dr. White. Except for a few shivering pedestrians, the streets were deserted as he walked to the stage office, stopping on the way at Oliver's confectionery to buy some bonbons for the many children at Darby.

He caught the nine o'clock stage and should have reached Darby before ten-thirty had not the driver stopped at Sorrel House Tavern, where a hot toddy helped Dr. Squibb thaw out a little. He did not reach his destination until after eleven.

Christmas dinner was, to use Dr. Squibb's word, "capital," but the family counsel on the subject of naval service for a Quaker was inconclusive. Uncle Edmund Bonsall quoted the seventeenth-century declaration of the English Quakers to Charles II: "We utterly deny all outward wars and strife, and fighting with outward weapons, for any end, or under any pretense whatever; this is our testimony to the whole world." There was nothing equivocal, he pointed out, about this fundamental testimony.

Josiah Hoopes, the nurseryman, who was related through the Hamiltons and whose mother was Sarah Hoopes, the celebrated Friends preacher, remembered that William Penn had once said, "A good end cannot sanctify evil means. . . . Force may subdue, but love gains; and he that forgives first, wins the laurel."

Aunt Hannah thought that since Edward would be a ship's doctor—if he *should* decide to go to sea—and therefore would be healing people instead of killing them, maybe his joining the Navy would not be quite the same thing as making war.

Complete nonsense, said Joseph Dodgson, who thought he had surprised his daugher Martha casting admiring glances in Cousin Edward's direction and who wanted no renegades in the family. Once a man donned the uniform of an officer of the Navy, there was nothing for his Meeting to do but disown him.

Grandma Bonsall spoke only once. "Thee must decide for thyself, child," she said.

Aunt Mary Bonsall merely cut another piece of mince pie for her nephew.

In Philadelphia next day young Dr. Squibb consulted Uncle Jacob Squibb at Sprague's store. Uncle Jake had always been ready to lend the young man a dollar or two in a moment of need, and he was even more generous with advice. He asked a few questions on the subject of pay. When he learned that an assistant surgeon on sea duty received only $1,700 per annum for the first five years of service, Uncle Jake concluded that it would be a cardinal violation of the Peace Testimony to join the Navy, even as a doctor.

The young man did not consult his brother Robert, who was working at the Altemus book bindery, or his father, whom he had been helping to support during six years of helpless illness. Neither did he seek advice from Grandmother Squibb, although the counsel she offered impressed him greatly.

"I have always known thee as a God-fearing Christian lad and a good Friend," she said. "Thee has only to decide which thee would serve—God and thy conscience or the monthly Meeting."

He made up his mind the first week in January 1847. He had been discussing his problem with his friend Sam White over two dozen Chincoteagues in Davy Gibbs's Oyster Cellar in Chestnut Street. Young Dr. White had no such problem. Although he, too, was drawn to the sea, he was going home to his family plantation in Georgia. Milledgeville, he had decided, needed another doctor more than did the United States Navy.

When they had finished their oysters, the two medicos took a walk which, either by accident or by Sam White's design, led past Mattson's tailor shop. There was a smart-looking naval uniform in Mattson's window. Dr. Squibb was a handsome young man and he was certainly aware of the fact that he would indeed make a striking officer in a Mattson's uniform.

Dr. White must have seen a look of resolution come into his friend's eyes, for he held out his hand and said:

"Best of luck, Ed. When you get back and find you need money to get you started in practice again, don't hesitate to call on me. The Whites have it."

Next day Dr. Edward Robinson Squibb began filling out papers applying for appointment as assistant surgeon in the United States Navy.

IV

DR. SQUIBB'S APPLICATION was an impressive document. When he presented it to Commodore Stewart at Philadelphia Navy Yard, it was accompanied by letters of recommendation from such notables as Surgeon John A. Kearney of the United States Navy and Dr. Franklin Bache, grandson of Benjamin Franklin and young Squibb's chemistry professor at Jefferson Medical College.

Before Squibb was granted permission to appear before the Naval Medical Board of Examination, General Zachary Taylor had begun his overland invasion of Mexico from the north and had defeated the Mexicans at Buena Vista. On March 10, however, Dr. Squibb was summoned to the Philadelphia Naval Asylum and given his examination. He passed fourth highest.

On March 27, under cover of the Gulf Squadron (Flagship, U. S. Frigate *Cumberland,* flying the flag of Commodore George Read) General Winfield Scott captured Vera Cruz. A month later, on April 26, Dr. Squibb was notified of his appointment as assistant surgeon and ordered to report aboard the brig *Perry* at Philadelphia.

Luckily, Mattson's had already been working on his uniforms, so the new assistant surgeon was able to go aboard the *Perry* on May 4, ready for duty.

He was an attractive young officer. His oval face tapered from a broad forehead to a round chin. His full lips were framed by pronounced rictus furrows and a long, deep dimple on his upper lip. There was a humorous tilt to the tip of his nose and an eternal question in his frank, intelligent blue eyes. He wore his wavy light brown hair parted on the right side and combed long over his temples, almost to the lobes of his prominent ears. There was plenty of gold ornament on his high-crowned, short-visored uniform cap, although the braid on his sleeve was only silk. His pleated white shirt had a turn-down collar almost hidden by his huge black bow tie. His jacket boasted a velvet collar and lapels six inches wide. There were lapels on his uniform vest, too, and eight brass buttons, the top two of which he left unbuttoned. The loop of his heavy gold watch chain was caught in the second.

When the *Perry* sailed from Philadelphia on May 16, Assistant Surgeon Squibb had not yet been officially commissioned. The Mexican War was over, the peace treaty practically concluded, before Dr. Squibb's commission as a naval officer had been signed by President James K. Polk, countersigned by James Young Mason, Secretary of the Navy, and ratified by the Senate on January 19, 1848.

The brig *Perry* was at sea for two years, three months, and seventeen days before returning to home waters. It had put in at Vera Cruz for a rendezvous with the Gulf Squadron, but by that time General Scott was well on his way to the envelopment of Mexico City, and there was no longer much activity on the coast. The *Perry* then proceeded to Rio de Janeiro to join the Brazil Squadron, principal objective of which was to break up illicit slave traffic under the Act of 1819.

If Dr. Squibb kept a personal log of the cruise of the *Perry*, as he did of subsequent cruises, it has long since disappeared. We do know, however, that the *Perry*'s tour of duty consisted largely in patrolling the equatorial Atlantic between the bulge of Brazil and the bulge of tropical Africa, pursuing the swift, clipper-built slave ships and protecting the legitimate trade of the newborn Republic of Liberia, then scarcely a year old. It was an active two years, and while the *Perry* may not have been as busy as the sloop of war *Cyane*, ace interceptor of the squadron with seven "blackbirders" to her credit, it was an exciting way for a new assistant naval surgeon to get his sea legs.

9

The *Perry* was just the kind of craft to put a quick crust of salt and barnacles on the hide of a Quaker landlubber. She was a mere cockleshell of a boat, just 280 tons and carrying but ten guns. She sat low in the water and when she was running before the wind in a heavy sea, with full canvas on both masts, her flying jib taut and her spanker set, she was certain to sail her leeward rail under. Although a fairly new ship— she was only four years old when Dr. Squibb came aboard— she already had a history. In 1844 she had brought Caleb Cushing home from Canton with the first commercial treaty between the United States and China.

The *Perry* returned to American waters and dropped anchor at Hampton Roads, Virginia, on July 10, 1849. Two days later the brig was paid off at Norfolk and on Saturday, July 14, Dr. Squibb left for Philadelphia on a theoretical three-month leave.

When he got home he found that during his absence he had been disowned by the Philadelphia Orthodox Meeting of Friends—for being a Hicksite!

The Cherry Street Meeting had also disowned him, but on the grounds that being a naval surgeon was a violation of the Quaker Peace Testimony. The Hicksite Friends, however, had taken a long time to reach that conclusion. The vote to disown Dr. Squibb had not been taken until April 25, 1849— two years after he had been notified of his appointment to the Navy.

Edward Squibb received the news of his rejection by his coreligionists with great equanimity. He was at peace with his conscience and his God. He had done no violence to the ideal of peace. He had helped those who were fighting the slave trade. He had fulfilled a humanitarian mission of binding up wounds and healing the sick. He had done harm to no man.

He held no rancor for the Friends who had sat in judgment upon him and cast him from their midst. He was tolerant of their presumption that they could stand between him and his God. On his first Sunday at home, accompanied by many of his numerous relatives, he made a point of attending the Darby Meeting of Friends.

V

THE NAVY'S PROMISED three months' leave turned out to be three weeks. On August 8, Assistant Surgeon Squibb was ordered to report to Captain McKeever, commandant of Brooklyn Navy Yard, for duty aboard the storeship *Erie*. He reported three days later and spent another three weeks fitting up the sick bay and stocking the dispensary, not only for the *Erie*'s own needs but also to supply the Mediterranean Squadron. On September 5 the *Erie* sailed from New York for the Mediterranean.

His second cruise found the assistant surgeon a salty, weather-wise, duty-seasoned blue-water sailor. His self-assurance, justified though it was, was surely taken for cockiness by many of his shipmates. He had strong and stubborn opinions about everything and everybody and made no effort to keep them secret. Aware of the gaps in his own experience and education, he worked constantly and systematically to fill them. But to hide the gaps from others, he was sometimes as arrogant as only youth can be. Rank was no protection from the lash of his quick, frank tongue. He respected authority only when it was accompanied by competence. And as the United States Naval Academy had been founded at Annapolis only four years earlier, competence was not yet standard equipment for officers of the Navy. The captain of the *Erie* inspired Dr. Squibb only with "absolute contempt."

A detailed appraisal of the characters and ability of the *Erie*'s complement is recorded in the journal which Dr. Squibb began on his Mediterranean cruise and continued faithfully until a few days before his death. Always a man who combined tremendous drive with precise method, he would record every thought, observation, opinion, and emotion of the day, filling page after page of a big ledger with neat, even lines of bold, copperplate script. Thoroughly nautical by now, he would conclude each entry with a record of the weather, the sea, and the ship's position at noon.

True, his duties in the sick bay of the *Erie* were not a great drain on his time and talents as assistant surgeon. The *Erie* was a small ship of some six hundred tons displacement, four guns (largely for ornament), a crew of only thirty-four, and a dozen passengers apparently bound for Europe on government business. Dr. Squibb kept a meticulous medical log, however, in addition to keeping the accounts of the officers' mess, for the wardroom had elected him "caterer," the nineteenth-century equivalent of mess officer.

His spare time was carefully rationed. His reading was methodically apportioned to the contemporary Macaulay and the already classic Gibbon (to give him historical background for the unknown continent he was about to discover); *Les Contes de l'Atelier* by a French author named Masson (to give him a new language); Butler's *Analogy* (the better to "comprehend the evidences of Christianity"); and finally the New Testament. ("The Acts," he wrote after one session with the Apostles, "was evidently not written by any of the recognized writers of the New Testament, for the style and diction as well as the orthography are unique. It bears the stamp of human nature more strongly than either of the Gospels, and in many points gives evidence of that spirit which has since divided Christianity into its various sects, and what is worse, perhaps, embitters them against each other . . .")

Time not utilized officially or in reading was also carefully scheduled. After meals the assistant surgeon usually allowed himself a few games of chess—with Fauntleroy, the executive officer, a man "with forcible and sustained prejudices . . . an inordinate profanity and ribaldry in expression," and a habit of singing, whistling, and drumming on the chessboard which often put Dr. Squibb off his game; with a mathematics professor named Yarnall; and, for the first twenty-eight days of the voyage from New York, with Mr. Horatio J. Perry, secretary to the Legation of the United States at the Court of Their Catholic Majesties, for whose express benefit the

Erie was calling at Cadiz. Dr. Squibb did not greatly enjoy chess with Mr. Perry, even when winning, because usually Mr. Perry "generously attributed my having beaten him to his unusually bad playing."

From sundown to tea, the young doctor habitually took his "solitary promenade on deck, with my most companionable thoughts of far-off home." When he departed from his schedule, he was bothered with guilt feelings. Every Saturday evening was "Sweethearts and Wives Night" in the *Erie*'s wardroom, and on one occasion the assistant surgeon reproached himself because after "the usual quantity of sardines, toddy, sweetmeats, &c was consumed at tea," he was "seduced into smoking a cigar and talking away most of the evening on deck, planning a trip to Leghorn, Pisa, Florence, and perhaps Genoa, should fortune favour us."

Fortune did not favor the *Erie* at Cadiz. Neither Mr. Horatio J. Perry nor any member of the ship's company was allowed to land. When the supply ship anchored outside the Spanish port, the Cadiz health authorities were holding all foreign-flag ships in quarantine because of "the cholera." Early on the afternoon of October 4, according to Dr. Squibb, "a pilot came alongside and asked in bad English whence we had come. Mr. Perry with his usual self-consideration answered before anyone else with the very definite word 'America'; this the poor pilot mistook for 'Malaga' and at once came on board. Soon the health officer came alongside and informed us that we could not land on account of quarantine and that we could therefore proceed or remain on board at anchor. . . . The communication took place at a distance and the scrap of paper on which the names of the ship and commander were written had to be placed in a bucket of vinegar and water from which the officer took it."

So the *Erie* went on to Gibraltar, carrying with it Secretary of Legation Perry as well as the unfortunate pilot, who had nothing with him—no money or change of clothes—"save a few paper cigars."

At eleven that night the *Erie* was furrowing the historic

waters of the Battle of Trafalgar, a fact duly noted by Dr.
Squibb.

VI

ALTHOUGH THE LIGHT gave out in Dr. Squibb's cabin before
he had finished his late reading, it is doubtful if he slept much
that night. The exciting prospect of setting foot for the first
time on European soil, the sense of entering upon the continuity of history, was terribly stimulating to the assistant
surgeon.

The Europe he was approaching was in a state of flux. For
more than a year the Continent had been swept by unrest and
revolution. From Ireland to Lombardy, peoples had been
smitten by a feverish, epidemic desire for freedom, and there
was bloodletting by the leeches of status quo. Louis Philippe
had been dethroned in France and the Second Republic declared. Ferdinand I had abdicated the Austrian throne in
favor of Franz Josef I, and Lajos Kossuth had declared the
independence of Hungary. There was trouble in Venice, in
Denmark, and in Schleswig-Holstein.

Although the Hungarian bid for freedom caught Dr.
Squibb's imagination most vividly, perhaps because of the
personality of Kossuth, he was more than vaguely aware of
the whole world situation. And as he gazed at the Rock of
Gibraltar during the five days the *Erie* lay in quarantine in
Gibraltar Bay, he did not hesitate to record his thoughts on
global politics or to assay the strategic value of the Straits in
terms of the alignment of nations he knew only at second
hand.

After musing upon the fact that for a long time even the
English had not fully realized the value of Gibraltar, inasmuch as George I had been ready to give it up at the Peace of
Utrecht as a barren, useless rock, Dr. Squibb wrote in his
journal:

"Now on the other hand its value is overrated, for combinations and treaties and alliances between nations are and prob-

ably always will be a check upon the power or oppression of anyone whenever such may be attempted. Thus if Gibraltar, or even England and Gibraltar were both sunk in the sea, with all their boasting, Italy, the Germanic Confederation, even the Northern Powers, would one or all forever prevent the conquest of Spain and Portugal by France or Barbary. 'Balance of Power' is now too well understood and appreciated ever to allow of great extension of conquest on the part of any nation for the future."

Aside from its military significance, Dr. Squibb also realized that Gibraltar was the spot where the War of 1812 was until recently still being fought in miniature, although Gibraltar was "the place where English officers were taught to be more civil and more sparing in their spiteful, opprobrious epithets toward our officers and countrymen after the last war. This lesson they learned upon their own impregnable ground. Our Mediterranean ships at that time frequently came in here to buy supplies, and as the officers were very commonly insulted in the streets, duels were by no means uncommon and generally terminated in favour of our side."

As an example, Dr. Squibb related a story of the last visit of the *Erie* to Gibraltar, when its commander was the then Captain, now Commodore, Robert Stockton, who had since distinguished himself in helping wrest California from Mexico. In order to avenge a gross insult by an English officer to the American consul "who was a peaceable old man of family and did not resent the affront," Stockton challenged the officer to a duel. Before he had finally received satisfaction, the "fire-eating commodore" had killed one Englishman, maimed another, and "challenged the whole regiment for their dishonor and bad faith to him."

The American consul who greeted the *Erie* in quarantine in 1849 was "young, good-looking, and gentlemanly" and arranged to supply the ship "with a profusion of fresh provisions and fruit, the grapes, apples, and pomgranites [sic] being very fine. In consequence of this kindness we had a delightful fresh dinner of which I partook greatly to my detriment, not having felt well since. I do wish I could learn to control my appetite."

As the quarantine period dragged on, more and more fresh foods came aboard—figs and oranges, and beef from Barbary which was "tolerably good." The complicated process of transacting business in quarantine was described by Dr. Squibb as follows: "A health officer comes in every boat and always sees that the baskets in which things are brought on board are thrown overboard and well soaked before he admits them to be touched by the boatmen. The money paid for the provisions is dropped in a bucket of salt water and allowed to remain there for some time before they will touch it."

The last hours of quarantine were increasingly trying to the taut tempers of the ship's company. Dr. Squibb was successively tried in each of his various shipboard roles. As medical officer he complained that he had to devote too much time to "making palatable dyspeptic lozenges for the Purser, who over eats and drinks himself and has in consequence a dyspepsia of which he complains bitterly but which in all probability has saved him from dying of apoplexy of which he is the personification."

As mess officer, Squibb had a long and acrimonious argument with Horatio J. Perry, about to leave the ship, over the amount of his wardroom food bill for thirty-four days.

In the same capacity he became involved in an incident with the captain and the executive officer which brought his relations with his commander a step nearer the breaking point. As caterer, Dr. Squibb had ordered the mess boys to serve the passengers first, as they did not properly belong to the mess and therefore should be considered as guests, and to serve the officers afterward in order of rank.

"Now the captain's ideas of politeness and good breeding are that he should be served first," wrote Dr. Squibb, "and he consequently threatened to whip one of the servants for passing by him with a cup of tea, when Fauntleroy spoke and ordered the servant to help the captain first always. After tea I went to Fauntleroy and told him that he had formally reversed an order which I had been at some trouble to enforce and that I should certainly resign as caterer rather than submit to the course of which this seemed to be the precedent. That the captain . . . as a member of the mess must submit to the regulations of the mess."

Next day the caterer had a talk with Captain Porter on the subject of good breeding. "The result of this interview was perfectly amicable and good humoured, with a clear impression on the captain's mind that so long as I was caterer, my code was established for observation."

Release from quarantine relieved tension all around and made for four days of frantic activity ashore. Dr. Squibb attacked the business of sight-seeing with the eager enthusiasm of a schoolboy and the naïve, openmouthed wonder of any American tourist on his first trip abroad. His journal echoed with double adjectives and bristled with exclamation points as he dashed from landmark to landmark, recording the sights and sounds of streets, bazaar and garrison, describing in detail the motley populations of the Rock, buying curios avidly (Mr. Perry unfortunately had drained the market of inkstands made from pieces of the Rock, which Dr. Squibb had set his heart upon); steel engravings of San Roque, Ragged Staff, Southport Gate, Ronda, and Europa Point; provisions and groceries for the mess; and a guidebook at Mr. Bertolosa's stationery store—a "very unsatisfactory guidebook, evidently written by someone totally unqualified for the purpose"— which was later of no help in locating the Moorish Castle for the assistant surgeon.

Dr. Squibb picked up several bits of news while ashore, some good, some bad. The U.S.S. *Portsmouth* had just arrived from New York in nineteen days ("A remarkably quick passage," wrote Dr. Squibb, "even with the two days added, these being commonly necessary to truth in such cases.") The *Portsmouth* sailed next day for Naples with "despatches for our squadron growing out of some French difficulties at home." The *Portsmouth* would take the *Erie*'s mail.

The bad news struck Dr. Squibb quite forcibly: The valiant bid for Hungarian independence by Kossuth, the poet-patriot Josef Petofi and their freedom fighters had been brutally crushed.

On the last day of the *Erie*'s call at Gibraltar, Dr. Squibb was laid low by "an attack of disordered stomach resembling Cholera Morbus." He refused to give up, however, and went ashore anyhow. Although he could scarcely stand, he would not return to his ship until he had finally acquired his rock inkstand and some paperweights made from a stalactite in Martin's Cave and marble from St. Michael's Cave and the Signal Station. He also found an old Genoese who as a great personal favor sold him some silver coins, just dug up, believed to date from "the reign of Charles IV of Spain," as well as some genuine antique cameos.

Once back on board, he went to bed immediately with "a fit of vomiting and purging, followed by considerable fever." The purser relieved his nausea by bathing his brow with cologne.

The assistant surgeon's illness had an important bearing on his own career and on American pharmacy generally. For a long time the former apothecary's apprentice had been mumbling to himself about the quality of medicines issued by the Navy. During the process of treating himself, he had been shocked to find that the rhubarb he had chosen as a stomachic was badly worm-eaten, and that there was a substantial proportion of sand mixed with the bicarbonate of soda.

Some day he would browbeat the Navy into furnishing decent drugs.

VII

THE NORMAL RUN from Gibraltar to Spezia, where the storeship was to meet most of the Mediterranean Squadron, was five days for a ship of the *Erie*'s type. Because of alternating heavy weather, adverse winds, and dead calms, all compounded—according to Dr. Squibb—by bad seamanship on the part of the captain, the *Erie* was three weeks reaching port.

The assistant surgeon's private war with his commander reached a decisive phase during this period. The morning after sailing from Gibraltar (October 15), the boatswain piped "all hands to witness punishment." As it happened, there were almost as many being punished as there were witnesses. Dr. Squibb commented as follows:

"After breakfast this morning 15 out of our crew of 34 were whipped at the gangway, and all except one for drunkenness and faults growing out of a shortsighted policy of our senseless captain in permitting the men to bring as much liquor as they please aboard the vessel, with the stipulation that they pay the penalty of being whipped for drunkenness. Six or seven others were whipped at one time on a previous occasion since we left New York, making in all, I feel pretty sure, more whippings than occurred on board the Perry in two years. There, too, we had a well disciplined orderly and obedient crew, but there we had men of sense and judgment for commanders."

It should be noted that flogging was still legal in the United States Navy in 1849. Although as early as 1844 Senator Hall had introduced draft legislation to abolish corporal punishment aboard American ships, the bill was pigeonholed in committee and was not passed by Congress until 1850. Captain Porter's floggings at the gangway of the *Erie,* while in perfect accord with naval regulations, not only increased Dr. Squibb's disgust with his commander, but started a train of thought which was to affect his philosophy of life in later years.

As the *Erie* beat her way along the Spanish coast, tacking ineffectually in the light and fluctuating winds, the captain found new ways of passing the time. One afternoon, Dr. Squibb records, he "amused himself by firing the old, rusty, dangerous nine-pounders which we have on board—or rather one of them—making a great racket and exposing the limbs and lives of all concerned to no purpose apart from caprice. Government is very wrong in putting such guns, or such captains, and perhaps the captain would add, or 'such doctors,' on board their ships. If they are only for show or form, dispense with them. If intended for use, let them be good and useful ones."

Later the captain joined in the cruel sport of a precocious, dirty, redheaded youngster named Billy Eversfield. Billy was traveling with his father, a former Army commissary and premature unreconstructed rebel, and his uncle, a "Virginia gentleman and rigid member of the Church," who insisted on ten-year-old Billy's learning his catechism every Sunday. Despite this religious influence, wrote Dr. Squibb, "Billy's inordinate appetite for wines and spirits is almost daily encouraged by gratification, and his father and uncle both boast that he can drink more than either of them without becoming drunk, or, in quotation, 'tight.'"

Billy wore a very dirty straw hat which was so much too big it rested on his ears, "thus acquiring the collateral advantage of hiding one half of the dirt by hiding one half of his face. . . . A coarse dark blue flannel shirt tied at the throat and breast by two pairs of red tape strings . . . a pair of pantaloons of the same material, cut sailor fashion . . . a pair of socks, the primitive color of which must be classed with the Eleuthinian Mysteries. . . . This was precisely Billy's rig when I used to visit him in bed, sea sick, off Sandy Hook, with this exception: that the colouring of the then new flannel shirt came off very freely, giving a delicate blue color to the dirt of his skin. This advantage has now worn off the flannel and would probably have worn off the skin only that an occasional sprinkling of rain renews it from time to time."

Little Billy's favorite pastime on the voyage from Gibraltar to Spezia was picking off the shore birds that were following the ship along the coast. Several birds were "caught or frightened to death in a cage, while others have been knocked over and killed with potatoes and other missiles while picking up crumbs about the decks." In this Billy was encouraged by his father and uncle. But when Captain Porter himself joined in the fun, ex-Quaker Squibb intervened. Two weeks out of Gibraltar he wrote:

"Two little birds that have somehow miraculously escaped destruction during the last week still remain with the ship although we have been in sight of land all day. One of these little fellows has become so tame that he comes into the rooms and wardroom quite frequently and catches flies and young cockroaches by the dozen. I caught the captain today amusing himself by throwing potatoes at these little passengers as they would light on the decks or rigging, and I believe made him ashamed of his senseless destructiveness: and as caterer, forbidding him from taking potatoes for such purposes."

By this time Dr. Squibb had "absolute contempt" for Captain Porter as a man (he wondered "what kind of woman Mrs. Porter can be, as wife of a man filthy in 'moral' as well as 'physique' "), as a commander of men, and as a gentleman. He now found himself in a position to criticize the captain as a sailor. After several days of perfect calm, with everything aboard flapping and banging as the *Erie* rolled idly in the ground swell between the French coast and Corsica, a dry gale arose during the night, blowing from the very point of the compass toward which the *Erie* was bound. Squibb wrote:

"From the captain's seasickness, timidity, or from some other cause, the ship has been kept under close-reefed topsails all day. The want of sufficient sail to steady her has added to the motion of this short, jumping, head sea. . . . All kinds of moveables lie in confusion throughout the ship, and one is not only obliged to keep his own position but also to defend it against the slipping and sliding movements of messmates, servants, chairs, &c. . . . Add to all this that we are receding rather than approaching our destination, and that besides having killed the last of our poultry today, a gust of wind carried away nearly all our potatoes from the stern netting. All day long the Captain, Eversfield and Billy have been pretty industriously engaged in wasting the few fresh provisions that remain by alternately gorging and disgorging."

The gale lasted two days. Three days after it had blown itself out, the *Erie* was within sight of Spezia, but not nearly at the end of her voyage. Squibb reported:

"Yesterday at ten o'clock we were little more than 20 miles off our port. . . . A vessel of this class and condition should beat, at the lowest calculation against a head wind, 50 miles in the 24 hours, and with a breeze as good and water as smooth as we have had, much more. Notwithstanding all this, we are still 6 or 8 miles off, and heading off shore. I may add to all this that I do not believe there is a passed midshipman or midshipman on board that would not have had the vessel in port two or three days ago. The topsails are now closely reefed, in a calm, and have been reefed three times in the last 24 hours, and yet the weather has not been bad, or in the least dangerous to ship or spars. . . .

"Ship's position at noon, about 10 miles N.N.E. from the entrance to the Bay of Spezia."

Next day at noon the ship's position was 8 miles N.W.

The interim was occupied by Dr. Squibb in figuring up his accounts (he had only $66 left of his advance for sight-seeing in Italy, and no pay due for more than a month), and in reading the Old Testament (20 chapters in Genesis and Exodus: "very interesting and often instructing. There is, however, much of what we now consider moral torpitude; and much wordy repetition in style. Some passages are how-ever very beautiful, and some characters and traits of charac-ter well worthy of admiration.").

That night the *Erie* slid silently into the harbor by moon-light, although the navigators, according to Assistant Surgeon Squibb, "were extremely nervous, as could be plainly seen, and the helm was shifted from one side to the other with a frequency that clearly showed that the author of the orders did not know exactly which or what was right, equally frightened at everything done, and yet afraid to do nothing. Fortunately from a conspiracy of circumstances at about 11 o'clock we came to anchor just inside the mouth of the har-bour."

Next morning Dr. Squibb was informed by the Italian lazaretto that the *Erie* must hoist the yellow flag of quarantine for two days. He also learned that a number of ships of the Mediterranean Squadron were waiting at Spezia, notably the *Cumberland,* the *Constitution,* the steamer *Mississippi,* and the flagship *Independence.* More interesting still, he heard that at least two medical officers were anxious to trade places with him in the *Erie,* which was returning home as soon as the squadron was supplied. One of them was Dr. Robert E. Wall of the *Cumberland,* whom he knew from his Brazil Squadron days. The other was Dr. Hamilton of the *Mississippi.*

The man who went home in the *Erie* would have a real chore, for there were some thirty officers and men being ordered home in her "by medical survey." Dr. Squibb did not mind the prospect of work, but he was loath to make a quick turn-around without seeing more of Europe than the ant runs of Gibraltar and the lighthouses of the Ligurian Coast.

The decision was not really difficult for Dr. Squibb. It boiled down to the question of preference between the *Cumberland* and the *Mississippi.* As for the *Erie*—Captain Porter would still be in command on her voyage home.

VIII

DR. SQUIBB'S TRANSFER to the frigate *Cumberland* was easily and quickly accomplished. He chose the *Cumberland* for several reasons. First of all, he was a personal friend of Dr. Wall's and was glad to do a favor for a man who was anxious to get home. Second, he had always wanted to serve in a big ship and the *Cumberland* was a true man-of-war, 1,726 tons displacement, 44 guns, a complement of nearly 500 officers and men. She had a silhouette that would delight the eye and heart of any square-rigged sailor.

True, the commander of the *Cumberland,* Captain William K. Latimer, was universally disliked and on his one previous contact with Dr. Squibb had been brusque and rather rude. However, the *Cumberland* seemed to be a happy ship, and when approached to approve the application for transfer before it reached the commodore, the captain had seemed urbane and polite enough. Furthermore, Dr. Squibb had heard from all quarters that the wardroom officers of the *Cumberland* were of "excellent character."

On November 9, two days after the *Erie* had received her pratique from the health authorities, Dr. Squibb transferred his worldly belongings to the *Cumberland*. He had only two regrets in leaving the *Erie*. Executive Officer Fauntleroy had received news of the death of his wife in Norfolk, leaving a babe of eight months—news which truly shocked Dr. Squibb, for he was extremely fond of his ribald, noisy chess opponent and felt he was deserting him in an hour of need. He was also pained, although in another way, that the mess had chosen Eversfield to be caterer in his place.

Dr. Squibb was delighted with his new messmates, his new medical colleagues (for the *Cumberland* had a full staff of medics), and even his quarters, although they were below the water line and smelled somewhat of bilge water. He was less pleased to learn that lights-out was strictly observed at 10 P.M., and that he was allowed only four small candles—too small for reading purposes—a week.

During the first days of his new duties he would have had little time for reading anyhow. The *Cumberland's* sick bay had forty-eight patients in bed when he came aboard. The senior medical officer, Dr. Samuel Barrington, surgeon, was a pleasant, elderly gentleman, a little easygoing for the tastes of the energetic young Squibb. His fellow assistant surgeon, Dr. Edward Hudson, was also a warm, friendly person but not inclined to overexertion. What's more, Dr. Wall had left his records in rather bad shape, weeks behind. Wrote Dr. Squibb:

"Have discovered since I have been in this squadron the secret of my having received praise from the Department on the score of my accounts. They are really kept generally so loosely and with so little care and accuracy that they can be of little value."

And a few days later: "All day again in the Sick Bay, so closely that I have not seen the clear light of day. The worst of it is, the more I write, the more there seems to be to write: I can readily see a month's steady work ahead. It does not require half an eye to see that the younger part of our medical corps of this ship have not been too fond of work, and that the older is too easy and too good a man to interfere with their inclination."

Dr. Barrington was also too good a man to interfere with Dr. Squibb's inclination to work. He was delighted when his new assistant surgeon set about reorganizing the dispensary and medical storeroom with his own hands, and he saw that Dr. Squibb got carpenters and fitters to rearrange and remodel the sick bay around the patients. When the squadron sailed from Spezia, the lower decks of the *Cumberland* were abustle all the way to Naples.

In overhauling the *Cumberland*'s dispensary, Dr. Squibb threw overboard great quantities of medicines he considered unfit for human consumption. He discussed with Dr. Barrington the question of the filthy and impure drugs which the Navy seemed eternally determined to buy. The senior surgeon agreed completely that the quality of issue medicines was a shame and a disgrace, but he didn't see what could be done about it. Dr. Squibb saw no immediate remedy either, but he resolved again to take action at the first opportunity.

His messmates were quick to spot Dr. Squibb as a glutton for duty and a man with an overwhelming sense of responsibility. The *Cumberland* had scarcely reached quarantine at Naples before the officers named him ship's postmaster.

"I seem destined always to have some troublesome and thankless office on board ship," he wrote, "for it is impossible to refuse such things except one selfishly says that he is not willing to take a little trouble for the sake of accommodating his neighbours."

IX

DURING HIS THREE WEEKS ashore at Naples, Dr. Squibb was in seventh heaven. His journal was effervescent with superlatives describing activities hardly typical of a sailor ashore in a foreign port.

The Villa Reale was "the finest promenade of the kind in the world." The Neapolitan pears and grapes were "delightful" and "the cauliflower here exceeds anything of the kind that I have ever tasted." The sight of a snow-covered Vesuvius in the moonlight was "magnificent." The Teatro del Fondo (where he heard *The Barber of Seville* sung by a baritone "the finest I ever heard") was "much the largest and finest theatre I have ever seen . . . about the size of the Walnut Street theatre of Philadelphia . . . well lighted with gas," and the audience "possessed the characteristic air of intellect and refinement which belong only to the highest degree of taste and civilization."

But the height of Dr. Squibb's "almost fanatical" musical delight was the San Carlo Opera, which, although "miserably lighted," possessed an orchestra "composed of 97 musicians" which "in musical perfection far exceeds any conception that I had ever formed of talent, skill, and real magnificence." It was here that he heard the world première of Verdi's *Luisa Miller,* with the composer himself present, which was "decidedly and by great odds the finest opera I have ever seen." He returned several times, when he had shore leave, to hear the new opera again.

Unfortunately, Dr. Squibb did not have liberty on the Feast of the Immaculate Conception and thus missed seeing the troops reviewed by the King of Naples and the Two Sicilies, and more particularly the public benediction by Pope Pius IX, who was then "living in regal splendor" in exile at suburban Portici. The young doctor was a great admirer of Pio Nono, "whose liberal sentiments and reforming political actions have already turned Europe upsidedown, and exiled him from his throne and capital. . . . How unhappy must be this perhaps best and most liberal of all the long line of Popes of Rome."

Dr. Squibb spent days in the Royal Museum and devoted thousands of words of his journal to cataloguing the paintings and statuary and registering his critical reaction to most. He spent all available cash on books, maps, and "curiosities" —a glove box of cyprus wood from Sorrento, an opera glass, a reading desk of olive wood and one of walnut, and "a very fine collection of plaster medallions, copies of more than 100 of the finest statues and paintings of Naples and Rome," all in bas-relief, "really very beautiful and valuable," four cases of them, all for five dollars!

But it was his visit to the excavations at Pompeii and Herculaneum that inspired his most ecstatic prose. To have passed the day at Pompeii more than made up for the "hardships and deprivations . . . and the inadequate pay" of a seafaring life. Contemplating the great amphitheater, with its animal caves, gladiators' room, and tier upon tier of seats, he was overcome by "the silent, awful grandeur of such a tombstone of antiquity! No human being who has stood where I have stood and seen what I have seen, ever forgets the moment. . . . Man may be cold, selfish and stoical, but not here! His passions may govern, and his vices debase him elsewhere, but in the presence of the Eternal past, and its lessons that are forced upon him, how can he avoid the contemplation of his own insignificance, from which his virtues alone can ever elevate him."

It would be surprising, of course, if a man who took umbrage at the "moral turpitude" of certain passages of the Old Testament did not record some shock at the prurient paintings and phallic emblems of Pompeii, yet his journal gives only a few lines to the subject: "Some severe criticisms are made upon the morality of the ancients from the obscene mythological pictures upon the walls of the best houses in the city, many of which excite disgust. Such frescos are, however, found on the walls of the most private apartments, as the 'Venereum.' "

The day before the *Cumberland* sailed from Naples, Dr. Squibb wrote in his journal: "Have been all day long impressed by a singular and delightful dream of last night in which the most ardent desires of my life were gratified, and I awoke from happiness that alas proved to have been all a dream."

He recorded no details and offered no explanation.

This was December 15, 1849. Sigmund Freud was not to be born for another seven years.

X

FOR THE NEXT YEAR and a half the frigate *Cumberland* cruised the Mediterranean from end to end. Dr. Squibb was to grow ecstatic over more of Italy, as well as to add Egypt and the Holy Land to his map of lands seen. His collection of "curiosities" grew to such proportions that he was forced to suspend his trunk and boxes from the overhead beams of his cabin in order to allow himself deck space to move about in.

But the cruise of the *Cumberland* meant more to Dr. Squibb than a grand tour of southern Europe and the Levant. It marked his coming of age professionally.

The medical log of the *Cumberland,* prepared by Dr. Squibb in addition to the quarterly report of Dr. Barrington, the senior medical officer, is even today a masterpiece of scientific and statistical reporting, clinical observation, and differential diagnosis, particularly considering the limitations marking the medical knowledge of the period. We must remember that bacteria and the virus had not yet been identified as agents of contagion and infection, that therapy was largely empirical and medication far from standardized.

But the medical log was not only medical and pharmaceutical. It also contained economic, sociological, and anthropological observations, as well as advice to the Navy on administration, regulation, and architecture. It was based on a rich and varied experience which began fourteen days after the *Cumberland* sailed from Naples.

On New Year's Day, 1850, while the frigate was anchored off the Sicilian port of Messina, smallpox broke out on board. A few days later the first case appeared aboard the flagship *Independence*.

Within three weeks twenty cases had developed aboard the *Cumberland* and Dr. Squibb suggested to his superiors that some sort of floating pest house be devised so that the small-pox victims could be isolated from the healthy members of the crew. The proposal was approved by Surgeon Barrington and the captain and on January 24 the Neapolitan brig *Celive* was chartered as a hospital ship (at $3.50 a day), towed along-side the *Cumberland* and put in charge of Assistant Surgeon Hudson and sick-bay attendant John Gannon.

Patients continued to be isolated aboard the brig until February 28—sixty-one cases in all, varying from a mild varioloid to ten which "from their violence, the size and progress of the pustules, and the deep pitting of the skin, may be considered as true variola. Four of these were fatal." The *Celive* was fumigated on March 9 and next day returned to her owners, who billed the Navy for $161.

The epidemic puzzled Dr. Squibb, inasmuch as "All on board who did not exhibit satisfactory evidences of vaccination or small-pox, had been vaccinated some months before, but it was from a virus that may have lost its efficacy, as only one or two equivocal pustules could be obtained. It has been remarked, by surgeons of experience and observation, that vaccination does not succeed as certainly, or progress as regularly on board of ships as under the ordinary circumstances; and the history of this attempt strengthens the opinion, for the virus was carefully obtained and well kept." The average duration of the fatal cases was 12 days and for the varioloid 20.2 days. One man of about forty, "distinctly marked in the face by a small-pox that he remembered well," was fit for duty in three days.

The term "virus," as used by Dr. Squibb above, was the contemporary word for lymph taken from a vaccinated child or a person recovered from smallpox, collected on the point of a quill, and transferred to the person seeking immunity.

Dr. Squibb records 138 cases of "gastric derangement and dyspepsia," which, while of epidemic proportions, he explains by "gluttony" and "debauchery among men on liberty."

The gluttony cases followed a regular weekly pattern. Dr. Squibb explained: "Every Thursday the week's ration of flour and dried fruit are issued and made into a batter, with grease from the salted meats, technically 'slush.' This batter, when boiled in a bag, with an iron spoon in the centre of it, is called 'duff.' By the common appetite for this article of diet, it appears that the materials of which it is composed are highly important to the economy; but that, coming in this indigestible form, and once a week only, and forming then, with molasses, almost the entire dinner of the day, it excites gluttony and gastric disorder. . . . Flatulence, from which colic rarely arose, was very common, giving rise to the bad habit to which sailors, more than any other class, seem addicted."

Regarding disorders induced by shore leave, Dr. Squibb's log has this to say:

"Men would return, or be brought on board after twenty-four or forty-eight hours' liberty on shore, in a condition to develop or favour the progress of almost any disease. The time allowed them is not long enough to produce delirium tremens in men accustomed to the daily use of small quantities of spirits, and hence most of these gastric irritations bear the same relation to delirium tremens that the limited time does to the time necessary to the production of full delirium from the same causes. Other cases again approximate gastritis in the same way; while still another group presents degrees of persisting irritation, that, without being serious in themselves, affect very unfavourably the gonorrhoea and syphilis commonly commencing at such times."

Venereal diseases actually presented much more of a problem to the medical staff of the *Cumberland* than the epidemic diseases. Dr. Squibb reported 211 cases in all, including 18 of orchitis, 8 of balanitis, and 6 of phymosis. For, like the armies of Charles VIII of France who "took Genoa, Naples, and the pox," in the bit of ribald doggerel attributed to Voltaire, and gave the name "Neapolitan pox" to what the Italians called "the French disease," the men of the *Cumberland* were not fastidious in their pursuit of pleasure.

Dr. Squibb reported 106 cases of syphilis in 86 individuals. "Sixty-nine men had one attack only; 15 two attacks; 1 three attacks, and 1 four attacks. Of these, 7 were secondary, 1 tertiary, and 8 complicated with gonorrhea. . . . The syphilis, both primary and secondary, of the older writers, seems to have materially degenerated as it occurs on board ship; for, during two cruises, wherein about 20 per cent. of the whole number serving on board have contracted syphilitic disease once or oftener, the writer has seen no more than 7 or 8 cases of chancre as it is described by old authors."

There were 62 cases of gonorrhea brought aboard the frigate by 56 men, six of whom had it twice. The mean duration of a case during the first half of the cruise was 18.69 days; during the second half, 16.6. The eight cases of gonorrhea occurring in combination with syphilis were not tabulated separately. Dr. Squibb treated his gonorrhea patients variously, his most successful method being the "injection of sulphate of zinc and sulphate of morphia, one grain each to the fluidounce of water, with copious drinking of water or mucilaginous infusions. . . . Rest in the horizontal position in all acute stages, with cold water dressings and mucilaginous injections . . . where the inflammation ran high. Where such injections were ordinarily, that is, carelessly used, they seemed to do harm. The immediate effect of active purgation seemed to be detrimental."

Dr. Squibb's log of the *Cumberland* lists cases of epilepsy (6), delirium tremens (8), otitis (11), pneumonia (7), angina pectoris (2), worms (5), tonsillitis (61), hemorrhoids (6), hepatitis (only 3, despite the bibulous habits of the crew), erysipelas (1), seasickness (8), and mumps (8).

There were fourteen cases of Asiatic cholera aboard, three of them fatal, and a great many registered as diarrhea "which would have been called cholera in any general hospital report," but were not so registered by Dr. Squibb "where collapse and rice-water discharges did not occur." One epidemic of intestinal disease occurred in Egyptian waters.

"When, upon entering the harbor of Alexandria, cholera was found to prevail there, the surgeon of the ship advised the captain to have no communication with the shore. The captain's judgment, however, being opposed to the surgeon's advice, the ship rode out a quarantine of five days, during which she was 'filled up' with Nile water from the cisterns under the town. After the quarantine, another day passed at anchor, and by this time so many cases of diarrhoea and cholera had occurred as to render it expedient to go to sea. The ship was accordingly towed out the following morning. . . . The disease abated immediately upon going to sea, and upon desisting from the use of the Nile water."

Dr. Squibb also reported three epidemics of what he called "catarrhs" aboard the *Cumberland* in September and November of 1849 and March and April 1851—277 cases, plus 40 cases of bronchitis and dozens more of related diseases. The catarrhs "were almost exclusively pectoral, for it was rare to see a common coryza, or 'cold in the head,' during the cruise." Cases were registered only when the patient was too sick to stand watch.

When the *Cumberland* was paid off at the Boston Navy Yard on July 9, 1851, after 719 days in foreign waters, Dr. Squibb totted up his statistics and drew conclusions.

The frigate was at sea 178 days, at anchor 541 days, and covered 18,266 miles by log. Of her original complement of 493 officers and men, 13 died, 17 deserted, 70 transferred to other ships, and 52 were invalided home. Of the entire number, "only 92 escaped the register of the sick, and of these 9 had been on board less than three months."

Why? Dr. Squibb first broke down his crew by age and nationality. The average age was twenty-eight, the youngest fifteen, the oldest sixty-four, 56 were under twenty-one and 15 were fifty or over. Americans numbered 238, including 43 officers. Irish were next numerous (103), with English, Welsh and Nova Scotians grouped to number 60, Germans and Dutch 42, Italians, Sicilians and Maltese, 28. The average number of the ship's company was 453 (there had been 109 replacements), and the register showed 1,638 cases of disease; each man reported sick an average of 3.6 times for an average duration of 12.82 days per case. This cost the Navy, Dr. Squibb calculated, 23,626 days' labor lost by sickness, or more than 7 per cent, although the actual cost of operating the sick bay was only 7.439 cents per day per case, exclusive of salaries. The total cost, including officers' and stewards' pay, would have come to 44 cents per day per patient, although there had been a saving of $1,288 in rations stopped while the patients were eating the diet supplied by the hospital department.

Was all this sickness necessary? No, declared Dr. Squibb. Hard-shelled adherence to outmoded man-of-war routine and disciplinary measures, unquestioning acceptance of tradition, and blind refusal to admit change were major causes of conditions favorable to disease. Wrote Dr. Squibb in his summing up, which was actually an indictment of Navy methods:

"Diet, personal habits, moisture, and crowded sleeping places, are the most prominent among these conspiring conditions. . . . That men should be crowded into 18-inch spaces to sleep, on a berth deck, in order that the beams of a well-ventilated gun-deck may not be defaced by hammock hooks, is senseless. But when it is remembered that the fundamental element of efficiency is health; and that health should be robust in order to insure the necessary amount of resistance to an unnatural life, the climax must have surprised all who saw and thought upon the hygienic condition of a ship wherein the customs of past ages had degenerated into laws jealous of innovation, and therefore resisting improvement. Scanty ventilation, damp decks, and a diet that never varies, in climates and seasons always varying, and all these administered with a judgment that will not be enlightened by the means placed at hand, are not conditions under which a healthy, energetic, progressive race of men are properly represented to the world. There is probably no community of 453 individuals in any other condition of life that will exhibit 1600 cases of disease within two years; and yet nothing is spared in legislation or expense, whereby it is supposed that such a community may be well maintained, except that an imperfect executive judgment is sanctioned in its imperfections, and relieved of all responsibility for errors."

Dr. Squibb recommended consideration of the question of whether the customary issue of the spirit ration before, rather than after meals, was more conducive to health.

In conclusion, returning to his objection to shipboard dampness as pathogenic, Dr. Squibb suggested "that the surface of the planking of a ship's berth-deck might be so saturated and glazed with common yellow wax that water would not be absorbed. And that, like the tile floors of many French hospitals, they could be easily cleaned and kept clean. The facility with which such an experiment might be tried is additional reason for respectfully urging its consideration upon the Bureau."

Just in case the Bureau of Medicine and Surgery of the United States Navy might classify his observations and recommendations in the category of "File and Forget," Assistant Surgeon Edward Robinson Squibb sent a copy of his report to the *American Journal of the Medical Sciences,* which published it in full in its issue for January 1852.

The report made no mention of Dr. Squibb's growing preoccupation with the incredible quality of the medicines issued for shipboard use. This would come later, when he was ready not only to make constructive recommendations but to take concrete action.

two

THE RUBBING UP

I

FOR THE NINE MONTHS following Dr. Squibb's return to his native land, his private journals present a graphic evaluation of the state of American medicine in mid-nineteenth century from the viewpoint of a practicing physician revisiting his old medical school and of a resident attached to a large hospital.

When he was paid off at Boston, Dr. Squibb hurried back to Philadelphia with a promise of a three-month leave in his pocket. However, he still rankled from his previous experience with Navy promises. He immediately wrote to the Bureau of Medicine and Surgery, pointing out that he had been short-changed by more than two months between his *Perry* and *Erie* cruises, and requesting six months' leave to take a refresher course in medicine—a "rubbing up," it was then called—pointing toward examinations for promotion. After all, an assistant surgeon on leave had his pay reduced from the seagoing rate of $1,700 to $1,000 a year. The next grade—passed assistant surgeon—would give him $2,000 at sea, $1,800 ashore, and $1,500 on leave or awaiting orders. The Navy granted his request.

Dr. Squibb hurried to Delaware County, Pennsylvania,

salty with thousands of sea miles, scores of tall sea tales, and a mature sailor's point of view. He wanted to rest, to feel the land under him, to display his "curiosities" to eager friends and family, and to eat oysters, terrapin, and mince pies to his heart's (and stomach's) content. For several months he idled his time away in Darby, holding Grandma Bonsall and the scores of relatives enraptured with his pictures, his pressed flowers from the ruins of Pompeii, his reproductions of the fine arts of Europe, his souvenirs of the Holy Land, and his European music box.

Then, as Jefferson Medical College prepared to open its fall term, Assistant Surgeon Edward Robinson Squibb, U.S.N., moved into Philadelphia "to rub up." On the clear, mild morning of October 20, 1851, he loaded his trunk, his big washbasin, and his music box into the dearborn and drove into town. At a quarter before nine o'clock he arrived at Mrs. Blythe's boardinghouse on Chestnut Street below Broad, where he was to lodge for the period of his rubbing up. He agreed to pay Mrs. Blythe $24 a month, which was to include food but no heat. Since Dr. Squibb was already paying Uncle Jake $12 a month toward the support of his bedridden father, and he had to buy a ton of coal from his old friend Joe Bullock's coal yard at Broad and Vine—to say nothing of buying firebricks from Julius Fink, the cooking-range man, for fixing the grate in his room—there was not a great deal left out of his eighty-odd dollars a month for tuition, clothes, and pin money.

True, tuition at Jefferson was reasonable. Fees for the most expensive courses—anatomy, materia medica, and chemistry—were $14 each. Midwifery was $10. And by college regulations the total fees of the seven professors were not to exceed $90 a year.

Withal, Jefferson was one of the best, if not the oldest, of the medical schools in the United States. It had been founded in 1825 by Dr. George McClellan, a pioneer American pathologist before pathology became a separate and respected branch of medicine. In the face of opposition from the University of Pennsylvania, his alma mater, Dr. McClellan started his medical school in the old Tivoli Theatre on Philadelphia's Prune Street (now 518 Locust Street) near Washington Square, which he rented for $550 a year. In 1828 he moved into a new college building on Tenth Street, between what are now known as Sansom and Moravian streets.

The staff of Jefferson Medical College included some of the most distinguished names in American medicine: Dr. Franklin Bache, professor of chemistry, co-author with Dr. George B. Wood of the first *Dispensatory of the United States,* published in 1833; Dr. Robley B. Dunglison, professor of the Institutes of Medicine and Medical Jurisprudence; an authority on human physiology, therapeutics and materia medica; Dr. Robert W. Huston, professor of materia medica and general therapeutics; Dr. Charles D. Meigs, professor of obstetrics and the diseases of women, author of numerous standard texts on midwifery and female disorders, and inventor of the ring pessary; Dr. John K. Mitchell, professor of the practice of medicine, who, far ahead of his time, insisted on the parasitic origin of malaria; Dr. Thomas D. Mütter, professor of surgery, a cosmopolitan and a prima donna, undoubtedly one of the great surgeons of his day, whose collection of anatomical specimens still attracts attention, more than a century later, as the Mütter Museum in Philadelphia today; and Dr. Joseph Pancoast, professor of surgical anatomy.

When Dr. Edward Robinson Squibb came again to sit at the feet of this eminent group, after more than four years as a seagoing physician and surgeon practicing under conditions that were often primitive and frequently left him to his own resources, it is not surprising that he sometimes found that they had feet of clay.

His journal for the period recorded not only the three months of lectures in great detail, but also Dr. Squibb's attitude toward contemporary practices, the competence and integrity of his professors, and the theories of his profession, which showed him well in advance of his times.

It was a period in which personal skill and sound instinct were far ahead of basic knowledge. It was an exciting period, because revolutionary discoveries were being made that charged the atmosphere of the scientific world with an electric sense of expectancy, a kind of involuntary trembling on the verge of great things that were to change not only the practice of medicine but the fundamental concepts of physiology.

Rudolf Virchow had not yet formally announced to the world that the cell was the basic unit of the human body, but news of his work must have transpired to the profession. Dr. Squibb records that although Dr. Dunglison, in his lecture on the general composition of the body, described "the elementary tissues . . . as areolar, muscular, and nervous," and discoursed at length on "humoralism and solidism," he did refer to "the cell agency in pathology."

Pasteur had barely opened his laboratory in Paris and it would be seventeen years before Lister was to demonstrate to his English colleagues his method of sterilizing an operating theater, yet Drs. Mütter and Pancoast performed complicated surgery with great skill, without apparent fatalities, and often without the newfangled anesthesia that was just coming into general use.

Ehrlich and Wassermann had not yet been born; Koch was still a schoolboy; Roentgen was six years old and nearly half a century away from his discovery of the X ray. And yet Drs. Mitchell, Mütter, Meigs, Huston, et al., although they still discussed the techniques of bleeding in typhoid (by venesection or by a hundred leeches to the abdomen) and the use of guano poultices in chronic arthritis (Peruvian guano had been imported into the United States since 1824), could still make amazingly accurate diagnoses by the sound of a cough, the smell of a sickroom, and the color and dampness of the skin.

And they were all pioneers in the use of a new anesthetic called sulphuric ether. It was only five years since Dr. W. T. G. Morton, a Boston dentist, gave his much-publicized demonstration of ether as an anesthetic at Massachusetts Gen-

eral Hospital in 1846, although ether had been used to produce unconsciousness in surgery as early as 1842, when Dr.
Crawford Long of Georgia put a man named Venables to
sleep while he removed a tumor. Dr. Squibb was fascinated
by the possibilities of the new drug. He recorded every word
of Dr. Bache's lecture on the chemistry of ether. He duly
noted Dr. Huston's admonition that ether should never be
given in water, because it does not mix, and wrote down the
method of preparing oil of wine, a step in the manufacture
of ether. And he was at the surgeon's elbow whenever Mütter
or Pancoast used ether during an operation.

Dr. Squibb had two unqualified favorites among the faculty of Jefferson Medical College: Dr. Bache, with his patri-
archal white beard and distinguished lineage, whose subject
was closer to the Squibb heart than the younger man yet
realized; and Dr. Meigs, the clean-shaven, dramatic, Ber-
muda-born son of a Yale mathematics professor, whose subject—he was probably the most famous obstetrician and gyne-
cologist of his day—was one with which Dr. Squibb had not
had the slightest experience during his four years at sea.

"Bache, with his clear, plain, logical and unforgettable
definition of chemistry," Squibb wrote, "is the most forcible
teacher I have ever known. . . . He contrasts strongly with
some of the rest."

And Meigs, "descanting upon the pelvis generally in a
manner belonging only to himself," had "the originality of
idea, and erratic, familiar manner, curious postures and
gestures which would not fit well elsewhere. He and Bache
are as widely different as good and bad . . . and yet both are
capital teachers."

Meigs gave his classes a complete course in midwifery,
from conception through delivery. Dr. Squibb was much impressed by the obstetrician's skill and knowledge and by his
insistence on a gentlemanly manner for the physician in his
delicate relationship with a lady patient, from the examination cabinet to the lying-in chamber. Meigs often introduced
a touch of humor into his lectures on this most serious sub-

ject. To illustrate the curious ideas of parturition often held by young women, which a physician must correct, he told "of a French woman whom he had delivered for the first time and of the doleful expression on her face as she told him, '*Ah, mon pauvre docteur, c'est tout gâté pour jamais!*'"

Dr. Squibb also recorded the Meigs story of "Rachel and her father Laban, but he did not quote correctly, for it was Rachel who stole her father's images and hid them in her tent under the camels' furniture and sat down upon them. 'Let it not displease my lord that I cannot rise up before him, for the custom of women is upon me.' This was an excellent lesson in the way he gave it, that physicians should be gentlemen when they speak to women, not blurting out, 'How's your bowels?' and 'How's your menses?' as in the examples he gave."

The author of *The Science and Art of Obstetrics* and of *Woman—Her Diseases and Remedies* was a striking figure as he stood before his class, his sharp features animated, his long dark hair brushed back over his ears, his spectacles pushed up on his high forehead, as he illustrated the ovarian function by representing "the Grafian vesicle by india rubber hollow spheres."

Dr. Meigs was continually using models and apparatus to demonstrate his points. Dr. Squibb reports that the professor used a manikin and a sheet to demonstrate the proper technique for performing a metroscopy and the delicate business of examination *per vaginam*. He fitted crossed surgical bougies together to illustrate the proportional relationship of the diameter of the foetal head to the pelvis. He devoted weeks to the management and mechanism of labor, after reducing the fundamentals to four: flexion, rotation, extension, and restitution. Have patience, he urged; never meddle with a labor when the forces are natural and co-ordinate, for meddlesome midwifery is as bad as careless midwifery; respect the function of the perineum; laceration is deplorable and need not occur with proper care. "Remember the direction the head must take and hold the perineum accordingly. . . ."

Whether he was poetic, as when he spoke of the beauties of Carus' curve, or humorous, as when he deplored too many gynecologists' "turning cooks to fry the os uteri," a reference to his colleagues' reprehensible use of cautery instead of silver nitrate, Dr. Meigs was adored by Dr. Squibb.

Squibb admired the suave professional manner and glib lectures of Dr. John Kearsley Mitchell, too, but he did not greatly respect him, despite his impressive international background—he was educated at the University of Edinburgh, took his M.D. at the University of Pennsylvania, and traveled for years as a ship's surgeon in the Far East.

"Went to sit in the arena," wrote Dr. Squibb during his first week back at Jefferson for his rubbing up "and had a very good cursory clinic tinctured with Mitchell."

A tall, portly, handsome man, with sideburns and a deeply dimpled chin, Dr. Mitchell was the polished prototype of the highly successful society doctor. Dr. Squibb recognized his cleverness but suspected his sincerity. When the author of *On the Cryptogamous Origin of Malarious and Epidemical Fevers* occupied his hour with expounding his own startling, prescient hypothesis, Dr. Squibb found that while it was "ingenious, plausible, and better sustained than any other theory, I begin to suspect that he does not himself believe [it]."

And although Dr. Squibb accepted without question Dr. Mitchell's endorsement of the contemporary practice of cupping, of bleeding for typhoid, and prescribing alkalis for milk sickness (which Dr. Mitchell described as "The Trembles, a species of poisoned gastric fever now nearly obsolete . . . an inflammation of the meninges, spinal marrow and brain"), he was often critical of his clinical methods. "Mitchell's clinic was as usual," he wrote, "a good many excellent and instructive cases prescribed for very variously and instructively if not very soundly . . . and very tired I am getting of his arsenic, ointment of three, and iodide of potassium."

Dr. Squibb's innate sense of accuracy was offended by

Mitchell's "slovenly weighing of urine"; and the Squibb sense of cleanliness, which was perhaps an instinctive fore-knowledge of the principles of antisepsis, was shocked by Mitchell's clinical manners: "Washed all his instruments, and his hands, that he did not attempt to keep clean, in water that he afterward used for mops with which he introduced nitrate of silver solution into the patients' mouths, a lesson of ungentlemanly slovenliness that he might have spared."

Dr. Squibb watched the operations of Dr. Mütter, professor of surgery, and Dr. Pancoast, professor of surgical anatomy, with an admiring but not uncritical eye. He described one exhibition of plastic surgery in which both men took part—small, blue-eyed Mütter with his dark curly hair graying prematurely, and his finely-chiseled features, explaining every move in his clear, musical voice, while round-faced Pancoast, bald except for a monastic fringe, a spot of his full red lower lip showing below the twists of his sandy handlebar mustache, wiped his bloody fingers on his pocket handkerchief and his instruments on whatever was handy.

"The operation was an extensive one," wrote Dr. Squibb, "for deformity by cicatrix from a burn involving the entire anterior part of the neck and chin. The patient was a young, spare, healthy-looking man. The incision was made at the lower part of the cicatrix and a flap from the left shoulder was turned in to supply the desired tissue. . . . The operation was quite extensive and admirably performed, the patient being under the influence of Ether. When the sutures were all placed, there remained no surface exposed for granulation, but there was too much strain upon the sutures to be borne by them, and they will probably break loose if not otherwise well supported. . . . Pancoast assisted Mütter throughout the operation, and it was independently remarked by the gentlemen who sat on either side of me that it was a beautiful sight to see two great surgeons working so amicably and so harmoniously together, without any exhibition of envy or rivalry. . . . Whether as an exhibition of perfect good feeling, or of self control, or of a mixture of the two as is most probable, I must tell them of this circumstance, for such things have good effect."

Dr. Mütter, apparently, was the better showman of the two. Dr. Squibb described one of his operations as "the grand act exhibition of the whole performance: Barnum by Dr. Mütter. A Mr. Alberger, I think, a man of some 45 or 50 years, had a chronic disease and great tumefaction of the knee (right) joint which had resisted treatment and was wearing out the patient's strength and life. . . . The patient was not easily etherized, but was finally brought under the full effect and kept so during the entire operation, including the ligation of the arteries. The double-flap operation was performed just above the knee, the bone being sawed through at about its middle. . . . At the end, just before the dressing, the patient was asked if he felt the operation and replied that he did not know it was done. No groaning or noise during the operation, except as the anaesthetic effect would diminish and be renewed. The operation was very well and prettily and quickly done. Some notable bleeding from the end of the bone but probably not serious. A large audience and one case of fainting."

Dr. Squibb was much more critical of Dr. Pancoast, particularly when the latter had to perform a difficult operation without an anesthetic, when the patient's blood and tears detracted from the artistic effect. He was even disparaging of Dr. Pancoast as a lecturer. He called the Pancoast lecture on the topography of the abdomen "the most bungling demonstration I ever saw, particularly the peritoneum part of it." And in his comment on Pancoast's description of the femoral artery and its operation, Dr. Squibb pointed out that while the surgeon "spoke of the care necessary to avoid the saphena nerve," he "seemed to forget the anastomotica. Also seemed to forget the rule for finding the artery in any part of its course by a tape. In fact, he does not probably prepare at all for these lectures; but like some of his colleagues is rendered careless by success and self suffi-

cient by position and prospects. . . . Did not give the anatomy of the artery and its branches at all."

Dr. Squibb made no attempt to conceal his opinions of his
professors and openly discussed his differences with them.
They in turn frequently invited him to sit with them in the
arena of the amphitheater during their lectures, and to visit
them at home. He brought Dr. Dunglison's wife a recipe for
macaroni au gratin that he had written down personally in
Naples. He went to Bache's medical-club meeting at the
Bache home in Spruce Street, where he met not only the
faculty of Jefferson Medical, but Dr. George B. Wood, the
distinguished co-author with Dr. Bache of the first American
Dispensatory, to whom Squibb refers as "two men for whom
I feel more respect than any others known in the profession,
both absolute authority in anything they speak or write of,
and both liberal and accomplished scholars." At Bache's
club strictly professional conversation was prohibited by rule,
so the principal topics of the evening were "Kossuth, Franklin, Johnson, and homeopathy."

At Dr. Pancoast's party there were ice cream and chicken
salad. Dr. Meig's student party added oysters to the ritual
chicken salad and ice cream, and so Dr. Squibb and Dr. Sherman (another rubber-upper) went around to Harmer's afterward for "a little brandy to keep down the rebellion in our
stomachs."

All in all, the rubbing up was very friendly as well as instructive, both in human nature and in the art and science
of mid-nineteenth-century medicine.

II

WHEN DR. SQUIBB returned to his native land and the bosom
of his family, flogging in the Navy had only recently been
outlawed by act of Congress. The last half of his cruise in
the frigate *Cumberland,* therefore had been accomplished
without benefit of cat-o'-nine-tails. Observing the effect of

the painless regime in comparison with the orthodox system of flagellation, Dr. Squibb's views on corporal punishment, already taking shape aboard the *Erie,* had now become crystallized. And he was convinced that Congress was in error.

Not one to keep his opinions to himself, and never a man to avoid taking pen in hand, the seagoing Quaker decided to tell the country, the Congress, and the Secretary of the Navy just what was wrong with the new legislation. Therefore, in addition to his morning, afternoon and evening classes at medical school, his detailed recording in his journal of the lectures and clinics, and an extremely active social life, Dr. Squibb worked for several weeks on a 2,500-word indictment of the new Navy humanitarianism.

He discussed his project with his friends, Navy and medical, and even old acquaintances who were neither. He recorded that one fine November day he was "coming down Walnut Street in admiration of the beautiful houses and the character they gave the street, when I saw George Chapman sitting at the window. Went in and talked to him for half an hour and had his opinion about my punishment article." Later the same day, after Dr. Pancoast's lecture, "walked to Chestnut Street with Pancoast, talking of Punishments in the Navy."

If he had been hesitating about whether to send his opinions directly to the Navy or to appeal first to the people, he must have been influenced by his first journalistic success—the acceptance of his medical report of the *Cumberland* by Dr. Hays, editor of the *American Journal of the Medical Sciences.* The sight of the proof sheets of the *Cumberland* piece apparently decided him to offer his flogging argument to the *Philadelphia North American and United States Gazette.*

Dr. Squibb's journal entry for November 15, 1851, records that "at 10 went down to Dr. Hays with the corrected proof sheets [of the *Cumberland* log]. Then on down through the driving rain to the North American office with my paper on Punishments in the Navy. Dr. Bird, the editor, was not in, so

left the paper and a card and was to call again at 2 o'clock."
Dr. Squibb went on to Uncle Edmund Bonsall's store "to try
to borrow some money, being reduced down to four cents,
not enough for an omnibus ride on this wet day. Uncle was
not in town, so this failed. Then up to Sprague's store to see
Jacob, with better success."

Later that day, after Mütter's lecture, he "returned to the
North American office and after waiting a few minutes Dr.
Bird came in. He seemed like a gentlemanly person but
thought my paper too long for them to publish. He wished
to read it so I left it with him."

The piece occupied nearly half a page in the *North American* for November 19, 1851. It was headed "Punishments in
the Navy" and signed only with the initials "E.R.S." It was
a verbose, logical, lucid, and reluctant apologia for corporal
punishment aboard ship, and was here and there reminiscent
of the *Cumberland* health report, particularly in reference
to shipboard hygiene and the author's characterization of
the Navy as "the national representation to the congress of
the nations of the world."

Without mentioning the *Cumberland* by name, Dr. Squibb
wrote:

The law abolishing flogging operated in this ship nearly as
follows, imprisonment and capital punishment being then the
only resources:

The slight punishments habitually resorted to for slight offences were the first to be impaired; for men who should get tired
of standing in the rigging, or of carrying a crowbar round the
decks, would defy their officers and orders, and be put in the ship's
prison, where they would have what was better suited to their
general character—idleness, the regular ration, and a companionship of their own class, while better men must do their portion of
duty.

Imprisonment is scarcely a punishment to the lazy and dissolute, who most require to be punished. But it is not so slight a
punishment to the eight better men of a maintop gang that they

should have the duty of ten men to do because two are in prison for crime; nor to the man who is called from his legitimate leisure, or his game of draughts, to take an oar in a boat in place of a man imprisoned for desertion or rum smuggling. . . .

A ship's prison is as close, damp, filthy, and unhealthy as any dungeon and as inhuman, as degrading, and as unphilanthropic as any flogging can be, without producing the desired salutary effect. . . . It may be mentioned that the huddling of criminals together, under such circumstances, is liable to the charge of producing other evils, of a kind that need not be glanced at.

Examining a proposed set of amendments to the antiflogging act, Dr. Squibb warned Congress that the proposal "to introduce a system of rewards for merit; and to put prisoners upon a diet of bread and water; and deduct the cost of time lost by imprisonment from prisoner's pay" would not work out. He declared that "bad men" could not be made to aspire to rewards, "for a loss of the spirit of emulation generally precedes all sorts of vice."

As for the proposal to put a man on bread and water for twenty days,

even if he should come out without developed disease, it will yet require 20 other days to fit him again for exercise as a full hand upon a topsail yard, or at his gun, or in any other position where physical strength is required. . . .

Let a ship go into action with 20 men on bread and water, or just come off of this diet, and, everything else being equal she will be whipped by a full handed vessel of her own metal because she has in those 20 weak men the equivalent of two silent guns. . . .

There is no doubt that the punishment by flogging was abused, but yet the writer has never seen a man flogged who seriously represented that he would consider it a moral degradation. . . . The tyrannical or passionate abuse of flogging . . . have led gradually and naturally to the present reaction. A medium seems now desirable wherein the abuses may be corrected and discipline maintained against all the idle, dissolute, vicious, and criminal that must of necessity enter largely into the peace service of any navy.

Should war happen, better men could soon be had, and patriotism, pride, and emulation would overcome vice and crime better than prisons. . . .

Had Congress interfered with the Articles of War only so far as to establish drum head courts martial for the trial of offences less than capital and entrusted to these alone the punishment of offences not absolutely trivial, abolishing flogging entirely except by sentence of such court, the evil would have been remedied and discipline maintained.

On publication day Dr. Squibb read his handiwork with a critical and not-too-friendly eye. With the typical attitude of author to editor, he wrote: "After breakfast looked over my piece in the North American and found it altered in two or three places and by no means for the better, and published on a supplementary half-sheet with proposals for the Mail Contracts and an extract from Lynch's new flimsy book.* Don't at all like the society in which it appears. If they could not have given it a proper place in the paper, they should not have published it at all. I had rather he had refused it, for then I could have offered it elsewhere."

Later the same day Dr. Squibb repented of his petulance. "Walking down the street after the [Mütter] lecture," he wrote, "met [Captain] Garland who told me that my Punishment article had been editorially noticed in the paper, a circumstance I did not know before, so that I had done the editor an injustice by supposing he had hid the article by placing it in the supplement."

The author then sent marked copies of the North American to his old friend Dr. Sam White; to Dr. Bache, of course; to Dr. Barrington, the surgeon of the Cumberland; to Dr.

* Narrative of the U.S. Exploring Expedition to the River Jordan and the Dead Sea, by W. F. Lynch, U.S.N., commander of the expedition, which Dr. Squibb read word for word, although he subsequently referred to it as "Lynch's heroics."

C. T. Guillon, another Navy surgeon; to Dr. Thomas Harris, chief of the Navy's Bureau of Medicine and Surgery; and to William A. Graham, the North Carolinian who was President Fillmore's Secretary of the Navy.

The medical report on the cruise of the *Cumberland* did not get nearly as wide a circulation; Dr. Squibb had some trouble wheedling author's copies out of Dr. Hays, editor of the *American Journal of the Medical Sciences*. He finally had to settle for "a package of sheets (waste)" although he had asked for the complete *Journal*.

Curiously, however, Dr. Squibb seemed more engrossed in the subject of flogging than in his medical log. When Commodore Stockton, once the fire-eating skipper of the *Erie* and the hero of the war in California, made a surprising speech in favor of the antiflogging law, Dr. Squibb read the text in the Philadelphia *Public Ledger*. "I came home and read it—read it all—milk and water as it is," he commented in his journal. "His side of the question is not worth much if they cannot produce better speeches and arguments than that."

III

MRS. BLYTHE'S CHESTNUT STREET boardinghouse was the focus of Dr. Squibb's existence during his winter of rubbing up, largely for economic reasons. He took all his meals there, walking home at noon (for dinner) and in the evening (for tea) except when he was invited to eat with his numerous relatives or (rarely) his old friends. And while he spent long hours writing in his room—his journal, his journalism, and a voluminous correspondence—he also managed to carry on a surprisingly complex social life.

Part of his social life centered at Mrs. Blythe's, beginning at the breakfast table. Often, after a breakfast of short ribs and coffee, he would go to his own chamber and carry back to the breakfast room original oil paintings or sketches of the Bay of Naples, largely for the edification of a pair of mature ladies named Mrs. Dana and Miss Peters. His relationship with the Dana-Peters pair sometimes extended into the evening hours, when he would exhibit his Bohemian glass, his scrapbooks, his plaster medallions from Italy, or his music box. He occasionally played chess with Mrs. Dana, who sometimes beat him although she played badly. And early in the winter he took his music box to outside parties, until he found "it would not play the polka fast enough to dance by."

He paid social calls by the dozens, and since there was no telephone at mid-nineteenth century, he expended a great store of foot power and many calling cards in the process. One November evening he records that after Pancoast's lecture he "walked down Sansom street . . . to Garland's. He and his wife were out so I walked up to Harry Serrill's. They also were out so I turned homeward, buying some molasses candy on the way to soothe my feelings after having walked 44 squares, at least 3 miles, for nothing. Came home and journalized until 10 o'clock and soon after retired. Weather clear, fine, and cold, with the wind from the N.W."

He went to art exhibits and concerts and recorded his impressions with the care and fastidious taste-decisions of a James Huneker. Coming home from a Philharmonic concert, he reported: "A Mr. Turner, ballad singer, sung as falsely as though he had no command of his notes, and yet had a pleasant voice. . . . Biscaccianti was the great attraction and sang with great taste and skill . . . and an exquisite finish that reminded me strongly of Tadolini. She sang . . . in a manner as far beyond Jenny Lind's conception . . . as is possible."

The man who was caterer of the *Erie's* wardroom and postmaster of the *Cumberland* would naturally inherit an equally thankless job wherever he was. And Edward Squibb, during his winter rubbing up, was the man to collect Jefferson Medical College's quota (one dollar per M.D.) of a subscription to erect a monument in London to Edward Jenner, as a belated centennial memorial to the man who introduced vaccination to Europe.

Dr. Squibb exercised his profession, too, during his refresher course—mostly for relatives and friends, but occasionally for modest fees. One such case he records: "Found a note upon my table from Ned Atmore, asking to see me with regard to taking charge of his family professionally. This I must undertake, as he is in pecuniary difficulty, and their doctor, Lieper, dead—notwithstanding that they live in 6th above Green."

A week earlier Dr. Squibb had tried to borrow money from Uncle Jake to pay his board, as he was broke until payday.

He was in regular correspondence with Sam White, who was still a little wistful over not having joined the Navy with his friend in '47, and who repeated his offer to stake Ed Squibb to a fresh start in private practice any time he wanted.

Dr. Squibb continued to ignore the stigma the Quakers had put upon him. On October 26, 1851, a rainy Sunday, shortly after taking up residence in Philadelphia again, he records that he "borrowed an umbrella from Mrs. Blythe and went down to Cherry St. Meeting to an accustomed seat not occupied before for nearly five years. Three or four old faces were around me there, but some were missing. Gone! Gone where?" Afterward he went around to see Grandmother Squibb and his father.

On alternate Sundays he went to Darby to see Grandmother Bonsall (who had a slight stroke that winter), to return an empty pie plate to Aunt Mary Bonsall, to see his numerous more distant relatives, and to attend the Darby meeting. At one meeting he reports that he heard "a good because short exhortation from Jane Price. . . . After meeting, during the whole of which I had aunt's mince-pie plate and napkin buttoned under my coat spoke to many friends and walked down with Dodgsons." To Martha Dodgson, whom he had long admired greatly and respectfully, he gave a copy of Dr. Meigs's memoir on a deceased colleague named Morton.

December of 1851 was a cold month. Dr. Squibb, who

still ended his daily entry in his personal log in a nautical manner, frequently wrote some such notation as "Thermometer in Bringhurst's door at 10 A.M. 14°, at 2 P.M. 20°, and at 4 P.M. 21°. Clear, fine and healthy atmosphere but dusty. Wind westerly."

On Christmas Eve Lajos Kossuth came to Philadelphia. Dr. Squibb was determined to see the man he had long admired and in whose presence in the United States he had a semiproprietary interest, inasmuch as the U.S.S. *Mississippi* of the Mediterranean Squadron had spirited the Hungarian patriot out of Europe. The doctor was making a professional call at the Atmores', he wrote, "and literally pushed through a Kossuth crowd from Chestnut to Race Street. All Sixth Street seemed alive at the windows and doors, and the pretty faces, God bless them, were not a few upon this ante-Christmas Kossuth. . . . Finally got through and read all the huge 'welcomes' until I got below Market Street, and here an immense picture arrested my admiration strongly, in its downward course. A very Lady-Macbeth-looking Liberty . . . wrapped tightly in a star-spangled banner had a fast hold of a tombstone-looking affair with a bust of Washington, and was looking back over her shoulder with the air 'you may come as much as you please but I'm d--d if you shall have this shrine of Liberty nohow.' A monstrously theatrical looking Kossuth stood a little way off with his legs rushing toward Liberty while his body hung back, determinedly clinging to a stand of colors. Farther still from Liberty was a huge Snake hissing visibly if not audibly, and with a golden crown on its head. Some links of chain separated, not broken, lay on the ground denoting what? Underneath all this was a welcome to Kossuth to the shrine of freedom; on one side was a large American Flag, and on the other a scarlet flag with 'Auction Sale this Evening.' In going up Chestnut Street saw Powell on Jones' steps, and we walked up to my room together, I having previously however, gone to the college and found there would be no lectures on account of the procession . . . a large number of amateur soldiers, amounting in all to some 3000 and at the end or near it, surrounded by the City Troop as a body guard, standing up in an open barouche was the famous Kossuth, a man of common stature with a good, intelligent-looking face as far as could be seen for the beard, and very large expressive eyes. His dress reminded me instantly, and his manner fixed the idea, of a Hamlet who had escaped, and was getting into a good humor, for he smiled at every bow. How much of Hamlet there may be about Kossuth I do not know but certain it is that he has the mantle, cap and feather. A number of carriages two abreast and the usual number of 'chief marshals' and 'aids' made up the procession, and it was a very long and creditable one—creditable to its real object, that of sympathizing with the country of Kossuth as represented in his person."

Dr. Squibb not only loved parades, but was also a fire buff, a hobby which Philadelphia twice gratified hugely during the last days of 1851. On December 27, fire broke out in Hart's Building at Sixth and Chestnut and burned down Johnson's law-book establishment. "A great deal of property destroyed and what is worse, three lives at least," wrote Dr. Squibb. "The old Eagle Hotel, fortunately, is among the ruins, for it was a very low, disorderly place."

Next day the doctor stopped by to watch the hook-and-ladder men pull down the smoking walls, noted that the thermometer in Bringhurst's door stood at 18° at 2 P.M., and heard "that the water thrown from the engines froze and fell as hail from the houses, and that many fire plugs were burned down in attempting to get water from them."

Two nights later he had the good luck to witness the spectacle of the year—appropriately enough at Barnum's Museum—which he described in detail in his journal. He had just come from Mason's, the engravers, where he had left his seal stones to be appraised ("He told me they were all good but one") and was nearing Seventh Street when he "heard the cry of fire, and looking up saw that the top of Barnum's Museum, in Swaim's immense block on the corner of 7th, was all in a flame and fire coming through two of the windows of the upper story."

He wrote: "Saw there was such a rush as to preclude the possibility of being of any use, and when satisfied of this took a stand in the doorway of a closed furnishings store just above the corner of 7th and from this spot watched the whole immense building burn story by story down to the very ground. It was a grand and fearful sight, for the fury of the flames was far beyond control. It was an episode in the eternal warfare of man with the Elements wherein the latter were altogether victorious from the outset, for no effort of man seemed of the slightest avail to the fated house.

"Commencing at the very top, and at the corner where the Drummond Light was, it enveloped story after story and burst forth from window after window down to the very ground. In Henderson's Bookstore on the corner the gas lights were burning tranquilly, shedding a pale, sickly sort of light around the deserted store, while the whole building above seemed swimming in an atmosphere of flame,—red, angry, furious flame. Finally, floor after floor falling through, the lower story caught and blazed from the doors and windows. Still the little gas light burned away, offering its most curious contrast of tranquility to the furious, devouring confusion around. As though frightened a little by the crashing, falling beams above, it would now and then tremble a little, but regaining at once its steady pale flame, it burned serenely and silently amid all the destruction until surrounded by clouds of flame it was finally crushed out by the falling of the floor above.

"This was one of the impressive lessons of the scene, for it was the perfect type of that quality so desirable in the human mind, which is so eminently the gift of wisdom. To be tranquil, steady, firm and constant, amid scenes of confusion, destruction, and danger, with inevitable fate in full view, is human greatness. . . .

"The east wall fell first and seemed to crush Fisher's house beneath its ruin. Then a part of the Chestnut St. front fell, after bowing most curiously. Then another part of this same front, and lastly the whole line of the west front came down with one awful crash. . . .

"Came home around seven, the whole building having burned to the ground in two hours. . . . Weather cloudy, rainy, foggy and mild all day, with filthy sidewalks and streets deep with slush and mud. Most disagreeable weather, much worse than the cold."

Next day, the last day of the year, Dr. Squibb walked out to look at "the ruins of the two great fires. People were engaged in carrying wax figures that had been saved and scattered about in neighbouring houses. . . . When I reached the Custom House, found the steps and pavement crowded with people to see the funeral of a Mr. Healy, whose remains have recently been recovered from the ruins of the 6th St. fire . . . and that of a watchman named Baker . . . just about to start from the U. S. Hotel."

A week later Assistant Surgeon Edward Robinson Squibb received a great personal shock.

He was ordered to sea.

IV

DR. SQUIBB HAD CARRIED on a considerable correspondence with Surgeon Thomas Harris, chief of the Navy's Bureau of Medicine and Surgery—the rank of surgeon general was not created until fifteen years later—regarding his future. Although he should have known from past personal experience that the Navy's starboard command did not always know what was going on to larboard, he believed he had reached an agreement with the bureau that he should not be sent to sea again at least until he had taken his examination for promotion to the rank of passed assistant surgeon, and perhaps even longer, if his pet project of making decent medicines could be developed. And yet when he came home to Mrs.

Blythe's for dinner one noon early in January, he found a yellow document staring at him from a corner of the dining-room mantelpiece—orders to "proceed to New York and report to Captain Salter for duty on board the Steamer Fulton."

As Dr. Squibb had never heard of the *Fulton* "except as an experimental wreck," the news spoiled his appetite. Yet he acknowledged receipt of orders, wrote privately to Dr. Harris asking for an explanation, and spent a busy few days preparing to depart.

He took leave of his patients (Mrs. Atmore's weeping nearly moved him to tears). He arranged for Andrews' trunk establishment to repair and ship his luggage. On saying good-bye to Grandmother Squibb, he was presented with a family heirloom—a pair of "gold sleeve buttons that had belonged to Uncle James Robinson," which he took around to Mason the engraver to have made into a seal ring, his old one "having become too small after 8 years of wear." He turned in to Dr. Dunglison the subscription list for the Jenner monument, and the money he had collected ($10, including his own dollar) and had his hair cut at Goebel's.

On Sunday he rode out to Darby to say goodbye to Grand-mother Bonsall and the family there. He arrived late at the Darby Meeting "which was silent and rather short." He reclaimed the uniforms and seagoing bedding stored in Uncle Edmund Bonsall's attic and arranged to have his room furniture and Bohemian glass brought from town to be stored there in return. He enjoyed Aunt Mary's "promised terrapins," and bade a tender but dignified farewell to Cousin Martha Dodgson.

Next morning he "saw as he was dressing the first rosy tinges of the morning sun, with its warm hues, over the cold, snow-clad scene. It was a most beautiful sunrise and made the wintry morning feel less wintry. . . . Breakfast about 8, and then started with Uncle and my tin box of uniforms, 'Nance' soon spun us over the smooth icy plank road and by a little after half-past eight we were at Mattson's door, where I wished to take my box of clothing. Spent half an hour or more with Mattson in trying on coats for alteration and repair and in devising means for avoiding the expense of a new full-dress coat."

He continued to attend his medical lectures until the last moment, even while attending to dozens of errands. He rode to the Navy Yard to get his pay and have his account transferred to New York. While there he learned that regulations for naval officers' uniforms were about to be changed, so he had to hurry back to Mattson's to countermand his orders for new uniforms and for changes in his full dress. He also went to Kerrison's, Tenth Street above Spruce, to have his music box cleaned and delivered to the Richard Levicks for their use during his absence. He walked to Sprague's to say good-bye to Uncle Jake and borrow ten dollars; to Horstmann's to see about a sword and uniform buttons; and to Schiveley's to leave a requisition for surgical instruments for the U.S.S. *Fulton.*

By half past nine of a cold bright Wednesday morning, January 14, 1852, Dr. Squibb had tipped Mrs. Blythe's servants, loaded his trunk into a hack and set out for the Walnut Street ferry. As the horse clop-clopped along the icy streets, he brooded upon his misfortune in having to leave the most friendly city in the world, snapping the ties of home and family that he had been so happy to find again, abandoning the warmth of feminine society for long months of an all-male world and the loneliness of the sea. As he was to write that night: "How beautiful and blooming the ladies looked as they tripped along with their fresh rosy color and their smiling faces and bright eyes on this winter's morning. How cheerful and bright and bustling the shops and shopmen looked, and how the beautiful little girls skipped along by Washington Square with arms loaded with books. . . . The very housemaids, as they brushed out entries, seemed to look bright and smilingly out, as if they wondered how anyone could possibly be so unfortunate to leave so bright and happy a place."

At ten o'clock the ferry *Dodo* crunched her way across the frozen river, found the Market Street steamer *Merchant* caught in the ice of the canal through the island, and pushed her out of the way to reach her slip at Camden, where the steam cars waited.

For three hours, as the train chuffed its way across New Jersey, Dr. Squibb occupied himself with the Philadelphia *Public Ledger* and the New York *Herald*, reading about the Forrest divorce case, Congress, and Kossuth's speeches.

"About 1 o'clock," he reported, "we reached South Amboy and embarked in the steamer John Potter. Calling nearly opposite for exchange of passengers and stores, we were soon again under way, and obliged to go round Staten Island and up through the Narrows in consequence of the regular passage being frozen up. Got a glimpse of Sandy Hook and Navesink, and saw the steamer Africa just going out. Went on the upper deck to see the Narrows and harbour in their winter clothing but it was much too cold to remain there long. At 10 minutes past 3 we were at the slip."

It took Dr. Squibb another half hour via the Broadway stage to get uptown to the Bond Street House, where he had stayed before and which "somehow or other" he rather liked, despite the fact that it was against his principles to stay at a hotel where there were only Irish servants.

"It was fortunately soon 5 o'clock," he wrote that night, "and the dinner horn, and after bathing face and hands, I sat down hungry as a hawk. Some little decline in the table since my last visit, the dishes and Irish servants being less clean and the latter more stupid."

Next morning, he went by omnibus and ferry to the Brooklyn Navy Yard, where he reported to Captain Salter and was told that the *Fulton* would not sail for a fortnight. Moreover, he found that he would be obliged to take odds and ends that had come home in other ships, and he feared he would have to put to sea with rusty instruments and miserable drugs. When he went down to the wharf to look at the *Fulton*, however, he "found her a good-looking craft, with a much better

Dispensary than I had expected, and with a very comfortable wardroom with six staterooms, and each an airport—quite high enough for me to stand erect. If she escapes going to the bottom, she will be a very comfortable vessel as far as quarters are concerned. She is very low in the water and must of course be very wet at sea.

"After inspecting her pretty thoroughly, returned to the yard dispensary and we went again on picking out instruments &c. A young Irishman named Joseph Prosser presented himself as a candidate for my hospital stewardship, and being rather prepossessed by his appearance, I told him all the hardships that he would have to pass through, and then took his references—an Irish Dr. Kelly in Fulton Avenue. When we had gone through the requisitions, it being half past 2, I went with the yard steward, who was drunk and had a broken arm, by the way, down to search for this said Dr. Kelly. When we reached his shop he was not there, and I was obliged to wait until after 3 o'clock. He came finally, however, and gave Prosser such a character as determined me to take him, even taking his and the doctor's nationality into consideration. He is to come to the Yard tomorrow at 10, when we will close the contract if he does not back out, for I gave him a clear description of all the deprivations and hardships he must undergo, and left him to sleep on the matter. . . . This done came across and . . . went up to my cold little room and wrote the necessary letter to the department on reporting for duty. To this letter I added, in as brief and forcible manner as I could, the state of my case in regard to the coming examination, and asked diplomatically that the Board might be ordered at once, and I permitted to go before them before sailing."

Preparing for sea duty did not interfere with Dr. Squibb's social life. He spent an evening with the Thornes on Washington Square, ending with the traditional (in New York, at least) sardines, olives, and claret punch. He spent a pleasant (if puzzling) evening with the De Mottes, friends of Captain Salter's, who delighted him with their cake and wine but bewildered him with their house guest, a Miss Evertson, who seemed very dull indeed early in the evening but who later produced exquisite "music from her mandolin music box—the most charming 'Fashionable Polka' I ever heard; could scarcely sit still for it." The riddle of Miss E. seemed to be her relationship with the Navy Yard commandant. Dr. Squibb seemed at first to think they were engaged, but he learned later that Captain Salter was already married.

With his characteristic energy, Dr. Squibb was requisitioning carpenters and materiel to rebuild the *Fulton*'s dispensary. He was rudely reprimanded by Captain Salter because he "did not go all the way home to get a uniform coat in which to appear in his august presence" while asking for an order to get an old shipmate, Dr. Edwards, shipped as an associate aboard the *Fulton*. And when he went aboard the receiving ship *North Carolina* to see that his new steward, Prosser, was being properly processed, he discovered that another old shipmate, Dr. C. T. Guillon, was aboard.

Dr. Guillon, it developed, had been aboard the *Fulton* during her trial trip, and he swore "she had really made some $8\frac{1}{2}$ miles of Pilot's measured distance in 28 minutes in smooth water, and nearly as much in the swell of the sea off Sandy Hook."

Dr. Guillon, in Dr. Squibb's opinion, was a character, although an influential character. Dr. Guillon offered to cut corners in the processing of Prosser, and to show him the ropes. Dr. Guillon then, according to Dr. Squibb's journal, "took me down into his perfectly French room on the lower gun deck. There were the striped red and white curtains spangled with gilt stars. There were the nude plaster and bronzed figures all around—and there, too, were the pictures of naked women, bathing, dressing, flying in gauze &c, all in perfect keeping with himself; and there also was Pierre, the French 'darkey' of old, putting all the French finery in order as of old. On a nail near the bed hung a brass key of the Commandant's private gate through which the Commandant's wife had given him the privilege of passing into the

Yard at all hours of the night, the public gates being closed at midnight—all quite in character. The said doctor was dressed in citizen's clothes, and had the same old prolonged mustache which in itself was much more a breach of uniform, or quite as much, as my daring to go before the Commandant dressed as a gentleman. Yet he goes to the Commandant in this French clown-and-dancing-master compound appearance and escapes without insult."

Still smarting over his "unjust orders" for sea duty, Dr. Squibb walked over to the Brooklyn Naval Hospital, where he discovered two old colleagues: Dr. Edward Hudson, his fellow assistant surgeon of the frigate *Cumberland,* and Dr. John L. Burt, who had also been rubbing up in Philadelphia. Each had welcome news for Dr. Squibb. Hudson was anxious to go to sea again and offered to take the Squibb post aboard the *Fulton.* Burt had recently been married in Philadelphia, and he wanted Squibb to meet his new wife, reputedly of an excellent family.

"It was now 2 o'clock, Dr. Squibb wrote that night. "I accepted an invitation to dinner from Dr. Burt . . . and sat down to a most frugal dinner with them. If all married Assistant Surgeons must live this way, I beg to be preserved from such matrimony. Beefsteak, mutton chop, potato bread and butter, and beets, and the doctor's whiskey and water formed the entire dinner, but served nicely and cleanly and well cooked.

"After dinner, which was not prolonged . . . I asked for pen, ink and paper and . . . wrote a private letter to Dr. Harris, stating all the circumstances that had come to my knowledge today and saying how acceptable would be orders to this hospital and how acceptable, probably, would be the orders to the Fulton to Dr. Hudson. Showed the letter to Burt to show him that I had not compromised Hudson—took a copy of it for my Letter Book, and then went to look for Dr. Bache to read it to him before closing it. He, however, had gone to town. . . . After waiting some time in the porter's lodge for an omnibus, rode to Fulton Ferry, crossed, and walking up to the Post Office, mailed my letter and paid the postage."

The Dr. Bache whose approbation Dr. Squibb sought was a nephew of the revered Dr. Franklin Bache of Jefferson Medical College and the *Dispensatory;* he was Dr. Benjamin Franklin Bache, a great-grandson of Benjamin Franklin and commandant of the Brooklyn Naval Hospital. He was an old Navy man, a product of Princeton (class of 1819) and the University of Pennsylvania Medical School, who had been fleet surgeon of the Mediterranean Squadron in the early 1840s and of the Brazil Squadron while Dr. Squibb was an assistant surgeon in the brig *Perry*. With him, too, Dr. Squibb had often discussed the crying shame of drugs issued by the Navy to shipboard dispensaries, and they had pledged themselves informally to do something about the sad state of affairs if the occasion ever presented itself. The occasion was apparently at hand.

The next day being Sunday, Dr. Squibb remained in his room at Bond Street House, bringing his journal and letter book up to date. (Carbon paper not yet having come into use, he laboriously copied each letter he wrote into a ledger, leaving space in which to paste the reply.) He fled, however, when the maid came to make up his room—"a sweet specimen of the Emerald Isle she is, too. Filthy and untidy as the best of them, and loquacious beyond endurance. I always rush downstairs General Putnam fashion when I hear the jingling of her beads."

What appeared to be a rankling, deep-seated, bigoted dislike of the Irish was actually only skin deep. Some of his dearest friends and associates were to be sons and daughters of Erin, and after he had reached a position of affluence he was a frequent and generous contributor to Irish charities.

Dr. Squibb's Manhattan nights were spent largely with friends who served sardines and claret punch, who perhaps entertained a Hungarian refugee or two, and who had young lady friends who sang and gentlemen friends who could discuss flogging and etherization.

Within a few days the Navy gave way under the combined pressure of Dr. Bache and his friends, Dr. Hudson and his friends, and Dr. Squibb. As a result, Dr. Hudson was to go to sea in the U.S.S. *Fulton,* and Dr. Squibb was to be assigned to Dr. Bache at the Brooklyn Naval Hospital.

The pet project was under way at last. The United States Navy was about to get pure drugs for its sick bays.

At least that is what Drs. Squibb and Bache thought.

V

WHEN THE ORDER detaching Dr. Squibb from the *Fulton* arrived, however, there was no mention of his assignment to the Brooklyn Naval Hospital. Instead, he was posted as "waiting orders," and it began to look as if he would go to sea again in the brig *Perry* for service off the coast of Africa. He immediately applied for and received permission to go home to Philadelphia—where, three days later, he got his orders to join the staff of the Brooklyn Naval Hospital. Borrowing nine dollars from Uncle Edmund and five from Uncle Jacob, he promptly complied.

On his return to Brooklyn January 26, he found a notice to present himself for examination at the Naval Asylum in Philadelphia on February 16.

At least he had three weeks to settle himself in his new quarters, familiarize himself with his new duties, and perfect his plans for the big project.

Dr. Bache and Dr. Squibb had agreed that buying drugs the way the Navy did—like rope and oakum, from the lowest bidder—was a crime. Congress had approved and President Polk had signed a measure prohibiting the importation of impure pharmaceuticals as early as 1846. Yet two years later a Dr. Edwards had memorialized Congress in these words: "The United States has become the grand mart and receptacle of all the refuse merchandize . . . from the European warehouses [and] the whole Eastern world." Rhubarb was worm-eaten and decayed, unfit for human consumption. Peruvian bark was mixed with willow bark, chalk, and plaster of Paris. Opium was adulterated with Spanish licorice paste. Scammony root was mixed with clay and vegetable matter.

Dr. Huston at Jefferson Medical College had written a monograph pointing out that insufficient and inefficient inspection had made the Act of 1846 practically a dead letter and that domestic practitioners of adulteration were reaching a very high degree of skill, almost the equal of European and Oriental falsifiers.

Dr. Bache and Dr. Squibb were resolved that Brooklyn Naval Hospital, at least, and if possible the ships it supplied, would have chemically pure drugs of standard strength.

Brooklyn Naval Hospital was a collection of two- and three-story whitewashed brick buildings set in a high-walled, neatly landscaped reservation across Wallabout Channel from the Navy Yard. Since there had been no smallpox cases in some time, Dr. Bache proposed to let Dr. Squibb have the upper floor of the pesthouse for a manufacturing laboratory. He had already priced a steam engine and a mill for grinding crude drugs. He was relying on Dr. Squibb, the old apothecary's apprentice, to outfit the plant on a shoestring.

The laboratory operation was of course to be in addition to Dr. Squibb's regular duties as house physician. He was to take care of the southern wing of the hospital and Dr. Burt the northern. He was not favorably impressed by the current state of the wards, "finding most of them in a dirty condition and one or two smelling horribly." However, Dr. Bache had told him he could make any changes he saw fit, so he immediately began moving empty beds out of occupied wards and regrouping cases according to their seriousness. He also climbed to the roof and shoveled snow, trying to locate leaks.

He was quite pleased with his private quarters—a parlor and a bedchamber, each with a fireplace—upon which he soon placed his personal imprint by moving furniture and arranging space for his books, his pictures and scrapbooks, his

Bohemian glass, and his music box when it arrived from Darby. He explored the market possibilities of Fulton Street, elected Story's as his grocer, and discussed menus with Ellen, the officers' cook. Ellen, he recorded, made excellent soup and capital meat pies and could do a beefsteak or a pork tenderloin to a turn, although she at first forgot that Dr. Squibb liked his hominy every day.

The assistant surgeon was not entirely happy, however, for he was forced to live on credit for the first ten days of February. He had been fighting a running—and for a long time a losing—battle with the Navy's paymaster corps in an attempt to collect his just emoluments. Purser S. P. Todd of Brooklyn Navy Yard insisted that Dr. Squibb's accounts would naturally have been transferred from Philadelphia Navy Yard to the U.S.S. *Fulton*. The purser of the *Fulton* had never seen a Squibb pay sheet. Dr. Squibb prepared certified copies of his orders detaching him from the *Fulton* and those assigning him to Brooklyn Naval Hospital and filed them with Purser Todd, Purser Douglass of the *Fulton,* and Purser McBlair at Philadelphia Navy Yard. Nothing happened.

He was then informed that the accounts had been received by Purser Todd "and went down to the Navy Yard by appointment to Purser Todd's office to get my pay. When I reached the office, was told by his clerk that my account was probably at the Purser's house; that he had not been down to the Yard since Thursday, but that if the weather should be fine on Monday, he would probably come down, for if he turned out when the weather was damp, he would get the gout worse. . . . Four times have I been to see another of the corps before I could get my account transferred to this office. And now three times to this office, and am yet without pay due me."

On Monday Dr. Squibb returned to the Navy Yard and found that "Mr. S. P. Todd had not been at his office since Thursday, although the weather was fine. Of course my account had not come. Immediately started for his house on the principle that a conscience that would rest easy under a three-days' absence from business for which it received large pay, might rest easy for three weeks or three years. His house, No. 74 Willoughby Street, was another long walk, and when I reached it, was told he had just started for the Navy Yard. Went back at once and sure enough, there he was and there was my account."

With his pay in his pocket, Dr. Squibb paid his grocery bill, took the ferry to New York (although the harbor had been frozen that morning, and many people had walked across before the noonday sun started the ice moving), and bought soap, essences and a toothbrush at Milhau's, ordered picture frames at Williams, Stevens and Williams on Broadway near Leonard, had his hair cut at the hairdresser in Niblo's building, and walked up Broadway looking for cravats, finding none he liked.

When he returned to the hospital, Dr. Burt borrowed a dollar from him "on the plea of having nothing less than a 20-dollar piece, and having I suppose gone over to New York and got fuddled upon it."

Although Dr. Squibb regarded the clumsy fumbling of his payroll as the equivalent of war between two branches of the Navy, Mr. Todd of the paymaster corps—whom Dr. Squibb called "that villainous-looking old purser"—had only the kindliest of feelings toward the Bureau of Medicine and Surgery and continued to use the professional services of Brooklyn Naval Hospital without fear or suspicion, just as if nothing had happened. Dr. Squibb bore witness to this in his journal entry for February 16, 1852, which records that "some farther writing and talking brought dinner time and two patients from Dr. Guillon on board the North Carolina. After dinner had to place them in wards and see beds prepared for them, and then to examine and enter their cases. This done, there was a bottle of one of Mr. Purser Todd's secretions to analyse, an occupation that filled up the time till tea."

VI

FEBRUARY 16 WAS THE DATE originally set for Dr. Squibb's appearance before the Naval Board of Examination in Philadelphia. However, correspondence with the Navy Department developed the information that through some oversight or clerical error his name had been omitted from the list and his examination date was reset for February 26.

Dr. Burt, however, left to be examined on schedule, much to the relief of Dr. Squibb, who did not have the highest regard for his colleague's competence. Even Dr. Bache had serious doubts about Dr. Burt's ability to pass the examination. Besides looking after Dr. Burt's cases and his own, Dr. Squibb was swamped with the work of justifying the proposed new laboratory. First he, Dr. Bache, and the hospital apothecary, an English-born chemist named Beaton, went over the list of drugs habitually furnished to ships of the United States Navy, struck off those they thought ineffectual or outmoded, and added new ones. Next they compiled a list of the current New York prices for every product in their revised catalogue. Then, at Dr. Bache's suggestion, they checked prices year by year back to 1844. And finally they drew up an estimate of the cost of manufacturing the same drugs in the proposed laboratory. The entire report was then forwarded to the Bureau of Medicine and Surgery.

During all of this period Dr. Squibb was busy superintending the carpenters who were turning the floor above the isolation ward into a laboratory, re-establishing discipline in the syphilitic ward, overseeing the repairs to the leaking roof, examining pus with Dr. Bache's new microscope, administering to the dying, and calling twice daily at the porter's lodge to treat Old Lafferty, the Irish gatekeeper, who had fallen down the north stairs.

The mortality rate was rather high at Brooklyn Naval Hospital that winter, and Dr. Squibb not only eased the last moments of the dying with opiates and words of comfort, but he made and witnessed their wills, wrote to relatives, summoned Chaplain Chase when necessary, and walked with the chaplain at funerals, since few windjammer sailors had mourners. He was also his own pathologist—in an era when Bellevue across the East River had none, and a quarter-century before Johns Hopkins was to open its doors, with William Welch to spread the doctrines of Virchow and usher in a new era of American medicine. Dr. Squibb performed his own autopsies and wrote detailed reports which noted not only the direct cause of death but analyzed the conditions which induced the disease. "Poor Henry Porter," for instance, "having contracted a consumption . . . dies a martyr to improper treatment and improper distribution of duties on shipboard." And the post-mortem examination of "poor Naudweck," another tuberculosis victim, prompted him to summon Dr. Bache, who was "puzzled to know how he should possibly have lived so long under such a condition of both lungs." When he had finished Naudweck's autopsy, Dr. Squibb dissected "almost all the arteries of the body, getting knowledge from the dead to be applied to the living. This done, it required an hour to get my hands clean."

Having returned to his own quarters by one o'clock that cold murky February day, Dr. Squibb "sat down to write out the notes of the post mortem until dinner time or two o'clock, having directed dinner to be deferred until the funeral was over. . . . Mr. Chase [the chaplain] was late at his appointment so we did not get through the funeral service in the Chapel till near three. This was fortunate, for the only friend who came to follow poor Naudweck to his grave arrived just before we started, the Chaplain and I in advance of the bier, and this one friend coming after. These are our funerals here."

That night, after making his evening round of the wards, Dr. Squibb called on Dr. Bache. The doctor was playing cards in the dining room with "some gentlemen company," so Dr. Squibb sat in the parlor with Mrs. Bache and her sister, a Miss Cook from Philadelphia.

"Sat with them for some time," he reported. "Took some supper, heard Mrs. Bache sing some airs, and finally came home about 11. It seems of late that ordinary music I hear gives me no pleasure. I used to like all kinds but now I had rather hear none, than bad music."

It may be that the doctor's captious mood was the result of his lugubrious occupations of the morning and afternoon. It is also possible that he was subconsciously comparing Mrs. Bache's voice with the opera singers who had thrilled him so much in Italy. But it is more probable that he was occupied in looking at Mrs. Bache's sister rather than in listening to Mrs. Bache's singing.

Although he made no mention of the fact while writing his journal later that snowy night, Miss Cook was an extraordinarily pretty girl.

VII

"HAD CONGRATULATED MYSELF, on leaving this morning, that I should be for a few days at least free from the responsibilities and anxieties of the sick and dying," wrote Dr. Squibb on the first night of his return to Philadelphia for his examinations, "and yet get here into its midst again where it comes close to home."

He had scarcely arrived when he learned that his father was sinking rapidly. He hurried around to Cherry Street and found his father in a very low condition but still able to recognize him, although he had lost all voluntary motion and most faculties. He sat for an hour at his father's bedside, listening to Grandmother Squibb recall that it was just twenty-four years ago to the day that her husband Robert, Edward's grandfather, had passed away in his sixty-second year. And now, nearing eighty, she was about to lose her son—whom she had nursed as an invalid for twelve years—at the age of fifty-six.

Dr. Squibb's professional eye told him that his father's death, while probably a matter of days, was certainly not a matter of hours. Its inevitability would therefore hang over him in addition to the dread suspense of his naval examination.

Next morning he put on his uniform coat and vest and walked to the Naval Asylum to meet his fate. Drs. Dillard, Blacknall, Hunter, and Mosely made up the Board of Examiners. They first had him fill out a form giving the history of his naval career, the variety of his service and its effect upon his health and general condition. He was next set to describing the symptoms, diagnosis, and treatment of pneumonia, while other candidates fidgeted and walked up and down and another doctor popped in occasionally to bluster encouragement.

"The result of all this," recalled Dr. Squibb when he had stopped perspiring, "was that I wrote weakly and badly, and as for the handwriting, I could scarcely have recognized it. Words incorrectly spelled, words omitted, lines crooked, and all else that was bad, rendered worse by a shocking inkstand, thick ink, and a bad rickety table to write on. The only part satisfactory to look back upon is that I got hold of my subject fairly, and omitted nothing that so limited a time and space might well include. When finished I sent in my two papers and my Letter Books, with the letters [which were pertinent to Navy matters] marked, and then Dr. Dillard came and told me that they had finished with me today but would expect to see me tomorrow by 11 o'clock."

It was then one-thirty. Returning to his hotel—he was stopping at the new Girard House—he changed into "citizens" and went around to Cherry Street. Grandmother Bonsall was there and went up with him to see his father. The elder Squibb was sensibly weaker "with clear indications that the end was not far distant." Dr. Squibb therefore wrote to Brooklyn asking Dr. Bache's permission to prolong his absence.

Despite the double tension of the examination and his father's impending demise, Dr. Squibb was enjoying Girard House. He found the food excellent and was greatly impressed by the newfangled sanitary plumbing arrangements. He must have mastered the unfamiliar contraptions quickly enough to be able to chuckle at his fellows, for one day in the midst of his mental and emotional turmoil he wrote: "Up about half past 8, and through breakfast and the complicated water closets by half past 9. What a capital opportunity is afforded to the negro man there for making extended observations upon the condition of people's prima vice!"

Before starting for the Naval Asylum again, Dr. Squibb had time to glance over Wilson's *Anatomy* to refresh his memory on the cranial nerves—a subject that was not even mentioned by the examiners. He later described the second session of the examination as follows:

" 'Brown' Homer . . . went at me at once, hammer and tongs, upon the formation of the orbit, coats, and then general anatomy of the eye, descending very much into particulars. Thence he went to the shoulder joint, elbow joint and wrist joint, and then asked how I would tell the phalanges of an ourang outang from those of a man. I at once told him I knew nothing of natural history and could not answer the question. This seemed to determine him to going on upon that subject, and he asked the class, species, & some other questions with regard to the place and rank of man in the animal kingdom. Then Dr. Mosely commenced with me, commencing with strabismus, and going successively to purulent ophthalmia, syphilis, hernia, fracture of the leg, thigh and forearm, and finished, I believe, with dislocation of the hip. Then came Dr. Blacknall upon affinity, Blue Pill, Ether, Chloroform, and perhaps a few more items but he troubled me neither much nor long.

"Then Dr. Hunter on the general properties of metals, their number, relative importance, and their combination with oxygen, and I could not for the life of me remember Chlorine. Had also stumbled very much in the matter of physical characteristics of metals. Asked then what arnica was. What specific gravity was, what a barometer was, and how used for measuring heights, and asked how the barometer would stand at the top of the highest mountain, which I could not tell. Also stumped me upon who had first observed the pressure of the atmosphere, and told me it was Galileo, a fact new to me.

"Then Dr. Dillard stumped me at once upon the first question, what is fever. I neither knew anything about the history or the theories and could give him neither that of Cullen nor Brown. Then asked what diseases were those of the chest. Then those of the larynx, the difficulties of prognosis, treatment, &c. Then those of the trachea and upon croup particularly, and this is all I can remember of the examination except that he and Homer took me to the corner with the splints, and having become confused before starting, continued confused throughout. . . . Confounded the splint of Hartshorne with that of Hagedorn, and other silly nervous stupidity. . . . They then told me they had finished and complimented me upon my Letter Books, and signified I was at liberty to retire, Dr. Dillard asking me kindly to his house during my stay."

After going home to change into civilian clothes, he went to see his father, who seemed better. Then on his way to dinner he "determined upon a piece of lavish extravagance upon the strength of being examined and passing, for I had no doubt of the result, from the leniency of the Board, notwithstanding my blunders—so went into Benton's Gold Pen establishment in Chestnut above Fourth and after a long selection paid five dollars for the large pen with which I am now writing so badly for the first time."

As the elder Squibb continued to linger, the doctor profited by his Philadelphia visit by taking care of a dozen errands, both personal and professional. He paid his uncles the money he had borrowed a month earlier and went to Mattson's to be measured for the new uniforms he would want as soon as the pay increase that went with his new (he hoped) rank took effect. He renewed his acquaintance with William Procter Jr., a Quaker and a prominent pharmacist, whom he had met a dozen years before at a meeting of the

Society for the Acquisition of Useful Knowledge. He consulted Mr. Procter about the pharmaceutical apparatus he would need for the proposed laboratory in Brooklyn and was told that Williams the tinman could "make anything that he could be made to understand and would undertake anything." He also visited Browning's store to see specimens of drugs powdered by a new process, and he ate two dozen oysters at Lecount's Eating House with Uncle Edmund Bonsall.

On March 1, 1852, a bright, sunny day sparkling with white frost, James Squibb "passed from this life very quietly, with no convulsion, and to the common eye nothing but the gradually longer coming breaths, like sighs, but not of pain." The family was all assembled and had been waiting for hours in silence, except for Old Maria, the maid, who insisted on going through with her daily cleaning and dusting, undeterred by the imminence of death. Uncle Robert Squibb, whom the doctor had not seen in two years, arrived in time for the end. Cousin John Squibb was there from Ohio, and Aunt Jane. Everyone behaved with philosophic resignation except for Ruth Bonsall, who had hysterics and required the professional attention of Dr. Squibb.

The funeral was held on the third, with Undertaker Bringhurst (whose outdoor thermometer had been Dr. Squibb's weather guide earlier in the winter) making the arrangements. Burial was at Fair Hill, the new Friends graveyard, a cold and dreary hour's ride from town.

It was a hard, sad leave-taking for Grandmother Squibb, but the old lady bravely went through the ceremony of officially constituting Edward the head of the family, now that his father was gone. She turned over to the doctor her marriage certificate and for two hours dictated the "succession and ages of all her children, which with the dates, and those of grandfather's and her own birth, were to be copied onto her marriage certificate." She also gave him a paper written by his father with data regarding Aunt Hanson's family, and some locks cut from the hair of his three sisters, Sarah, Mary and Ellen, at the time of their death, wrapped and endorsed by his mother. "These," wrote Dr. Squibb, "are to be put with my valuables, for the endorsements alone are the only pieces of mother's handwriting that I possess."

It was his last visit with Grandmother Squibb. She, too, was to die that year.

On the day of his father's funeral Dr. Squibb learned that he was now Passed Assistant Surgeon Squibb, that the Board of Examiners had rated him No. 1 in his group, and that they had advanced him seven numbers on the Navy Register.

He also learned with a twinge of regret, even though he had expected it and could not quarrel with the justice of the verdict, that Dr. Burt had been rejected.

Before arranging for his luggage to be shipped back to New York, he dropped in at Davy Gibb's Oyster Cellar to savor two dozen oysters.

three

THE FLOWERING

I

THE MOST EXCITING PERIOD of his life was awaiting Dr. Squibb in Brooklyn. The next two years were to see the realization of his pet schemes—and the sudden blossoming of a happiness he had not even dreamed of. He was to get official Navy blessings for his laboratory, he was to invent a method of making pure ether safely and of standard strength, he was to fall in love, and he was to become a father.

He returned to New York in a heavy snowstorm, so heavy that the hack drivers waiting at Pier 1, North River, for the South Amboy ferry with the Philadelphia passengers, asked four dollars to take him home to Brooklyn.

"This I resisted," wrote Dr. Squibb, "and finally got a porter for my baggage and followed him on foot to the Fulton Ferry. Crossing, took a carriage and came home."

By the time he had a fire going in the grate of his parlor, he was to find that the upstairs nurses, a pair of hearties named Silcox and Young, were roaring drunk, and that "a poor fellow named John Berry, servant to Dr. Potter, [was] about to breathe his last."

Bemoaning the fact that he had sat at five deathbeds in as many weeks, Dr. Squibb spent the first morning of his return to duty in the dead house, where his autopsy revealed that poor Berry "had died from chronic pleurisy of very grave and extensive character, together with effusion and some softening of the brain."

For the funeral, "Mr. Chase, the Chaplain, being sick, Mr. Shackleford, an Episcopalian pastor with a fine voice, read the service in the chapel. Except the half-drunken sailors, and his room mate then, I was the only one to attend poor Berry to his last abode, it being too wet for the parson to go to the grave! It will be dry enough for him to go some day!"

As the winter waned, however, and the sap began to rise in the trees that fringed Wallabout Channel inside the hospital compound, Dr. Squibb's life grew less funereal. Not only was more and more of his time devoted to setting up the new laboratory, and less and less to ministering to the sick and dying, but a new and tender interest seemed to be flowering in his life. With the subconscious feeling of security that came with his promotion and increased pay—his annual stipend jumped from $1,400 to $1,800 for shore duty, plus commutation of rations at 30 cents a day—together with the approach of spring, Dr. Squibb's interest in the opposite sex was rising sharply.

He made frequent trips to Manhattan by the Fulton Ferry, once to buy some metallic arsenic at Milhau's to make Donovan's solution, and to buy a patent inkstand at Jerolimon the stationer's; once to buy a black silk cap to keep the dust out of his hair while carpenters and masons were busy converting the pesthouse upper floor into a laboratory, and to get his hair cut ("very badly") at Christadoro's, where he had a running fight with a barber who was determined to rub cologne and grease into his scalp; and once to call on Uncle Bonsall at the Astor House and walk up Broadway to Lockwood's bookstore for a copy of Mitchell's *Dream Life*. And each time he spent the evening with some young lady of his choice. Miss Julia Talman he found pleasant and sociable, but Miss Thorne—whom he had met in Italy just a year before, when her family had come aboard the frigate *Cumberland* and he

76

had gone with them all to visit Virgil's tomb—he found fascinating.

"With no auxiliaries whatever," he wrote, "simply our two selves and our respective chairs, Miss T. and I manage to spend what to me are very pleasant evenings, so that I almost invariably outstay propriety, and in all human probability make her desire to go to bed before she has the opportunity. But somehow I never recollect how time passes until, as last evening, it was nearly 11 o'clock. It was therefore near 12 when I reached home and retired without the customary late round through the house."

Suddenly the pattern changed. He was a more and more frequent visitor to Dr. Bache's quarters. True, he respected Dr. Bache professionally, for Benjamin Franklin's great-grandson had been a Navy medico since Dr. Squibb was nine years old, a full surgeon with service in the seven seas behind him. But personally Dr. Bache impressed Dr. Squibb as a consummate bore. He was eternally reminiscing about yellow fever in the frigate *Brandywine* at Rio, when Dr. Bache was fleet surgeon for the Brazil Squadron and Dr. Squibb was a green assistant surgeon in the brig *Perry*. Dr. Squibb was also a little chary of Mrs. Bache, a woman of his own age who had married Dr. Bache, nearly twenty years her senior, after the death of her first husband, a man named Hart. Mrs. Bache seemed a little too worldly-wise and more than a little too loquacious. But Mrs. Bache's younger sister Caroline was something else again.

Caroline Cook was not quite real. She was something quite out of Dr. Bache's world, out of Mrs. Bache's world, out of Dr. Squibb's world, out of *this* world.

Caroline Cook was eighteen. She exuded a cool, fresh loveliness that was uncommon in Navy circles, in Quaker circles, in any circle that did not include eighteen-year-olds and in many that did. Her beauty burst upon Dr. Squibb like the glory of sunshine upon a man who has sat for years in darkness. He would never forget the way she looked the first time he saw her.

Her oval face was crowned by thick chestnut tresses parted above the center of her broad forehead and twisted into heavy braids that almost covered her small ears. She had long blue-gray eyes that seemed to be eternally dreaming of things far away and recondite, challenging Edward Squibb to discover their secret. She had a small, fine nose and a rounded, willful chin. Her generous mouth was frequently twisted into a curious, asymmetrical smile that was at once disdainful and inviting, innocent and cynical. Except for the smile, it was a child's face.

Even the voluminous crinoline fashions of the day could not disguise the fact that she was well and generously proportioned. Her velvet-bordered bodice, burgeoning yet wasp-waisted, was modestly sealed with a high collar of white embroidery, fastened at the throat with a heavy gold brooch. She wore another gold brooch at the waist of her basque, anchoring the gold chain from which a gold cross hung into her lap. The fingers which emerged from the flaring bouffants of open-work embroidery at the end of her sleeves were slender and expressive.

She moved with a lively grace and a subdued vitality which seemed to promise great warmth and understanding.

On his thirty-third birthday, Edward Robinson Squibb for the first time in his life found himself violently in love.

Until that time, he had cherished very definite and long-thought-out ideas about the kind of woman a serious man should marry. For years he had been recording the specifications of the ideal wife.

First of all, Dr. Squibb was not looking for physical attraction. In fact, he rather shied away from it. In describing the daughter of a medical colleague, a Dr. Lowber, only a few months before he met Caroline Cook, he wrote in his Philadelphia journal: "Found Miss Fanny to be a pleasant, intelligent young lady. One of your good, sensible girls wherein a mine of gold is covered over by only common, homely earth. Passed the evening discussing books and their authors, and in looking at the doctor's pencil sketches."

78

And the previous October he had called on the Harry Serrills on Buttonwood near Sixth in Philadelphia and found Mrs. Serrill to be "A perfect jewel of a woman and a perfect pattern of a wife. . . . It makes one feel better to see so good and happy a woman. Upon me, I think no Sunday sermon or reflections have nearly so good an effect. There is nothing abstract or incomprehensible here. . . . And the whole of this original goodness lies in the woman, for the man, subjected to the corrupting and slowly, steadily-wearing influences of the world, must have such a home and such a guardian angel to renew oftener than every morning the keenness of those finer sensibilities so rapidly blunted by friction with the wide world's interests and passions. Conjugal love in such women is the shrine of virtue in the world, and he who fails morning and evening to approach it with bowed head and bended knee loses his only security against vice and forfeits the promotion of his own happiness and goodness."

Uncle Robert Squibb's wife, Aunt Jane, had a sister Harriet who also impressed Dr. Squibb as a paragon. After meeting her again for the first time in many years, he found her "a most excellent girl, and having lived well for many years upon her own exertions as a teacher of school, she stands a living monument to the existence of virtue in the world, and eulogizes poor human nature more loudly, more eloquently and to more practical good than all the tombstones that ever were planted. Should like very much to cultivate her acquaintance."

The pattern for a perfect spouse, as Dr. Squibb saw it, was something on the order of his cousin Martha Dodgson—an intelligent, sincere, warmhearted, rather plain woman interested in the serious things of life such as religion, homemaking, children, and the triumph of virtue over the vicious things of the world, self-effacing yet quietly and eternally working for her husband's comfort and welfare, completely devoted to his family, to his work, and to his every word and thought.

Caroline Cook bore only the faintest resemblance to this

idealized portrait. She was beautiful. She laughed a lot. There was no doubt that she was virtuous, but there was a fleeting hint of mischief in her smile that sometimes disturbed Dr. Squibb deeply, although far from unpleasantly. She was passionately interested in dress and adornment. When she visited Dr. Squibb's bachelor quarters—properly chaperoned, of course, by her sister Elizabeth Bache—to look at the doctor's "curiosities," she admired the wrong works of art, did not show great enthusiasm over the Bohemian glass, and made facetious remarks about the oak cane from the castle of Spezia and the dried plants from Pompeii.

Nothing would have made any difference to Dr. Squibb. She was the only possible woman in the world for him. Had he needed to rationalize, he could have quoted his own early hypothesis that a bachelor does not know his own mind. While serving aboard the *Erie* he once wrote that "no man's character can be foretold or judged of fairly until it has been subjected to the modifying influence of the woman he marries."

Edward Robinson Squibb married Caroline Lownds Cook on October 7, 1852—a year which saw such lesser events as the coronation of Napoleon III as Emperor of France and the publication of *Uncle Tom's Cabin*.

II

Dr. Squibb married not only Caroline but the entire Cook family, a fact which he accepted with good grace inasmuch as he himself was a pious devotee of the cult of the family. The Cooks were almost as populous as the Squibbs and the Bonsalls.

Caroline's parents were Lois Crowell and Elisha Worth Cook, who were married in Philadelphia in 1817 and produced nine children, two of whom died young. Only her brother William was younger than Caroline. Sister Elizabeth (Mrs. Bache), who was thirty-four, was the oldest. Then came brother Sam, thirty-one, and Mary Jane, who was married to Theodore F. King, a prominent New York physician. Mary Jane was twenty-five, two years younger than brother Albert. Sister Sarah, whom everyone called Sally, was twenty-three and married to Charley Fellows, who had a jewelry store in Maiden Lane, in Manhattan.

There was also Aunt Lownds, who had a country place 'way out on Ninety-first Street in New York; Cousin Cecilia Lownds; and Cousin Jennie Letson, whose husband was a department head at A. T. Stewart's big store in New York. Uncle Pearson Yard lived with his family at Eleventh Street near Race Street in Philadelphia.

Dr. Squibb regarded them all as very fine people indeed in that gloriously happy and busy first year following his marriage. They were frequent visitors to his home; he had moved from his bachelor's quarters to the more commodious apartment just vacated by Dr. Burt and his wife, directly beneath Dr. Bache's quarters, a handy arrangement for the oldest and youngest of the Cook sisters.

The Naval Laboratory was getting into full swing at about the same time. Dr. Squibb had been spending more and more time "crossing over," buying glassware at Quettier's, brass cocks and couplings, hoses at the india-rubber houses, webbing at Harmer, Hayes, in Beekman Street, and blow-pipes and various piping fixtures from Stratton. He had already been making ammonia, blue pill (a mercuric laxative), potassium iodide, syrup of squill, citric acid, and zinc cerate. He had been making tincture of opium. He made tincture of tolutana by using the resins from the tolu tree (today it is made synthetically from coal tars). He made tincture of colchicine from colchicum seeds he ground up in an old coffee mill.

The Naval Laboratory began making drugs not only for the hospital and for ships calling at Brooklyn Navy Yard, but for the Pensacola naval station. Dr. Squibb, from his own seagoing experience, devised a standard set of all-purpose splints which would take care of all probable fractures aboard ship, including a long splint for the lower extremities, a short carved splint for the inside of the thigh, a double inclined plane (with lower part so arranged as to be easily detached and used separately as a fracture box when required), and a set of leathered wooden splints, complete with two sheets of cotton wadding and a package of tow. (Cost to manufacture: $15.63.)

And, finally and triumphantly, he began to manufacture ether and its by-products: sweet spirit of niter, oil of ether, and Hoffmann's anodyne.

One thing that had impressed Dr. Squibb deeply during his rubbing up at Jefferson was the variation in the effect of ether in anesthetizing patients of similar age and physique. Why, he wondered, were some people more difficult to put to sleep than others? Was it a question of idiosyncrasy—or of the ether? By the spring of 1853 he thought he had the answer.

He bought samples of all the commercially manufactured ether he could lay his hands on and put them through the most painstaking analysis he could devise. He found astounding differences in their degree of purity, in their color, limpidity, and specific gravity. The variations, he concluded, were due to careless manufacture and to the use of diluted alcohol and of sulphuric acid of less-than-standard specific gravity. And the variations in the ether, he decided, were the cause of the differences in anesthetic effect.

His project for the year, he resolved (with Dr. Bache's approval), was to discover a method of manufacturing ether of standard strength and purity. Nothing, he was sure, could make him happier than a foolproof system of distilling ether free of residual water, alcohol, or sulphurous oxide. Nothing.

He was wrong, of course. There were other and greater sources of happiness—such as the knowledge that he was about to become a father.

Dr. Squibb achieved paternity on September 30, 1853, and although he had for weeks been mentally rehearsing all that he had learned in Dr. Meig's course, the actual event did not go off with quite the methodical calm he had planned. He had thought he was quite competent to handle the delivery without the help of outside midwifery, but when the time came he was not much better than most frantic fathers. He recorded the occasion in some detail:

"On Friday morning just about daylight and just before gunfire . . . Caroline told me she had been awakened by a sharp pain, which went off and was repeated again after 10 or 15 minutes. I soon suspected she was in labour, and about 6 got up and dressed. By 8 o'clock the pains were only a few minutes apart, and had become more severe, leaving little doubt of their character. Found the hard head of the child presenting, high up, but no bag of waters. . . . The pains increased in severity and with shortening interval till near noon when there was scarce any interval at all, and her suffering almost beyond endurance. The head was then engaged, but I could not make out the position, and mistook a large sugillation of the scalp for the cord, and was very much worried and very anxious for the life of the babe."

At this point Dr. Squibb tried desperately to remember what Dr. Meigs had counseled about rotation, and the ratio of the diameter of the foetal head to the pelvis—in vain. "Believe that I was so excited as to have lost all judgment and skill in the matter and scarcely know what I did or said."

So he ran upstairs for Dr. Bache. Caroline's sister, of course, came along and more or less took charge.

"As soon as [Dr. Bache] made his examination, the case became all plain and simple again. The character of the pains now changed. They became expulsive, the head naturally and slowly descending. About two o'clock . . . the head was born and soon after another pain pushed the body out as far as the hips. The child breathing and crying well, lay in this position some four or five minutes when another pain expelled it entirely at about twenty minutes past 2 o'clock. Half an hour later a very large placenta came away naturally, and the labour and suffering of my precious wife were over. . . . The child was a fine large fat boy and weighed in the evening 12 pounds with a blanket which was afterward found to weigh 1 pound. No bleeding or other accident occurred and the poor dear felt as though in another world."

On Sunday Father and Mother Cook came up from Philadelphia, Charley and Sally Fellows dropped in for tea, and Aunt Lownds came in later, and "all of course were very much surprised to find a baby."

The baby, by the time he was ten days old, proved to be very fretful, crying almost constantly when not asleep or nursing. "He seems to be much troubled with colic," wrote Dr. Squibb, "passes quantities of wind, and bids fair to be a troublesome . . . child."

Choosing a name for the new baby also proved troublesome for the doctor. As far as Caroline was concerned, the boy's name would be Edward, like his father's. The father, however, had a great distaste for his own family name. It had, first of all, an unpleasant onomatopoeia. Second, he had never quite adjusted to his naval colleagues' calling him "Doc Squills"—squills being bulbs of the lily family then widely used as diuretics and expectorants—or "Doc Squeegee."

"His mother names him Edward Squibb," he wrote, "to which I add his paternal great-great-grandmother's maiden name of Hamilton. This I insist upon in consequence of the great disadvantage that I have suffered during life from so odd and ugly a name as that of Squibb. These disadvantages I do not feel myself justified in entailing upon my children."

Dr. Squibb seriously entertained the quaint notion that somehow his son would grow up to be known as Edward S. Hamilton.

Before the boy was a month old, however, both parents, for unexplained reasons, were calling him "Shang."

III

SHANG HAD NOT YET cut his first tooth before another cherished seed planted by Dr. Squibb came into fruition: President Pierce's Secretary of the Navy, a Carolinian named

James C. Dobbin, paid a state visit to the new laboratory over the unoccupied pesthouse. Accompanied by an extensive retinue which included admirals, commodores, the chief of the Bureau of Medicine and Surgery, and the top brass from Brooklyn Navy Yard and the warships anchored in Wallabout Bay, the Honorable Secretary inspected the modest three-man assembly line Dr. Squibb had organized to pack uniform sets of splints and bandages for the sloop *Cyane* and the brig *Bainbridge,* listened to Dr. Squibb explain the maze of glass tubing and the fuming retorts, nodded wisely at the pumps and boilers and grinding mill, and clucked approvingly at the revolutionary Squibb scheme for distilling ether by the use of steam. At the conclusion of his inspection tour, the Honorable Secretary declared himself pleased with what he had seen and promised to secure sufficient funds to expand the laboratory according to the plans of Drs. Bache and Squibb.

A few days later Dr. Squibb was detached from duty at the Brooklyn Naval Hospital and ordered to report aboard the U.S.S. *Allegheny*—an order which should not have surprised him in view of his previous naval experience, yet which did rather daze him in the light of the Honorable Secretary's promises. He protested to Washington.

A few days later the order was changed. Dr. Squibb was detached from the *Allegheny* and ordered to report aboard the U.S.S. *Mississippi!*

His second protest must have reached the Secretary himself. Previous orders were countermanded. The Naval Laboratory was established as a unit distinct from the Brooklyn Naval Hospital, although still under Dr. Bache. Dr. Squibb was relieved of all hospital duties and ordered to devote his time exclusively to the laboratory.

The time previously given to the wards, the casebook, and the dead house was immediately transferred to the complex problems of ether. In addition to the prime question of uniformity and purity, Dr. Squibb was also vitally interested in safeguarding the manufacture of a substance so volatile and so dangerously inflammable. As he was to write nearly thirty years later, while arguing the case of tin containers as against glass: "The writer has seen ether take fire at a measured distance of fifteen feet between the source of the escaping vapor and the source of the fire, and many times has seen it take fire at shorter distances between a broken bottle and a gas light. In his experience . . . he can recall five disastrous fires involving many lives and serious injuries and over a million of dollars of property, which were directly traced to the breaking of bottles of ether."

To eliminate the hazard of distilling ether over an open flame, Dr. Squibb began designing a still which would operate on a moderate head of steam. It took a year of experimentation before he was ready to test his apparatus.

On October 27, 1854, he connected his still to the steam vent, set the glass gauge tube with plaster of Paris and candle wick, and fitted the beak to the large glass Liebig condenser which in turn was fitted to the still.

"Then," he wrote, " got the new condensers out of the cellar and washed the coal dust from them, setting them in place and fitting the eduction pipes. Then fitted a piece of lead pipe to connect the Liebig to these tin condensers, soldering on an eduction pipe for the acid liquor, alcohol &c that I expect to condense with the glass condenser. Then luted all the joints, attached the hose, and had everything prepared for work in the morning."

By nine o'clock next morning an assistant named Watson had the steam pressure up to 91 pounds, and another assistant, Mr. Clarke, had charged the still according to the formula prepared by Dr. Squibb: 52 pounds of sulphuric acid of specific gravity 1.845 at 68°, and 12¾ gallons of alcohol of specific gravity .820 at 70°.

The mixture began boiling only a minute or two after the steam was turned on. Dr. Squibb had drawn off six gallons, testing each half-gallon separately for specific gravity as it came over, when "the sulphate of lime luting of the glass gauge tube gave way, and the contents of the still commenced escaping, charring all the wood, &c, and making a terrible splashing, ruining all our clothes &c. In trying to arrest or catch the hot fluid I scalded my right thumb and Clarke got some hot acid upon a cut upon his hand. Finally we had to let it run, and catch as much as possible of it, losing a great deal. . . ."

Changing the luting to putty and white lead corrected this fault, but the density of the yield was too high. Changing the pressure of the steam was no help. "The whole yield from both processes was opalescent with a leaden sediment."

After several days, Dr. Squibb concluded that the sulphuric acid furnished by Dr. Bache was below official strength and was causing all the trouble. "I told Dr. Bache that in consequence of the weak acid I had lost a quantity of alcohol and failed to get Ether—and that this was quite an unnecessary expenditure of trouble and clothing. He promised to go over in the morning and get a carboy of strong acid."

The carboy arrived from New York, but its specific gravity tested at only 1.817 at 66°, some 3 or 4 per cent weaker than the acid already on hand.

Dr. Squibb's journal for the next months was filled with page after page of accounts, of experiments; columns of figures of specific gravities, temperatures, amounts and costs; tests of sulphuric acid for impurities; changes in the design of his condensers.

Little by little he discovered he could wash away most of the impurities in ether with potassium carbonate and redistillation. He also satisfied himself that he could definitely produce ether of uniform strength by using steam.

Instead of rushing to patent either process or apparatus, Dr. Squibb gave both to the world with considerable pride. The *American Journal of Pharmacy* for September 1856 contained a detailed diagram of his design, accompanied by an article entitled "Apparatus for the Preparation of Ether by Steam."

Nearly thirty years later, Dr. Squibb wrote:

The modifications of this apparatus, now in successful use, vary very little in design and not at all in the principles involved from the original as published, although very much larger. The same general form of still and internal steam coil of heavy lead is followed by a cast iron purifier, the larger lower chamber of which contains a solution of potassa renewed every day. This chamber has a wire gauze diaphragm, always immersed in the solution, to divide the bubbles of vapor, and has a steam coil to keep the solution heated above the boiling point of alcohol, so that the vapors of ether, and of alcohol which has escaped etherization, are finely divided and thoroughly washed in the alkaline solution.

Surmounting this chamber are five smaller, plunger chambers of the same form and arrangement as the chambers of an alcohol column. In these the mixed vapors are still kept above their condensing points, are washed five times in succession by a descending current of hot distilled water coming from above. Escaping from this series of washings, the vapors, now consisting chiefly of alcohol and ether, and uncondensable gases, enter a second purifier. This consists of a large block-tin worm which terminates in a central cylinder furnished with wire gauze diaphragms, upon which rest about two inches of round pebble stones. From the bottom of this cylinder a small block-tin tube leads the liquid condensed by it to a small, cold, condensing worm from which the liquid is conducted to the feed-back of the still, where it is received into the fresh supply of alcohol for the still. At the top the cylinder communicates with the large block-tin worm for the purified ether. The block-tin worm and the central cylinder which constitute this second purifier, are placed within a large sheet-iron tank supplied with water at a temperature of 35° C. or 95° F., kept at a constant temperature throughout, by means of a long upright shaft supplied throughout its length with propeller blades. This shaft is kept in motion by the power of the current of water which supplies the final large condensing worm.

The still is first charged with about thirteen gallons of alcohol or clean spirit, and into this about two carboys, or 360 lbs. of concentrated sulphuric acid, is run slowly in a small stream. The still is then closed and heated to the etherizing point of about 130° C.

or 266° F., the purifiers being charged and heated up at the same time. . . . The present apparatus is of such a capacity as to etherify about one barrel of clean spirit each working day of nine and one-half hours, and, with the exception of two to three months of summer when even the well water is not cold enough to give an economical condensation, it is run from year to year. If the spirit or alcohol be of good quality and clean, the sulphuric acid does not require changing oftener than once in each running, and then only because it gets so dark and tarry by the charring of the impurities of the alcohol as to render the mixture in the still liable to frothing.

The one charge of acid will generally etherify, without much inconvenience, about 120 barrels of clean spirit, when it becomes economical to throw it away and put in a fresh charge. In splitting the alcohol into ether and water, both distil over, leaving the acid unchanged, except for accidental foreign matters in the spirit— the water accumulating in the lower chamber of the first purifier, to be run off with the solution of potassa at the end of each day. . . . Nothing short of the grossest carelessness or inattention can interfere with the uniformity of the product.

Today, more than a century after Dr. Squibb made his first successful steam ether still, the giant still at the Squibb laboratories in New Brunswick, New Jersey, although it has a hundred times the capacity and is fitted with more efficient condensers and automatic controls, is basically of the same design as the one he developed at the Naval Laboratory in Brooklyn.

four

FREE ENTERPRISE

I

WHEN DR. SQUIBB had learned how to make pure ether of uniform strength, he turned his attention to chloroform. And when he had learned how to make chloroform, he began to think of making money. The sequence of developments covered some three years, a period which also saw changes in Edward Robinson Squibb the man.

Marriage, fatherhood, and professional achievement were powerful catalysts in his evolution. He was still intolerant of incompetence and stupidity in high places, but he began to look with a little more kindliness on the foibles of lesser humans, and with more mellowness in his generalized judgments on special groups.

His priggish attitude toward the fugitives from the Potato Famine, apparently acquired at sea (one in every four of the crew of the *Cumberland* was a native of Ireland) and nurtured ashore, was completely transformed during this period. When the time came to hire a nurse for little Shang, he was quite happy to engage a bright-eyed, red-cheeked, square-jawed colleen of nineteen summers, name of Mary Jane Fogarty.

Mary Fogarty was not sure where in the Old Sod she had

been born, or the exact date, but she was about the same age as Caroline Squibb. She was not quite illiterate, and not at all stupid. She had never learned to write but had somehow managed to learn to read her prayer book and, eventually, the newspapers. She had a rippling sense of humor, loved children, and was devoted to the Squibbs. In fact, before Shang was a year old she decided to make a career of being devoted to the Squibbs.

The devotion was mutual. Whatever ideas he may have had of the Irish as a bachelor, as a husband and father Dr. Squibb took Mary Fogarty to his heart, and she became a member of the Squibb family for life.

During this same period, it must be said, relations between Dr. Squibb and the Cook family deteriorated somewhat. He still adored Caroline with all the love and blind worship due a radiantly beautiful goddess. But as he had allocated to himself the role of husband and father, lover and tutor, he found himself in the equivocal position of being both slave and master. Although she was the mother of his son, Caroline was after all a lovely, inexperienced child, not to be burdened with such mundane matters as household bills, marketing, and menus. What was more natural than for the former caterer of the wardroom mess of the U.S. Storeship *Erie* to order groceries and plan meals for his darling? And what more natural than for Passed Assistant Surgeon Squibb to protect the precious health of one so young and charmingly fragile?

The only drawback to the paternal approach, however, was that Caroline had a mind of her own and insisted on eating sweet potatoes, even when she knew they did not agree with her. She would also neglect to change her wet shoes after walking in the rain, because she was too busy talking to one of her sisters, and would consequently catch cold.

On such occasions Dr. Squibb would give her a hot foot bath, put her to bed right after tea, and read aloud to her from such divergent works as Miss Bremer's *Homes of the New World*, Miss Strickland's *Queens of England*, Bulwer-

Lytton's *The Last of the Barons,* Smollett's *Humphry Clinker,* and Relstab's *1812.* When she fell asleep, he would fall to journalizing or to reading *Scientific American, Harper's,* or *Punch.*

He also read *Punch* during the visits of Dr. Mayo, who succeeded Dr. Burt and whom Dr. Squibb found to be even more boring and egotistical than his predecessor.

The decline of Dr. Squibb's admiration for his wife's family appears to have begun with Caroline's eldest sister Elizabeth, to whom he always referred as Mrs. Bache. He was particularly annoyed by what he called her "Commodorial propensities." She always referred to Dr. Bache as "the Commodore," a rank to which his thirty years' service would no doubt have entitled him, except that medical officers were not accorded line rank by the pre-Civil War Navy. Mrs. Bache, he wrote, "seems to think that she has all the authority of her husband in his absence, and talks of reporting matters to the Commodore, and orders and interferes with people in a way that is very wrong and disagreeable."

Mrs. Bache also had the grievous habit of borrowing (with her husband's assent) members of the laboratory staff for her own personal chores. Robert, Dr. Squibb's messenger and boy of all work, was frequently not to be found because he was tending the cow which Mrs. Bache tethered on the hospital compound to provide milk for her family. And on several occasions she commandeered Mr. Buckley, the laboratory carpenter, to mend broken furniture in her apartment when Dr. Squibb needed him to crate supplies for the barque *Storm,* the East India Squadron, or the Chelsea Hospital.

But what really wounded Dr. Squibb the most was the fact that the Cook family was well off and made no bones about it. In fact, certain of its members began to flaunt the fact in Dr. Squibb's handsome face. During the early ether experiments, Aunt Lownds had invited the Squibbs to a party at her house. Caroline told her husband she had refused because she had nothing fit to wear. A few days later, when stopping at Mrs. Lownds's door with Dr. Bache, Dr. Squibb refused to come in because Caroline was not with him. Whereupon Aunt Lownds "seemed annoyed and said she had invited us to her house for the last time &c. Several persons were present, and I could not say what I wished at that time. Could not help feeling however that it was a piece of very great weakness, to say the least, in my wife, to sacrifice so much kindly feeling in her own aunt, to so frivolous a reason for not going, as the want of a new dress to wear, which dress she could not afford to buy in time. What a great misfortune it seems to be that a woman should be so brought up as to want what she cannot honestly have—or to marry below her income."

Mrs. Bache was no great help on this score, either, as witness Dr. Squibb's journal: "This morning Mrs. Bache presented Shang with 'a set of furs' for which I was not thankful but sorry. It is disagreeable that I or mine should receive presents, for it amounts to an obligation to return them. This I cannot afford, honestly, to do. I have told this to some of our relatives, and induced Caroline to tell the others, but it seems some of them do not heed it."

And when Dr. Squibb politely refused the invitation of Caroline's parents to spend Thanksgiving Day, 1854, in Philadelphia, only one person could have betrayed the real reason.

"Caroline received a letter from her mother today, saying that as they had heard through Mrs. Bache that the only reasons for our not going to Philadelphia on a visit were pecuniary, Mr. Cook had procured a free ticket for us which she enclosed. All this annoyed me very much, and placed me in a very disagreeable position in many respects, besides that I dislike being managed into anything by anybody."

So Dr. and Mrs. Squibb went to Philadelphia for Thanksgiving and stayed with Mr. and Mrs. Cook at 602 Spruce Street; and while there they celebrated Caroline's twenty-first birthday, on November 25.

However, Dr. Squibb did manage to take Caroline out to Darby to see the Bonsalls and to Cherry Street to see the surviving Squibbs—brother Robert and Uncle Jacob, notably. He also scurried around professionally for a few days, shopping at McAllister's for microscopes for Dr. Bache and for his old friend Sam White in Georgia; dropping in at Lindsay and Blakiston's bookstore "to see a cut of an instrument for cauterization of the urethra," and to talk to Mr. Lindsay "about the book I propose to prepare upon Pharmacy"; then to Lippincott's "to see upon what terms we could buy Wood & Bache and the Pharmacopoeia for the Laboratory."

He called on Dr. Barrington of the *Cumberland* and Dr. Franklin Bache, and he went back to Jefferson and shook hands with Drs. Mütter, Mitchell and Pancoast. He watched Pancoast "perform several small operations, as subcutaneous section of the periosteum of the radius. Removal of a sebaceous tumor near the outer canthus. Introduction of an animal tube for lacrymal fistula, and finally he crushed a stone in the bladder of an elderly man."

Dr. Squibb then returned to Blakiston's for a copy of Meigs on children "for Shang's particular benefit." When he finally caught one of Dr. Meigs's lectures at the medical school, he lingered a while and walked home with the great obstetrician. "The last part of his conversation was very characteristic," Dr. Squibb reported. "He asked me if I was saving any money, and before allowing me to go, made me promise him to lay by 25 dollars before the year was out. Then came home to tea. After tea Caroline, who had been shopping now for a day and a half, had some silks sent from Levy's to look at and select, and finally decided upon an expensive brown striped one which cost then 30 dollars."

Four days later the Squibbs were back in Brooklyn.

At Christmastime it was Caroline's sister Mary Jane King and her husband Dr. Theodore King who embarrassed Dr. Squibb. Dr. King gave Caroline a blue enameled lady's watch with a sprig of flowers on each side, set with diamond sparks. "It is a very pretty little watch indeed," wrote Dr. Squibb, "and exhibits a kindly feeling upon Dr. King's part, yet it makes me very uncomfortable, for it is altogether out of my power to reciprocate. . . . Beside this, Mary yesterday gave Caroline two silver butter knives—and the doctor this evening gave me a map of the city of Brooklyn. He bought some poultry yesterday and got two pair of chickens for us, so we weighed and paid for these and put them in our basket to bring home. Left there about half past 9, and went to the grocer's and bought cranberries while waiting for the cars."

An incident on Christmas Eve made Dr. Squibb feel much better about the world in general. His former steward on the storeship *Erie*, a man named Jump, called on him with a hard-luck story. He was out of a job, and his wife, who had been supporting him, "can no longer get any sewing to do, and their landlord has positively refused to let them occupy their rooms any longer, so he sees nothing but starvation and midwinter cold before them, as he can get nothing to do in any capacity. If such a story as his, in these Christmas times, fails to awaken charity and thankfulness to God, how shall I ever be able to look at the end!"

Dr. Squibb gave his former steward a $2.50 gold piece and almost immediately was given vivid proof of the value of casting one's bread upon the waters!

"In returning to Dr. King's this evening," he wrote, "Caroline found a quarter-eagle lying in the street. Just the coin and the amount of my little gift to poor Jump in the morning."

II

WHILE HIS ETHER EXPERIMENTS were gradually coming to fruition, Dr. Squibb was also delving into the mysteries of chloroform.

Although chloroform had been known to science for more than twenty years, its first use as an anesthetic was even more recent than that of ether. It had been discovered simultaneously and independently in 1831 by Guthrie in the United States and by Soubeiran (who called it *éther bichlorique*) in

France. Liebig in Germany produced the same thing a year later and called it carbon trichloride. Chloroform had been used as an anesthetic on animals in Paris in 1847, and two years later it was used on humans in Edinburgh, where it was called "chloric ether."

Dr. Squibb first tried making it in Brooklyn in 1855 from chloride of lime and alcohol. His journal calls it "chloroform" and describes his procedure, aided by assistants James and Clarke, as follows:

"The plan adopted was to mix the 20 lbs. of Chlorinated Lime with 4 gallons of water, grinding up the lumps and putting the whole through a sieve with a double mosquito netting bottom. While they did this, I filled the charge into the still, managed the heat, received the crude chloroform, and washed it. I commonly washed the five pints which came over first. Mixing a little water at first to precipitate the chloroform, and then washing this well with three times its bulk of water. These washings were used as so much water in the next succeeding charge. After the first five pints, I commonly distilled over 2 or 2½ gallons more from each charge. This also was used as water in the next succeeding charge, making up the amount of water 7 or 7½ gallons, sometimes 8. . . . The Chlorinated Lime used is a tierce recently purchased by Dr. Bache. It is pulverulent and dry, and mixes easily with water, without stickiness or without any degree of setting. It is dusty and exceedingly irritating to the air passages, rendering the work quite disagreeable. It has a quantity of black particles, perhaps sand, in it. It is very well charged with chlorine, much the best I have ever seen. The chlorine escaped from the delivery pipe of the worm this afternoon and was exceedingly uncomfortable. It has given me a persistent hard cough.

"The alcohol used is of two kinds. Some 8½ gallons of Atwood's alcohol I had reserved for this purpose, and this will be used as far as it will go. It is reduced to the officinal standard. The remainder is some of Lounsberry's rummy odor alcohol, also diluted to the off. standard. When I had collected the washed product of two or three first charges (very green) into a stoppered green bottle in the window, the stopper was exploded out with violence and the crude chloroform began to boil briskly and became quite hot. I set the bottle carefully into a basin of cold water, and set the whole out of doors, for the chlorine or muriatic fumes were extremely irritating. When the escape of gas ceased, the liquid was limpid and colorless, and had lost bulk considerably. Query: Was this a quadri chloride or formyle? Or merely terchloride holding chlorine in solution? . . . Managed to get over seven charges, working very late. . . .

"The first two or three charges were badly managed from the fact that it had not occurred to me to distill off as long as the taste of alcohol not 'sweet,' was markedly perceptible. . . . Found that cold water let into the still from the sprinkler, in small quantities, and frequently, very much diminished the escape of chlorine fumes—and produced a larger and less colored yield."

Several days later he wrote: "About three in the afternoon we finished the seventh and last charge and found there was 41 lbs. 5 oz. of crude washed chloroform. . . . The last charge was one pound short, being an excess over the seller's weight of the cask. It purported to have 500 lbs. but we weighed out 519 lbs. from it and had full weight each time. It cost 3½ cts. per lb. or $18.95 the whole cask. The first alcohol cost 91¢ and the last used 90¢."

Dr. Squibb, being very much a do-it-yourself type, did not stop at the stage of manufacture. Nor did he bother with laboratory animals. When he had managed to distill chloroform which he considered of officinal quality after careful and extensive tests, he did not hesitate to try it out on humans. Luckily for him, two of his wife's brothers appeared on the scene at this period: Albert, some years her senior, and William, the baby of the Cook family. Brother Albert was on his way home after the collapse of a great—and greatly speculative—lumber project. Brother William, who was to have been an assistant to Albert, was consequently thrown out of

97

a job and came to live with the Baches—and, wrote Dr. Squibb, "I fear not likely to get a situation easily. Besides, it seems he is in debt, having like his brother Albert, lived much beyond his means. They seem both more fond of dress and show than of work."

Brother William had an excruciating toothache. Dr. Squibb examined him, at his wife's request, and although he was not a dentist he could easily see that the tooth was hopelessly decayed. The doctor therefore gave young Cook a few whiffs of his newly distilled chloroform and extracted the molar with a pair of Mr. Buckley's pliers. William Cook did not feel the slightest twinge of pain, and Dr. Squibb managed, somewhat to his own surprise, to extract the whole tooth perfectly.

But the doctor did not devote his entire time to anesthesia. His records show that while he manufactured citrate of iron without trouble, he had some difficulty in straining the impurities out of his own chloride of iron for the manufacture of a tincture. He made considerable spirit of nitric ether and percolated sulphuric acid with alcohol, ginger, and cinnamon to make aromatic sulphuric acid.

He worked hard and successfully on potassium iodide and hydrocyanic acid. He purified ammonia and ground flaxseed. He analyzed the dye in a sample of blue flannel for the Navy and he manufactured silver nitrate from whatever silver coins he could lay his hands on.

His records on silver-nitrate experiments in April and May of 1855 are typical of his meticulous methods. His chief source of silver was French five-franc pieces, and he recorded the date and weight of each—Louis XVIII, 1814, 24.7927 grams; Louis Philippe, 1831, 24.8876 grams; Napoleon, 1809, 24.8407 grams.

On May 16, 1855, he turned in the following account:

63 five-franc pieces @ 98¢ and 1 Mexican dollar @ $1, $62.74
Nitric acid, 12 lbs. 1.68
Sol. Potassa, 8 pts. 64

Breakage of beaker 75
Fuel 1.85

Yield, 74 oz. av. $67.66

Cost, 91.43 cents per ounce.

The first practical use of the Squibb-made silver nitrate was to swab out Dr. Bache's throat, which had become badly ulcerated.

During this entire period Dr. Squibb carried on a running argument with Dr. Bache on the subject—destined to become an obsession—of impure drugs. While preparing to make syrup of squill one day, he complained in his journal, he found the recently bought squills so bad that he took them to Dr. Bache to protest their quality. Dr. Bache "said he had not seen them!!! but if they were bad they could be sent back."

On another occasion he found that a shipment of gum arabic contained 21½ pounds of sand and dirt recovered by "garble and riddle."

Applying the carbonate-of-soda test to some tartar emetic that Dr. Bache had bought for the receiving ship *North Carolina*, Dr. Squibb found it consisted largely of potassium bitartrate (cream of tartar). "Dissolved 100 grams in 2000 grams distilled water—or rather tried to do so, for all of it would not dissolve, so great was the adulteration."

He also found fault with the preparations of Mr. Beaton, the naval-hospital apothecary, whose subnitrate of bismuth he found "full of carbonate and altogether a bad preparation. Got permission from Dr. Bache to throw it out."

Dr. Squibb later told Dr. Bache "that our spirit of nitric ether was not fit to be served out in consequence of the bad nitrate of potassa used. After much urging, I finally got permission to throw it all out and substitute new, made from the new pure nitrate."

And further: "Examined the subject of phosphate of iron . . . induced Dr. Bache to let me condemn our stock which is evidently a bad preparation."

Dr. Squibb did not thoroughly approve of Dr. Bache's taste and judgment in the matter of wines and liqueurs, either. It was Dr. Bache's responsibility to buy brandy, sherry and port for medicinal use at the hospital and laboratory and on several occasions he asked his junior's opinion.

"Not one of his 6 samples of sherry would I buy," Dr. Squibb commented, "although one or two were not bad. Two samples of brandy were vile."

To show Dr. Bache the kind of wine and brandy he approved of, Dr. Squibb took the ferry to Manhattan and bought from a Mr. Toler a gallon each of brandy and sherry for his own use and got a sample of brandy he considered proper for the laboratory. The latter was Otard Dupuy at five dollars a gallon which "although new, is a perfect brandy for medicinal purposes, whereas the only sample that I tasted of his that was at all fit was 7$."

Next day: "Showed Dr. Bache the brandy I bought for myself at 6$ and the sample that I bought at 5$. He acknowledged them to be both very good. And we tasted his 7$ brandy in connection with them, and I think it decidedly inferior to either. If he buys it for 7$ for the laby., I shall think it a great shame."

Dr. Squibb also thought it a great shame and something of a shock to discover that Dr. Bache's interest in brandy was not strictly medicinal. Dr. Squibb himself indulged in an occasional convivial glass and was always ready to mix a sherry sangaree for his guests, but Dr. Bache had claimed to be a total abstainer since his marriage. It was therefore a great surprise to Dr. Squibb, in Manhattan to buy Brande's *Manual of Chemistry* at Ballière's and a book on the chemistry of dyes at Appleton's, to find Dr. Bache standing on a street corner near Stewart's store, acting rather strangely.

"On looking at him and speaking with him," wrote Dr. Squibb, "I soon found that he was intoxicated. Also smelled liquor upon his breath. Once or twice before I have suspected that he had been drinking pretty freely . . . although his wife and his friends give it out on all occasions that they are (he and she) 'teetotal temperance people.' Mrs. B. will not even touch Cherry Bounce when offered, on her husband's account, and yet she cannot be ignorant of his drinking."

It is quite possible that Mrs. Bache was so preoccupied with her approach to motherhood that she paid little heed to the doctor's use of alcohol. In any event, a few days before her confinement, both the Bache and Squibb apartments were overwhelmed by a very special calamity which might have driven anyone to drink.

"We have had a most disgusting time for two days past," wrote Dr. Squibb. "Dr. B's water closet has been clogged up with leather, glass, sticks and what not, and the filth and feces have run down upon our closet below, saturating ceiling, walls, carpet and everything, and all through their careless, shiftless mismanagement and through the ignorance and stupidity of Moran, the water man."

It was in this setting, shortly before midnight of May 16, 1855, that Dr. Squibb awakened Caroline to go upstairs to attend her sister at the birth of Benjamin Franklin's great-great-granddaughter.

III

IT WAS DR. WHITE who first put into Dr. Squibb's head the idea of going into private industry—the same Sam White who had first nudged him into joining the Navy and who was now trying to nudge him out. Early in 1855 Sam White wrote his old friend Ed Squibb a long letter, suggesting that eight years in the Navy was long enough to prove his patriotism; that it was high time he thought of making some money; and that he had better resign his naval commission and come down to Milledgeville, Georgia, to join his old pal Sam in the private and profitable practice of medicine.

Dr. Squibb's first reaction to the suggestion was negative, but the idea germinated for a full year, fertilized by such factors as the discovery that it was difficult for a family man to make both ends meet on the $1,800 annual pay of a passed assistant surgeon on shore duty; the pressure of trying to keep up with the Cooks; and the pressure of sincerely trying to satisfy Caroline's charming but persistent yearning for nice things.

The exact steps leading to his final decision will never be known, for his journal covering this period was destroyed by fire three years later.

It is almost certain, however, that the family legend which became the company legend is *not* true. The founder's son, Dr. Edward Hamilton Squibb—Shang—in his declining years made the statement that Dr. E. R. Squibb left the Navy in 1857 because Congress failed to appropriate funds and the Brooklyn Naval Laboratory was closed. This might very well have happened. There were certainly lobbyists in Washington at mid-nineteenth century, trying to keep the government out of the pharmaceutical business. Furthermore the chairmen of the naval-affairs committees of both Houses of Congress were Southerners and therefore anti-Navy (because the Navy had been interfering with the slave trade) and were always ready to slash a naval appropriation. Under Pierce, the Navy was a stepchild both on the Hill and in the Administration. In 1854, for instance, Commander David G. Farragut asked leave to observe the naval operations of the Crimean War. Instead he was ordered to Mare Island, California.

Nevertheless, Navy Department records show that the laboratory was not shut down until 1866. And the annual report of the Secretary of the Navy for 1857—the year that Dr. Squibb left the Navy—has nothing but praise for the laboratory and its work. That section of the report devoted to the Bureau of Medicine and Surgery, signed by the bureau chief, Dr. William Whelan, and dated October 26, nearly two months after Dr. Squibb was placed on inactive duty, reads as follows:

The naval laboratory at Brooklyn has furnished the entire outfit of all vessels commissioned for service during the year, as well as the usual quarterly supplies to various home stations and occasional shipments to the squadrons on foreign service.

In this establishment we have happily within our own control a sure means of obtaining pure and reliable medicines for the Navy at no greater cost, if indeed as great, as we had formerly paid for such articles too often made for sale, as are vended in the stores of our large cities. The adulteration of medicine amounts to a science and there seems no alternative to escape the mishaps attendant upon the administration of uncertain agents, than to commence the preparation and manufacture of our supplies upon the moderate scale commensurate with our wants. Three years' experience have removed whatever doubts might have been entertained of the success of the undertaking.

The report concludes:

The laboratory *continues* [italics added] to afford valuable facilities to other departments through analyzing flannels, whiskey, vinegar, soap, oil, and candles.

There is no doubt that Dr. Squibb's reasons for leaving the Navy were economical and personal, abetted by bureaucratic stupidity in the Department, something to which he had become accustomed. Here is the record:

On April 11, 1856, Dr. Squibb wrote to the Secretary of the Navy (through channels), asking an increase in pay. He pointed out that the pay of a passed assistant surgeon was disproportionate to the duties of an assistant director of the laboratory and begged that it be increased. He emphasized that the offices of the laboratory were nonexistent when the pay of medical officers was fixed by Congress, and therefore the duties of the position could not have been considered as embraced in the routine of naval medical officers as then envisaged. The duties were different in quality and quantity, involved personal expense and risk, and were laborious, extraprofessional and incessant, requiring close study and practical application of the collateral sciences of chemistry, pharmacy, and mechanics. He believed that his duties to the office as created by Departmental Order of October 31, 1853, were as profitable to the Navy as they were arduous to the incumbent.

It was a logical, eloquent, and sound request, and it was passed along with the endorsement of every intermediary: the director of the laboratory (Dr. Bache), the commandant of the Brooklyn Navy Yard, and the chief of the Bureau of Medicine and Surgery. The last-named (Dr. Whelan) added a special endorsement:

"I beg to commend Dr. Squibb's application for an increase of pay to the most favorable consideration of the Honorable Secretary of the Navy. Dr. Squibb is eminently deserving of a better remuneration for his valuable and unremitting services in a new department of the Navy."

The Honorable Secretary's reply was prompt. It was short but not sweet. It read as follows:

SIR: Your letter of the 11th Inst. asking for an increase of pay has been received. Your pay is fixed by law and cannot be increased except by action of Congress.

DOBBIN.

Dr. Squibb was disappointed and hurt, but he did not drag his feet. He went on making medicines and drugs as usual for more than a year. He may have brooded, but he was neither vindictive nor idle. He was looking for a way out with profit and honor in his own country.

His work at the laboratory had attracted considerable attention, and so, tempting as it was, he could reject Sam White's invitation to return to the practice of medicine. He had a new ambition: to be pharmacist to the medical profession.

He had a number of offers. Dr. Richard S. Satterlee, chief medical purveyor to the United States Army, talked long and seriously about setting up an Army laboratory—a project which was abandoned because of pressures from private industry. Out of the other offers, he selected one which seemed to have the most promise.

From Louisville came a proposition from two Kentucky gentlemen, Dr. J. Laurence Smith, a chemist and professor of chemistry, and Mr. Thomas E. Jenkins, who owned a drugstore in Louisville. Dr. Smith and Mr. Jenkins had raised enough capital to start work on a commercial laboratory they called the Louisville Chemical Works, on High Street near Thirteenth, and they offered Dr. Squibb a third interest in a new firm if he would run the laboratory.

After an extended exchange of letters, Dr. Squibb agreed to make a trial run of a year if he could get a furlough from the Navy. He must have been greatly intrigued by the prospects, for he offered to work for less actual cash than he was getting as a passed assistant surgeon.

In a holograph letter written from the Naval Laboratory and addressed to Dr. Smith on April 29, 1857, Dr. Squibb made the following points:

You furnish all the capital yourself (no matter whence ultimately) as well the present investment ($6000 as I understand it) as that to be invested, and for all this you receive the interest . . . so that the capital is not contributed by you as though no interest was to be paid upon it. You contribute, therefore, upon the basis of capital, your chemical knowledge and experience, and the risk of the money invested. Mr. Jenkins contributes his business capacities and knowledge of the business (a most important share), and I my experience in the manufacture. . . .

I become responsible for the interest of one-third portion . . . as fast as it may be invested, and that interest to be paid out of profits, and if the profits do not arise in sufficient amount or in time to meet the first installments of interest, I incur new obligations for it until paid. Then, as I must join the enterprise, if at all, empty handed entirely, I may be allowed to draw upon it in advance, 100 dollars a month for necessary living expenses, and the bonus of a life insurance for 5,000 dollars, say about 125 dollars per annum, these to commence only when I leave this place and am occupied entirely with the interests of the enterprize. . . .

Then my first connection with the enterprize is to be limitable to one year, at my own option, so that if I choose to withdraw at the end of that year, the amounts that I may have received not exceeding the above deputations may not be considered as a debt accumulated against me, but rather as a clerklike compensation for the services rendered.

A formal agreement was reached between Dr. Squibb and his two partners after two months of correspondence, and in July he traveled to Washington to see what deal he could make with the Navy. A new Administration had just come into office, and President Buchanan had chosen a Connecticut Yankee, Isaac Toucey, to be his Secretary of the Navy.

The new Secretary received Dr. Squibb personally and listened sympathetically. He promised to grant the doctor a year's furlough and agreed to Dr. Squibb's stipulation that he must not be recalled to active duty during that time because of the contractual obligation he was about to undertake to remain for a year in Louisville.

On September 1, 1857, Dr. Squibb left Brooklyn and the Naval Laboratory to try his hand at private enterprise.

He had scarcely had time to set up his ether still and install pumps, steam boilers, and grinding mill at the Louisville Chemical Works when he received orders from the Navy to report aboard U. S. Sloop of War *Marion*.

On December 1 Dr. Squibb wrote to Secretary Toucey recalling the understanding he thought they had reached during their July interview and resigning his commission. Four days later his resignation was accepted.

IV

LOUISVILLE COULD JUSTLY claim to be the birthplace of a concept that was in half a century to grow into a household word—E. R. Squibb & Sons.

It was in Louisville that Dr. Squibb definitely decided to enter the lists of private enterprise singlehanded.

And it was in Louisville that his second son was born.

The second Squibb of the seventh generation in America first saw the light of day on June 16, 1858, on the banks of the Ohio River. He was delivered by his father (a circumstance that was becoming a Squibb tradition), although with considerably less excitement and near-panic than was his brother. Dr. Squibb described the event in his journal, but with less detail:

"Awakened this morning soon after 4 o'clock by Caroline. She had awakened with pain about 3, but we thought at first that the pains were colic. About 6 o'clock, however, they became more regular, and showed their true character. While I was at breakfast they became worse and unmistakable and we sent off for the nurse [Mary Fogarty had refused to leave Brooklyn]. . . . our second boy was born about 8 o'clock. The pains were very severe and at short intervals, but very effective. Gave her some chloroform with good effect. The boy is quite small, but perfect as far as can be seen, and everything has gone on perfectly well, so that we have great cause for thankfulness."

Caroline was determined to name the boy after her sister Sally's husband, and so he was called Charles Fellows Squibb. From this day on, Shang—who was four going on five—became "Ed" and was given private lessons by his father every day at teatime.

From this day on, also, Dr. Squibb knew that he was going into business for himself when his contractual year was out. He began collecting samples of his own handiwork, putting them aside for the future, and scrupulously notifying Dr. Smith of his actions and purposes, so that the market value of the products might be charged to Dr. Squibb's monthly allowance. He put up for himself officinal ether and strong ether, chloroform, Hoffmann's anodyne, and spirit of niter—"to distribute if I should deem it necessary before I make them for myself."

He was not, however, stealing time either from the Louisville Chemical Works or from science.

For commercial purposes he was making, in addition to the

anesthetics and the by-products of ether, a varied list of pharmaceuticals which included the following: iron oxide, iron hydrophosphite, iron oxalate, iron iodide, iodide of mercury, nitrate of mercury, zinc chloride, potassium arsenite (Fowler's solution), iron subcarbonate, cantharides cerate and powder (Spanish fly, yield 105 pounds at 76 cents cost); extract of ergot, cubeb and rhubarb, and subacetate of lead—a product which put Dr. Squibb back on his crusading track against impure ingredients.

"On examining the solution of subacetate of lead this morning," he wrote a month after Charles Fellows Squibb was born, "found it much too low in s.g. and then found that the dry residue left on filtering weighed 3 lbs. 4 oz., far too much. On examining this residue and the litharge from which it came, found both to consist mainly of carbonate. From 5 lbs. 8 oz.—83 oz. used only 1 lb. 15 oz.—31 oz. had dissolved and this was probably the whole amount of oxide contained, say 37.35 per cent. oxide and 62.65 per cent. adulteration. This is a pretty strong case of home adulteration in the way of litharge and to come from such a source. Dr. Smith went over to their lead works and there got some good English litharge but containing a little copper. He said Dr. Wilson had told him that people would not give him a cent a pound difference between the two."

The "good English litharge" left no residue.

Dr. Squibb persisted in his plodding, methodical experiments to secure perfect ether and perfect chloroform. His journals for the Louisville period are crowded with page after page of meticulous, detailed tables indicating his quest for a standard. Testing officinal ether at temperatures varying from 33° to 83° Centigrade (boiling point of ether), he found that the specific gravity varied only .006 for each 10 degrees. In ether fortis, he found a change in specific gravity from .745 to .710 in a Fahrenheit range from 33° to 90.5°, while officinal ether varied from .758 to .734 between temperatures of 50° to 90° F. He also carried on a correspondence with

Dr. W. T. G. Morton of Boston, the dentist who first gave a public demonstration of ether as an anesthetic.

All in all, Dr. Squibb spent a happy year in Louisville, even though his home was without the newfangled plumbing he had admired in Philadelphia, and he was forced to walk a few blocks to the river of an evening to take a bath. However, he enjoyed tutoring his four-year-old son, whom he took for walks to the post office and to the Nashville Railway depot to see the "cars" come in. On the Fourth of July—his thirty-ninth birthday—after reading *Punch* and *Scientific American,* he took Ed to see the soldiers parade and then to the circus, where "he was greatly pleased."

Dr. Squibb also was greatly pleased to receive an invitation to read a paper on the U. S. Pharmacopoeia at the national convention of the Pharmaceutical Association (of which he was not yet a member) at Washington in the fall. He immediately set to work writing it at home in the evening, but the new baby was fretful and cried a lot that July and he made little progress.

Caroline, too, was fretful that summer in Louisville. She had frequent attacks of colic and of what Dr. Squibb described as "cholera morbus." On one such occasion he wrote: "Caroline better today but has no appetite and will probably worry herself sick again. Found her crying both at noon and night, filled with the idea that everything was wrong and bad and never would be better." That evening, after his walk to the post office, he brought her some ice cream.

It was in July that Dr. Squibb received a commitment from Colonel Satterlee, the Army Medical Corps chief procurement officer—or as close to a commitment as the Army could make. If Dr. Squibb would undertake to open a laboratory of his own, the colonel wrote, the Army would keep him going with the bulk of its pharmaceutical orders. Of course, the Army couldn't finance any such project, but if Dr. Squibb could find sufficient capital elsewhere . . . Dr. Squibb thought he knew where to find the capital.

He immediately went to Dr. Smith and proposed that the partnership be dissolved on August 20, the end of the contractual year.

The windup of the partnership was completely amicable. Dr. Squibb worked in the laboratory until several days beyond the agreed date, and even on the morning of his departure for Brooklyn he went back to finish checking a batch of subcarbonate of iron.

On the morning of August 25 Dr. and Mrs. Smith came by with a carriage (and some milk that Mrs. Smith had prepared for the baby) to take the Squibbs to the boat. Mr. Jenkins, too, came down to see them off on the mail steamboat *Boston*.

The steamboat sailed on a Tuesday noon. The trip up the Ohio River to Cincinnati was normally a leisurely overnight journey, but the *Boston* spent a good part of the night hung up on a sand bar and went aground twice more during the morning. They arrived in Cincinnati shortly before noon Wednesday. Parking Caroline and the children at Spencer House, Dr. Squibb called on several colleagues (most of whom were out) and on an alcohol manufacturer named Fletcher who gave him samples and a price list.

After a short and almost sleepless night (mosquitoes) the Squibbs were up at four Thursday to catch a train of the Little Miami line to Cleveland, where they changed at three in the afternoon for a Lake Shore train to Buffalo. It was midnight before they bedded down at the American Hotel (no mosquitoes).

Friday morning they arose in time to buy a fresh supply of lunch and of milk for the baby before catching the seven-thirty train for Albany. They were on their way again before Dr. Squibb discovered he had lost the remainder of his through tickets. An unsympathetic conductor only smiled at his suggestion to telegraph the hotel for verification of his story that the tickets were surely on the floor of his room, and made him pay full fare all over again.

Dr. Squibb thought he was overcharged also on the Hudson steamboat *Isaac Newton*, which they boarded in Albany at eight that night—$3.25 for supper and "a little bad state-room." However, he gave the baby a dose of paregoric, so he and Caroline got an excellent night's rest.

The *Isaac Newton* reached its Manhattan dock at six-thirty next morning. After getting the baggage under way by express, Dr. Squibb and family walked to the Fulton Ferry, crossed over to Brooklyn, and took the "cars" up to the home of Dr. and Mrs. King, who had invited them to stay until they got settled.

Immediately after breakfast Dr. Squibb set out in preparation for the Great Adventure.

five

ORDEAL BY FIRE

I

WITHIN A WEEK of his return to Brooklyn, Dr. Squibb was in business for himself. Every day he inspected possible locations for a laboratory—even the day he suffered from nausea "with a tendency to diarrhoea. . . . What the cause I do not know unless it was soft clams for breakfast." He visited many addresses in both Brooklyn and New York before he found a five-story brick building which had the proper water and gas connections. It was at 149 Furman Street, Brooklyn, on the harborside just under Brooklyn Heights.

On September 6, 1858, he offered the proprietor, a Mr. W. W. Green, $225 for yearly rental. Mr. Green countered with a two-year lease at $250 a year, with an option on three more years at $300. Mr. Green agreed to spend $50 fitting the building to the doctor's purposes and turned over the keys at once, dating the rent year from the fifteenth.

The sign "E. R. SQUIBB, M.D.," did not go up until some days later, but the doctor went into double action immediately. He ordered glassware, copper tubing, and basic drug supplies from Schieffelin. He shopped in Newark for a secondhand steam engine. Since his old friend Buckley was in the hospital and unable to work, he hired a carpenter named Summerfield for $1.75 a day. He wrote Mary Fogarty to hurry back home. He ordered bottle labels printed by a Manhattan printer named Hasbrouck. He hired a cooper named Riordan to make tubs for chloroform and other liquid chemicals. He arranged for Taylor & Campbell of New York to make some essential castings. He got two of his brothers-in-law, Dr. King and Charley Fellows, to agree to finance his minor preliminary expenses. And he wrote to dear old Sam White in Georgia to say that he was now ready to take advantage of his friend's rash promise, classmate to classmate, on the eve of Ed Squibb's joining the Navy.

While awaiting Sam's reply—which was an invitation to come to Georgia—in between supervising the construction in Furman Street, playing with his two sons, reading *Punch,* and making new sketches of his ether apparatus for a mechanic named Coggins, Dr. Squibb worked in a frenzy to finish a paper on the Pharmacopoeia which he was to read to the forthcoming Pharmaceutical Association convention at the Smithsonian Institution in Washington.

He finished the paper on September 12, read it over, was aghast to find it took two hours and therefore might with difficulty find a place on the agenda, but finally tied it up, ready for delivery.

Next day he rushed over to the South Amboy ferry for the first stage of one of the most important missions of his career. The introduction was hardly promising. As Dr. Squibb tells it:

"Before getting to the ferry discovered that I had left my paper behind and had to go back for it. In the mean time Dr. King had discovered it and started to bring it to me at the boat, and he only came just at the last moment. Then just as the boat was about to start and I went to buy my ticket, found my portemonnaie gone, my pocket having been picked. Thus all my money ($80.25) except a little change was gone. Fortunately I was in company with Leon Milhau [the New York druggist] and he paid my fare and dinner."

Dr. Squibb telegraphed to Charley Fellows from South Amboy, but he apparently did not have complete confidence in the efficacy of what God and Samuel Morse had wrought, even though the new electrical means of communication had been in common use for a dozen years. In any case, he made doubly sure by writing to his brother-in-law from Philadelphia, asking him to send fifty dollars to Washington.

At the first session of the Pharmaceutical Association convention he was elected a member of the association, and at the second session he was elected vice-president. At the third session he began reading his paper, but he did not finish until the fourth session. He received "a special vote of thanks."

After three days of convening and sight-seeing, Dr. Squibb crossed the Potomac on the Alexandria Ferry and took a train for Georgia. It took him the whole weekend, with long stopovers and bad connections, to reach Milledgeville and Sam White.

As life in the South proceeded with a leisurely rhythm, Dr. Squibb did not really get down to business until ten days after he reached Milledgeville. True, his visit was partly for the purpose of renewing friendship ties with Sam White and his family and friends. He visited the local penitentiary, hospital, and state asylum, exchanged visits with the numerous Whites (mostly judges and doctors), and surveyed the vast White cotton plantations. Whatever Quaker-bred Dr. Squibb —who had been raised in the Quaker belief that slavery was evil and whose early career had been involved in fighting the slave trade—thought of slavery in action he did not record in his journal. In any event, he never used the word "slaves"— only "negroes."

On September 29, 1858, Dr. Squibb gave Dr. White his note for $1,300—capital to start the first Squibb laboratory.

At five-thirty in the morning of Saturday, October 2, Dr. Squibb started home, changing trains and railroads several times a day, waiting for hours for connections. He changed at Gordon and Macon, Georgia; Wilmington and Weldon,

North Carolina, and Washington, D. C., finally reaching Philadelphia at 10:30 Monday night.

He spent three days shopping for weights, scales, and other lab equipment, and in visiting his family. Thursday night he was back in Brooklyn.

II

OCTOBER AND NOVEMBER were frantically busy months for Dr. Squibb, collecting and installing apparatus for 149 Furman Street and moving his family to Miss Simonson's boardinghouse nearby on Brooklyn Heights, at 43 Middagh Street, where the Squibbs occupied the entire second floor.

Much of his time was spent ferrying back and forth to Manhattan and to New Jersey—seeing about a pump at Worthington's, a platform scale at Fairbanks', and a shaking mill at Hewes & Phillips' place in Newark. He needed bottles and stoppers, labels and thermometers. The retorts he had ordered from the Jersey City Glass Works were not right and he had to make several trips back and forth before he got what he wanted.

In Furman Street the carpenters and mechanics, the masons and painters were finishing up the laboratory. The ether and chloroform stills were installed, the purifier and storage tubs were set up, and the boiler was bricked up in the basement. The first mason on this job was found dead drunk by Dr. Squibb, who fired him forthwith. The doctor juggled his other workmen, too, firing incompetents, looking for professionals. He hired one mechanic named McCarty at $6 a week.

He put up samples of ether, chloroform, Hoffmann's anodyne and spirit of niter for Dr. Satterlee, for the Surgeon General's office, for Professor William Procter, editor of the *American Journal of Pharmacy,* and for Grieve and Clark of Milledgeville, and sent them off by Adam's Express.

He had circulars printed, stating his experience and qualifications as a manufacturer of pharmaceutical products, and listing the officinal drugs and other remedies he was prepared to sell. On the evening of November 28 he folded circulars and addressed them by hand to 320 physicians and pharmacists in New York and Brooklyn. Next day he carried his New York list across the harbor to Boyd's Dispatch Post, where he paid $1.64 for delivering the circulars in Manhattan. Back in Brooklyn, where, he discovered, there was no penny post, he took his circulars to the post office, where he paid $3.11 for local delivery.

He was now ready to build up an inventory.

Actual production at the laboratory of E. R. Squibb, M.D., began on December 1, 1858. On that date Dr. Squibb loaded the first charge into his chloroform still, and on the succeeding days he recharged it a dozen times, making two casks of chloroform. It was not a very auspicious start. He had trouble with his boiler, which he decided was too small, and he inhaled so much lime dust that he coughed incessantly for five hours.

The first run of chloroform tested at a specific gravity of 1.49 after rectification, which was standard but not quite as high as Dr. Squibb had desired. However, on December 5 he put up eighteen pounds of it for a New York dealer in pharmaceuticals named Maxwell—his first order.

Next day he started his ether still and was well satisfied with the first charge, because he "got a large run, dirty at first but afterward very clear and good, requiring no rectification, and very strong." Subsequent runs were less satisfactory. He used too much heat and his acid turned frothy. After a week, however, he had things working smoothly and, having produced enough ether to put up, he started making the byproducts: oil of wine, sweet spirit of niter, and Hoffmann's anodyne.

Orders began trickling in. The circulars were doing their work, and Dr. Squibb mailed another batch to doctors and pharmacists in Philadelphia. His appearance at the Pharmaceutical Association convention in September had made a favorable impression, and word-of-mouth approval spread through the profession. Dr. Smith sent him customers from Kentucky. Schieffelin Bros. & Company asked for samples but would extend him no credit when he bought colocynth and aloes to convert into extracts. He was also making sulphite of lime on order and analyzing guano for another customer.

Less than three weeks after he had started production, Dr. Squibb found himself needing more capital for expansion. He needed cash for more raw materials and new equipment. He borrowed $100 from his brother-in-law Charley Fellows, to buy corks. He got another $100 from Dr. King to pay Hasbrouck, the printer, for labels and the circulars. He wrote to Sam White, asking if he could raise another $1,800 before next May.

He worked a sixteen-hour day. "Do not get to bed nowadays before 12," he wrote in his journal for December 20. He retained McCarty as a general roustabout and daytime assistant in the laboratory. He hired a teen-age lad named Michael Diver for $2 a week to help out afternoons and evenings, washing and filling bottles and putting up orders. He always went back to the laboratory at night, even Christmas Eve while Caroline was visiting the Baches.

It was a hard grind, but it was worth it to get a new business—his own business—well on the way.

The future was looking very bright indeed when, two days before the end of the year, disaster struck.

III

THE INSTRUMENT OF FATE was, ironically, the innocent youngster Dr. Squibb had hired as a helper a fortnight earlier.

On December 14, 1858, Dr. Squibb wrote in his journal: "Boy Michael Diver commenced work today and seems to start pretty well. Mixed the spirit of nitre this morning, got it ready for filling, and filled a lot of it before I perceived it was cloudy. This will have to be allowed to stand and be refilled. Boy Michael got very much affected in filling it, almost losing his volition, and looked very badly."

Patiently Dr. Squibb showed Michael the various precautions to take to prevent anesthetizing himself while handling ether and ethereal products such as oil of wine and Hoffmann's anodyne. Several times he noted progress.

"Occupied some time in teaching the boy about putting up spirit of nitre," he wrote on one occasion.

He also warned the boy again and again about the danger of using a light in the vicinity of so volatile a fluid as ether.

Either the boy Michael was not an apt pupil, or he learned so quickly that he became overconfident.

Late in the afternoon of December 29, 1858, winter's early dusk was creeping over Brooklyn Heights. Dr. Squibb lighted the gas lamp over the workbench of his top-floor laboratory at 149 Furman Street. He had separated the pulp from the seeds of colocynth and was weighing out the amount called for by his formula. He would have time, he thought, to start his cathartic extract macerating in a porcelain-lined tub before walking home to supper. On his way out he would tell the boy Michael to go home, too. It was getting too dark for him to work, and the character of his current job prevented the use of a light.

The boy Michael Diver was working on the floor below, pouring ether from a huge carboy into smaller bottles—half-pound bottles, one-pound bottles, and three- and four-pound bottles for hospital use. His eyes smarted from the pungent sweetness of the fumes, and he felt suddenly faint. Remembering what Dr. Squibb had told him, he turned his head away and held his breath. It did no good. He was about to set the carboy down when it slipped from his hands and smashed to the table top, cracking open a small bottle of ether.

A shimmer of vapor arose from the volatile liquid as it spilled out and rippled across the work table. A candle burned at the other end of the table where Michael had been waxing bottle stoppers. He was so terrified to realize he had violated Dr. Squibb's injunction about lights and ether that he did not think of blowing out the candle.

There was a faint puff of sound, a blinding glare, and the whole table was a writhing mass of flame. Michael Diver screamed.

"Dr. Squibb! Help! Dr. Squibb!"

The shrill note of panic in the boy's voice brought Dr. Squibb hurrying down from the upper story. By the time he had reached the scene, the river of fire was squirming among the filled ether bottles. One by one they popped like firecrackers, adding their contents to the holocaust. The blazing liquid poured off the table to the floor.

Dr. Squibb jumped over the flames to open the water tap in the sink behind the work table.

"Dr. Squibb, I forgot—"

"Run downstairs, boy. Send Mr. McCarty up to help me. Tell them all to come up quickly."

For Dr. Squibb the situation was well in hand. He filled basin after basin with water, emptied it upon the flames. The fire on the floor was reduced to a small patch. The table still blazed.

Michael Diver panted back upstairs.

"They've all run off, Dr. Squibb," he gasped. "I shouted after them but they wouldn't stop. Mr. McCarty said they were running to call the fire wagons."

"Then run yourself, boy. The stairs. Quickly."

The doorway to the staircase was already aflame as Michael ran. Three of the big hospital-size bottles had just exploded from the heat of the flames. There was a wall of fire stretching completely across the building now. And Dr. Squibb was behind it. At last he realized his position was hopeless.

He turned his back on the flames and hurried to the other end of the laboratory. All his books and papers were there— his precious journals with the records of all his experiments, all his formulas and scientific data, all his life work. He gathered up the thick, heavy ledgers into his arms and groped through the smoke and flames toward the stairs.

He coughed. The smoke was acrid with the smell of burning chemicals and shot through with weirdly colored flames. Something else exploded, spraying the room with shattered glass. The blast knocked him to his knees and he dropped his books. Gropingly, despairingly, he picked up the heavy volumes, one by one. He sank his chin into his upturned coat collar, closed his mouth and eyes, and jumped through the flames.

When he reached the stairway his clothes were afire.

When he staggered into the street, four floors below, his hair was burned off and his face and hands were seared black and bleeding. His arms still clasped his precious ledgers, although glowing caterpillars of fire crawled along the page ends.

"In the excitement of trying to save books, etc.," he wrote later, "I was not at first aware that I was burned, but the bystanders, and a numbness of my hands and face soon made me aware of the fact."

A crowd had gathered to watch the conflagration. Someone wrapped an overcoat around his smoldering clothing. Neighbors recognized him and led him home, dazed, blinded, heartbroken, and, when the numbness of shock had worn off, in agony. Before he reached Middagh Street he heard the fire engines clanging past. But Dr. Squibb, the fire buff who had stood for hours in the freezing cold to watch Barnum's Museum burn down, would not see the spectacular destruction of his own hopes and fortune.

Although he had lived in the neighborhood only a few months, he had already made friends with the score of doctors who lived around Brooklyn Heights, and who had taken him into their local medical society. So while Mary Fogarty hurried across town to the Naval Hospital to get Mrs. Squibb, who was visiting her sister, the neighborhood physicians were putting Dr. Squibb to bed in Miss Simonson's boardinghouse. Dr. McClellan was first to arrive, then Dr. J. C.

Hutchison and Dr. Isaacs, and finally Dr. Minor, who although he lived around the corner on Willow Street, had been visiting Dr. Dudley.

By the time Caroline Squibb had arrived with Dr. Bache, her husband had been given opiates and anointed with unguents. When she saw his head, arms and hands swathed in bandages, she closed her eyes and leaned against Dr. Bache for support.

Dr. Hutchison took her aside to tell her how severely her husband had been burned.

"He should be taken to City Hospital," he said.

Caroline shook her head. "I must nurse him myself."

"But he will need special care. His eyes . . ."

"Will he see again, Doctor?"

"We hope so. We won't be sure for days, maybe weeks."

He smiled sadly at the ironic thought that the man who had shown the world how to make ether by using steam to avoid the danger of an open flame might be blinded for life by an ether fire.

When the doctors left, much later that night, a boy was sitting on a curb in Middagh Street, crying bitterly.

IV

FOR THE GREATER PART of a century company legend, based on Squibb family say-so, has dated the disastrous Furman Street fire on Christmas Eve, 1858. There was sound foundation for this sentimental twist to a tragic story—a lapse of Dr. Squibb's own memory.

The last entry in Dr. Squibb's journal for 1858 is dated December 22—a dozen lines at the top of a page. Coming across this nearly blank page more than twenty years later, Dr. Squibb added a few lines in a tighter, smaller script as follows:

1882

Nov. 24.   On looking for notes not found here, I conclude
that the interruption was caused by the burning of
the laboratory on the evening of Dec. 24th, 1858,
after which I was laid up with burned face and
hands.

So Dr. Squibb, nearly twenty-four years after the fact, remembered the fire as having occurred on Christmas Eve.

Six weeks after the fire, however, he reported otherwise.
On February 15, 1859, his hands still swathed in bandages
although the pads had just been removed from his eyes, he
dictated a letter to Professor Procter, editor of the *American
Journal of Pharmacy,* which began:

"By the help of an amanuensis I am able to acknowledge
your kind favor of yesterday, and can proceed to give you
some detail of the disaster that has occurred to me. On the
afternoon of the 29th of December, a new boy whom I was
teaching to put up preparations, accidentally broke a small
bottle of ether. . . ."

The contemporary press also reported the date as December 29. The Brooklyn *Eagle* devoted two paragraphs of the
first column of page 3, in its issue of Thursday, December
30, 1858, to describing the event as follows:

FIRE.— About 6 o'clock last night fire broke out in the chemical
factory of Dr. Edward K. [sic] Squibb, No. 149 Furman Street.
The firemen were promptly on the ground, and obtaining a good
supply of Ridgewood water, soon suppressed the flames. About
9 o'clock it again burst out and the contents were totally destroyed. The loss is estimated at about $5000. Dr. Squibb was
somewhat burned about the face and hands in attempting to save
his books and papers. The fire originated in consequence of the
carelessness of a boy who was engaged in sealing chemicals.

At this fire the value of the waterworks was again made manifest, the hose tender of Engine No. 3 having connected to a hy-
drant and got a powerful stream before any engines arrived.

Engines were of little or no use, only three being used. The alarm about 9 o'clock was for the same fire.

It is interesting to note that the *Eagle* reporter was more interested in the functioning of those newfangled pressure fire hydrants than in either checking the extent of Dr. Squibb's injuries or finding out why the firemen had gone off and left something smoldering the first time out, so that the total destruction of the laboratory three hours later was actually a case of neglect by the department.

It would seem that the Brooklyn fire department was not really at its best that year. There actually was a fire on Christmas Eve, according to the *Eagle,* in a three-story brick house occupied by John C. Matthews in Warren Street, which was in the Third District. However, the City Hall bell rang for the Fourth District, and by the time the fire laddies had finally located the blaze, the Matthews house (which was near the dividing line) was pretty well gutted and the neighboring houses were being looted by local hoodlums who claimed to be firemen.

There was even a fire in Furman Street on December 24— the camphene and turpentine works of Farran and Fullum at No. 35.

The same column of the Brooklyn *Eagle* which reported the Squibb fire carried the following paragraph:

LECTURE.— Rev. Henry Ward Beecher delivers his lecture on 'Sympathy' this evening in the Clinton Avenue church.

V

THE ROAD BACK was long and painful. The burns were deep and cruel. Although there was doubt for weeks whether Dr. Squibb would ever be able to use his hands and eyes again, one thing was certain from the beginning: He would never again be called the handsome Dr. Squibb. His face would be marred for life.

Dr Squibb did not go to the hospital. Caroline insisted on caring for him herself, although she was sickened by the carbolic smell of antiseptics, the greasy feel of unguents, and the odor of burned flesh. When she slept or when she retired to retch in secret, Mary Fogarty took over.

There was a constant parade of physicians through Miss Simonson's boardinghouse, led by Dr. Minor. They allowed no visitors for weeks. But when the pain had lessened and the opiates had been stopped, they let a teen-age boy come up. Michael Diver had been coming twice daily to inquire about Dr. Squibb's condition, asking, with tears in his eyes, permission to go up and apologize.

Dr. Squibb could not see him, for his eyes were still bandaged, but he recognized the "Boy Michael's" tearful voice.

"It was not thy fault, boy," said Dr. Squibb, using the Quaker pronoun he had never before used outside his own family. "It was an accident. Don't fret. Thee has been a good lad."

The doctors first took the bandages off the hands, for there had been massive destruction of tissue and shrinkage of tendons, and they wanted to restore full use of the fingers if possible. Especially did they want to prevent the permanent stiffening of the fingers into claws, and the overgrowth of scar tissue to form webbing at the base of the fingers.

As healing progressed, the doctors asked Mrs. Squibb to massage the scar tissue several times daily to correct the tendency. It was a painful operation for both of them. Occasionally Dr. Squibb would wince and occasionally Caroline, nauseated by the smell of antiseptics and sickened by the sight of her husband's maimed hands, would steal away for a moment for a whiff of her scent bottle. His eyes still bandaged, Dr. Squibb would be unaware of her absence. "Don't mind me, Mother," he would say. "Keep pressing."

When the doctors removed the bandages from his eyes after five weeks, they were both heartened and saddened. The cornea had not been badly damaged. He would see again. But his eyelids would be permanently everted, and his tear ducts would never again be normal. His eyes would water constantly and he would always have to protect them artificially. By day, he would have to wear goggles against the cold, the wind, and the dust. By night he would have to fasten his eyelids together with strips of isinglass plaster, so that he could sleep with closed eyes.

When at last he was allowed out, he walked to Furman Street to stare at the gutted shell of the laboratories of E. R. Squibb, M.D.

For the next few days he spoke hardly a word. He was not bemoaning his misfortune or brooding over his disfigurement. He was thinking—thinking and planning the details of making a fresh start. The disaster was in the past now. The future was still his. After all, he was only in his fortieth year. Why should not he, like the phoenix, arise from the ashes of his own making?

Actually, he had taken the first steps even before the bandages were removed from his eyes. He had accepted with thanks the landlord's offer to rebuild the burned floors. The mechanics, who had scarcely finished building his apparatus and fixtures before everything was destroyed, had already conferred with him at his bedside and were ready to refit the laboratory from scratch again. The fire-insurance companies had been prompt in paying off on his policies. To be sure, their payments were some thousand dollars short of the actual loss, to say nothing of the loss of time and production, but the gap of a thousand dollars should not be too difficult to bridge.

Although he did not know it, many friends and unknown admirers had already begun crossing the bridge. Sparked by George Sampson, president of the Brooklyn Savings Bank, a committee of physicians, pharmacists and laymen had been active on both sides of the East River since early in the year, raising funds to help finance the rebuilding of the laboratory.

The Brooklyn committee consisted of Dr. C. M. McClellan, chairman; Dr. James M. Minor, treasurer; Mr. R. J. Davies of 12 Clinton Street, secretary; Dr. James Crane, Dr. W. H. Dudley, Dr. T. L. Mason, Dr. C. L. Mitchell, Dr. A. Otterson, Dr. G. I. Bennett, and Mr. J. W. Smith. The New York committee included Dr. Willard Parker, Dr. E. Delafield, and Dr. James E. Wood.

These men quietly collected contributions, ranging from ten dollars from T. V. Rushton, pharmacist at the Astor House, to several hundred dollars from Dr. Minor, who had built up an extremely remunerative private practice in the eleven years since his retirement as a passed assistant surgeon of the Navy.

On April 13, 1859, Dr. Minor, as treasurer of the committee, presented Dr. Squibb with nearly $2,100, accompanied by a florid testimonial of appreciation.

"We should do less than our duty," read the testimonial, "and fall far short of the promptings both of our feelings and inmost convictions, did we not give expression to our deep sense of the importance to the profession and the community at large, of the efforts you have made to relieve them from the manifold evils of adulterated and noxious drugs imposed upon them by the dishonesty and criminal cupidity of unprincipled manufacturers.

"You have brought to the work a sane consideration of practical chemical science, pharmaceutical skill, and professional attainment such as we had hardly dared to hope for. We look upon your cause as our cause, your enterprise as the inauguration of a new era, and yourself as the exponent of the great principles of Truth and Humanity, in array against dishonest cupidity."

Ten days later Dr. Squibb replied, thanking the committee for their confidence in "the enterprise which you have so warmly befriended," and promising "to endeavor to show . . . in the future better than by any words, that your confidence and munificence have not been bestowed upon a callous or ungrateful object.

"The liberal sum of money enclosed," he concluded, "I

shall invest in the enterprise and shall always hold it in trust for the interests and benefit of the medical profession, and I beg you, gentlemen, never to believe without good individual evidence that your investment or interests have been forgotten or overwhelmed in the current of commercial pursuits."

Dr. Squibb carefully kept a list of the names and addresses of the contributors, for he did not consider the funds as a contribution, but a loan to be repaid with interest. Yet the human side of the gesture moved him greatly, and he remembered it all his life.

Nearly twenty-five years later he received a letter from T. V. Rushton, the Astor House pharmacist, who had gone to Denver to start in business for himself and was having financial trouble. On March 15, 1883, Dr. Squibb replied:

I remember very well your contribution to Mr. Meakin on my behalf . . . and your kind note when I returned it to you, and I now double that contribution to you with the hope that it may be of service to you. Enclosed please find a postal money order for twenty dollars.

Very truly yours,

E. R. SQUIBB

six

BITTERSWEET

I

THE TRIUMPHANT REBOUND of Dr. Squibb from near-disaster, physical and financial, was tinged with bittersweet. The approach of the Civil War brought prosperity to his rebuilt laboratory and heartache to the loyal Unionist whose best friends were in the South. Moreover, the war years saw the beginning of a great personal sorrow.

The rebuilding of No. 149 Furman Street, however, was unalloyed, joyful excitement. By mid-March of 1859 the wreckers had cleaned out the gutted floors of the laboratory. Carpenters, masons and painters followed close on their heels. Bearded now, and wearing dark glasses, Dr. Squibb recommenced his complex rounds in New York and New Jersey to purchase new lab fittings.

By May he was accepting special orders and employing assistants. One of the first names to appear on his daybook for 1859 was that of Michael Diver. The boy Michael was to receive $2.50 a week, including night work, an increase of 50 cents over his previous pay as an apprentice.

Other assistants that steamy summer of 1859 were Henry Miner, who got $5 a week; Charles Banks, who got $9; and Charles Spanholz, who got $12. John W. Clark, who was hired at $20 a month, drew an advance his first week on the job and was discharged for drunkenness on July 8, in debt to Dr. Squibb for 77 cents. All got two weeks' vacation with pay.

By fall Dr. Squibb was back in full production and sending out his first list. The list was accompanied by a printed circular introducing himself all over again as follows:

THE SUBSCRIBER, lately a Passed Assistant Surgeon in the U. S. Navy, and for some years Assistant Director of the Naval Laboratory at New York, informs the Medical Profession that he has established a Laboratory at New York for supplying to the U. S. Army and such of the Medical and Pharmaceutical Professions as may desire it, a class of Medical Preparations that come fully up to the standard of the *National Pharmacopoeia.*

The common belief that much of the uncertainty of medical practice arises from the bad quality of medicinal substances, seems to acquire daily confirmation. Through faulty preparation and commercial competition, many preparations formerly regarded as of primary importance, are gradually going out of use, while others produce effects and cause accidents that do not properly belong to them, as described in the *Pharmacopoeia.* New remedies as suggested and offered for trial are often found so imperfect, and varying so much in chemical character and strength, that they are either condemned, or received upon false promises, both equally at variance with the proper progress in therapeutics. . . .

Several improvements, such as the printing of one or two simple tests upon the labels of some of the more important preparations, and in the mode of putting up such as are liable to deteriorate by careless keeping, are addressed particularly to the Physician and Pharmaceutist and can hardly fail of appreciation by either.

EDWARD R. SQUIBB, M.D.

LABORATORY,
No. 149 Furman Street,
(Near Fulton Ferry), Brooklyn.

The 1859 list contained 38 officinal preparations, from acetum opii to zinci sulphas, including of course ether and chloroform. It also contained 31 items on an "Unofficinal List and New Remedies." The new remedies were accompanied by such notations as:

"Chromic Acid, recommended by Drs. Heller, Sigmund, Marshall, and others, for the destruction of fungus and morbid growths, particularly about the genitals. See Dub. Quart. Journal XIII, 250, and U. S. Dispensatory, 11th edit., p. 1392." Or:

"Chloropercha. Solution of Gutta Percha in Chloroform, an excellent substitute for collodion in surgery.

"Sulphite of Lime—new chemical agent for arresting fermentation, used in certain cases of Dyspepsia, and in yeasty vomiting."

The list brought in a promising quota of civilian orders and a few Army orders from Colonel Satterlee.

Colonel Satterlee also sent Dr. Squibb a problem which both intrigued and surprised him: a request to analyze a sample of quinine sulphate prepared by Rosengarten & Sons. The Rosengarten firm was a pioneer Philadelphia pharmaceutical house, dating back to 1823, when it was known as Zeitler and Rosengarten, doing business on St. John Street. In 1840 a Frenchman named Denis had replaced Zeitler as a partner, and in 1853 Rosengarten *père* took his sons Samuel and Mitchel into the firm. Rosengarten & Sons was still one of the most reliable pharmaceutical houses in the country and Dr. Squibb wondered why the Army was questioning a Rosengarten preparation. After a long series of tests he found out.

Late in December he sent Dr. Satterlee three pages of notes and figures, accompanied by a letter reading:

I have examined the Sulphate of Quinia of Rosengarten & Sons sent by you and find it consists of

Sulphate of Quinia 69%
Sulphate of another alkaloid, probably
cinchonidia 31%

The result surprised me very much and I examined the reaction repeatedly and carefully. The foreign salt is *not* probably fraudulently added but results from the use of inferior New Grenada barks and working them too closely.

The fee for analysis was not high, and the drug orders for a standing army of 25,000 men were apparently not going to make Dr. Squibb a rich man. The total 1859 receipts of the rebuilt laboratory from May through December amounted to $5,161.31, of which $4,625.32 came from the medical and pharmaceutical professions and only $535.99 from the Army.

Nevertheless it was good to be alive and good to be in business again. Dr. Squibb, who had already raised the boy Michael Diver's wages to $3 a week in October, gave him a Christmas bonus of $3 and promised to raise his pay again in February to $4, including overtime.

II

THE YEAR 1860 MARKED a turning point in Dr. Squibb's fortunes. The rebuilt laboratory was soon working at full tilt, thanks largely to the Army and Dr. Satterlee, who, after a slow start, was more than living up to his promises.

Dr. Richard S. Satterlee, Colonel, Medical Corps, United States Army, was an old soldier from 'way back, the second generation of a military family. His father commanded Connecticut troops during the American Revolution, and he himself had been in the Medical Corps since 1822. He had served with Colonel Zachary Taylor in the Seminole War in Florida in 1837 and had landed at Vera Cruz during the Mexican War. He had served with General Worth's division at Cerro Gordo, Churubusco, Molina del Rey, and Chapultepec. He became Winfield Scott's medical director at Mexico City and established the base hospital there.

Dr. Satterlee was far more astute politically than most old soldiers. He foresaw the defeat of Stephen A. Douglas by

Abraham Lincoln in 1860, and, even before the secession of South Carolina that December, he discussed with Dr. Squibb a project for turning out bandages and splints. When eleven Southern states convened in Montgomery the next February, formed the Confederate States of America and elected Jefferson Davis their President, Colonel Satterlee doubled his orders to the Squibb laboratory. And when in the second week of April 1861, Beauregard fired on Fort Sumter and President Lincoln called for volunteers, Colonel Satterlee quadrupled his orders and began pleading with Dr. Squibb to enlarge his laboratories, a plea which was continued with swelling crescendo throughout the year.

The outbreak of civil war was a profound shock to Dr. Squibb. First of all, his Quaker-taught hatred of war had somehow survived his four years of service aboard men-of-war—an instinct in direct conflict, in this case, with his Quaker-taught hatred of slavery. And secondly, the war cut him off from his oldest and dearest friends, Sam White and his family and friends, slave-owning Georgians all, who had financed his first laboratory.

He continued to fill orders as rapidly as was consistent with his uncompromising standards of purity and uniformity. In the interests of humanity, he was more than happy to increase his output of pure ether and chloroform so that the pain of battlefield operations and base-hospital amputations could be eased. But it was only after General George Brinton McClellan was appointed Commander in Chief in November that Dr. Squibb was convinced that the Civil War was a serious business that might last for years.

Dr. Squibb had mixed feelings about the McClellan family. He had had nothing but the utmost respect for the late Dr. George McClellan the General's father, founder of his alma mater, Jefferson Medical College. He also respected the founder's brother, Dr. Samuel McClellan, professor of anatomy at Jefferson. Dr. C. M. McClellan, the founder's cousin—who was Dr. Squibb's own neighbor and dear friend and who had chaired the committee to rebuild the laboratory

—had both his love and his professional admiration. But the founder's two sons . . .

Dr. John N. McClellan had always irritated him at Jefferson by his unbased know-it-all attitude, his pathological need to talk loudly during lectures, usually in derogation of some colleague; and his more than slight tendency to circumnavigate the truth when it was most convenient.

And General George Brinton McClellan had always struck him as too ambitious and too successful a promoter. True, he was a West Point graduate and had served well in the Mexican War and as an observer in the Crimea. But why, after he had renounced the Army for the railways for five lucrative years, was he suddenly dubbed a major-general and handed, in rapid succession, the Army of Ohio and the Army of the Potomac? No, with McClellan running things it was bound to be a long war. Dr. Squibb decided he had better take Dr. Satterlee's advice. He began looking for land to expand his plant.

Shortly after the beginning of 1862 he located a block on Brooklyn Heights close to his Furman Street laboratory, between Vine and Doughty streets, on the steep slope that rose from the waterfront to Columbia Heights. A building could be erected here with entrances on two levels—on Vine Street, where Dr. Squibb planned to have access to his private office, and at 36 Doughty Street, which would be the customers' entrance. There were some structures on the land—an old distillery, and some outbuildings for nearby livery stables —but they were torn down a few days after Dr. Squibb took title to the property on May Day.

On May 25 the cornerstone of the northeast corner of the new laboratory was laid.

A few days before Thanksgiving—and just two weeks after General McClellan had been relieved of his top command by General Ambrose Everett Burnside—Dr. Squibb moved into the new laboratory.

Although builders George Joyce and Parmenas Cartner finished the construction job in six months, they did not skimp on design or materials. With the Furman Street fire in mind, Dr. Squibb insisted on "slow-burning construction" —heavy posts and beams, six-inch flooring, fireproof masonry vaults to store papers and valuable chemicals, and walls of hard-burned Haverstraw brick and cement mortar.

"It was almost monolithic," wrote one of Dr. Squibb's sons many years later. "To make any changes was a tough job. We could seldom get a whole brick out of the walls. The Big Boss was a stickler for pure cement."

The construction was financed, through the intermediary of George Sampson of the Brooklyn Savings Bank, partly out of profits and partly through mortgages held by Brooklyn banks.

Dr. Squibb had already repaid the volunteers who had helped him get back on his feet after the fire. On November 12, 1861, every contributor received a check on the Long Island Bank, accompanied by a printed form letter reading as follows:

DEAR SIR:

About April of 1859, when the undersigned had suffered a loss of apparatus etc. by fire, you and many others came forward through Dr. Jas. M. Minor, and by a subscription amounting to nearly twenty-one hundred dollars, made good the loss sustained.

The sympathy and pecuniary aid were most acceptable, and were gratefully received,—but in the case of the pecuniary aid, with the mental reservation that the money so liberally bestowed should one day be returned.

Since that time, principally through the preference given to a good class of medicinal preparations by the Medical Department of the Army, my business has been reasonably prosperous, and I now ask as an especial favor, to be permitted to return the amount of all these subscriptions, with the interest added.

In sending you the enclosed amount, be assured that it is with no desire to impair,—much less to discharge the obligation under which your timely sympathy and aid placed me. On the contrary, this obligation is one of the most grateful recollections of my life, and this duty of reimbursing you for the inferior part of your liberality once performed, the obligation will remain with me as an unalloyed pleasure, and a debt only to be paid with the great debt of nature.

Some of the major contributors, like Dr. Minor, protested that their contributions had been outright gifts, but Dr. Squibb would not hear of it. Whereupon a subcommittee crossed to New York, took their returned money to Ball and Black's at 565 Broadway, and ordered a table service of heavy silver, simple in design and marked with an Old English *S*. On New Year's Day, 1862, they presented the silver to Mrs. Squibb, but it was the doctor who "volunteered to try to convey our joint thanks to you all.

"She is very much obliged to you," Dr. Squibb wrote, "for your friendly appreciation of her husband's efforts to be moderately honest, useful, and grateful, and I am sure that no new year of either her life or mine was ever commemorated by so warm a greeting from such friends."

III

THERE SEEMS LITTLE DOUBT that a good deal of Dr. Squibb's medical preparations served the gray as well as the blue armies during the Civil War. In his monograph, *The House of Squibb* (1945), Francis Sill Wickware writes that Dr. Squibb not only met many of the needs of the Union armies, but "Indirectly he met some of the needs of the Confederate Armies as well, for a good share of his ether found its way into the Southern lines. It is even said that Abraham Lincoln himself chose to overlook the smuggling of Squibb ether to the South."

Although such kindly behavior would certainly have been characteristic of the Civil War President, it is much more likely that Squibb ether reached the South through the enterprise of Robert E. Lee's generals than by courtesy of Abraham Lincoln.

There is plenty of evidence in Dr. Squibb's letter books of the period to support this. For instance, a letter from Thomas P. Smith, pharmacist of St. Joseph, Missouri, enclosed a check for $182 but added plaintively that "the medicines have not yet been seen. The rebels seem to be having their way in Missouri."

Years later Charles F. Squibb recalled that "our chief distributor [in the South] was Gen. Banks. The Johnnies always managed to capture his well-equipped trains. Our goods went all through the Confederacy and were appreciated." He was referring to Major General Nathaniel P. Banks, who commanded a volunteer corps in the Shenandoah Valley early in the war, was defeated by Stonewall Jackson at Cedar Mountain, Virginia, succeeded Butler as commander at New Orleans, and lost to Taylor at Sabine Cross Roads, Louisiana.

Partly because of loss of medical supplies through capture and partly because of the expansion of the Union Army to a million men with casualties numbering in the hundreds of thousands, Dr. Satterlee's needs soon far exceeded even the increased facilities of the new Squibb laboratories.

The chief medical purveyor pleaded with Dr. Squibb to enlarge his plant even more, sufficiently to take care of all Army needs, but Dr. Squibb demurred. He was not sure that he could give a larger plant the close personal supervision required for the maintenance of the uniformity and purity of product that constituted his hallmark. Moreover, what would happen to the added facilities when the war ended and the Union armies were demobilized?

The Army then went ahead with plans to set up government-operated pharmaceutical plants, one of them at Astoria, Long Island, within a few miles of the Squibb laboratories. Dr. Squibb in 1863 commented on this move in a letter to a St. Louis colleague, to whom he wrote:

"The Surgeon General has decided to have laboratories of his own. Dr. McCormick is to have one near here and Dr. A. K. Smith one in Philadelphia. Dr. McCormick is just starting his at great expense and under such circumstances that I predict for it a disastrous and disagreeable failure. From all I can learn, Dr. McC. is, as the author and vender of a 'Magic Waverly Pill,' but little more than a great quack and I think an unreliable man, but Dr. Wood knows more of him than I do. It is, however, a great pity that the best interests of the Medical Corps of the Army should fall into such keeping."

The Army, however, thought well of Dr. Satterlee's activities in maintaining the flow of medical supplies, regardless of the quality, and the following year (1864) breveted him brigadier general at the age of sixty-six. The accompanying citation praised General Satterlee "for diligent care and attention in procuring proper army supplies as medical purveyor, and for economy and fidelity in the disbursement of large sums of money."

To Dr. Squibb, the South was not the Confederacy; it was Milledgeville, Georgia. The South was his old and dear friend Sam White, whose money had built the first Squibb laboratory; it was Fleming Grieve, the Milledgeville pharmacist; and of course their kinfolk, for all of Milledgeville seemed to be related in some way.

To be cut off from his friends by the war was particularly hard on a man as scrupulously observant of the letter of the law as was Dr. Squibb, for he would indulge in no subterfuge that might be interpreted as communicating with the enemies of the Republic. He was happy, therefore, to hear from Sam White via flag of truce or even via Nassau, although he himself would never use a means of communication that depended upon blockade runners.

Sam White's notes were terse, impersonal, and very short, partly because he did not wish to incriminate his old friend and partly because he was not quite sure what Dr. Squibb's feelings toward him might be, now that they were politically enemies. The letters merely reported that John Grieve was a prisoner in Maryland, or that Dr. Hall's brother Hartley was in Rock Island prison in Illinois, and that the Cousins Jones and Captain Tom White had also been captured.

Dr. Squibb immediately set about locating the Southerners

and helping them to the extent allowed by law. On November 3, 1863, for instance, he wrote to the commanding officer at Fort Delaware as follows:

DEAR SIR:

If not improper, nor against the regulations of your command, I beg you will allow the enclosed note to be given to a prisoner of war taken at Gettysburg and now believed to be in your charge, named John Grieve. He is a Georgian, and I believe was serving in the 2d Georgia Battalion.

Should he have been transferred from Fort Delaware, will you have the kindness to tell me where he may be found?

Should he still be in the Fort, and reply to my note, (which you will please read), be so kind as to guard me against sending him anything that will interfere with your regulations or compromise him.

Very respectfully
Your obed. servt.
E. R. SQUIBB.

The reply from Brigadier General A. Schorpf was written on the back of Dr. Squibb's note:

John Grieve was transferred to Pt. Lookout, Md. You can send him money or clothing by express—he will receive it—select any color except blue or gray.

Dr. Squibb sent both money and clothing, carefully charging it to Dr. White's account, which continued to earn interest all through the war.

Six months later another note came from Georgia:

Friend Squibb—

Col. Batt Jones, a kinsman of ours [he was a cousin of Dr. White's wife], is now a prisoner of war at Johnson's Island. Any aid, pecuniary or otherwise, that he stands in need of, and you can render, will be gratefully remembered by your old

Friend
SAM G. WHITE.

Johnson's Island had a dreadful sound to Southern ears. To some it was the Yankee Andersonville, although this was an obvious exaggeration. There is little doubt that what suffering there was was due chiefly to the severe climate—Johnson's Island prison was in Lake Erie, not far from Sandusky, Ohio—and to the lack of appropriate clothing. In any event, Dr. Squibb wrote immediately to Johnson's Island and Lieutenant Colonel Batt Jones replied at once. He was, he said "rejoiced that a kinsman of mine . . . should have sown good seed in soil so opportunely productive . . . and while receiving what strictly belongs to Dr. White I hope I may not ask more than is due."

Colonel Jones asked for $50, a sack coat for which he gave exact and detailed measurements, a pair of pants, two pairs of drawers and woolen socks, "all of durable materials and heavy enough to wear during the fall by which time I hope to be exchanged. . . . We are treated very well and I believe would be treated better, but for the conduct of some, who never know how to behave themselves anywhere."

By August, Johnson's Island prisoners were no longer allowed to receive provisions or clothing unless the packages were sent from outside the Federal lines. So when Colonel Jones wrote for another $50, plus a sack of flour, a firkin of butter, ten pounds of coffee and fifteen of sugar, plus shoes and blankets, Dr. Squibb had a box sent to Thomson & Burns, importers, at Yonge and Front streets in Toronto, paid duty on it, and had it forwarded to Sandusky.

He also inserted a personal notice in the New York *Herald:* "Lt. Col. Batt Jones, prisoner of war at Johnson's Island, is well. Richmond papers please copy."

The colonel broadcast appeals to friends in other parts of the country, asking not only that they send him food and clothing, but also that they pull strings to have him exchanged or paroled to Cuba. When this failed and the bitter winds of the last winter of the war swept across Lake Erie, Colonel Jones grew desperate. He wrote asking Dr. Squibb to participate in "a pious fraud" for "the preservation of my health." He suggested that Dr. Squibb send him 100 pounds of flour in a sack marked "Atlanta, Ga."; also "100 lbs. of bacon (hams & sides), 1 bushel corn meal sifted, 1 bushel dried peaches and 50 lbs. brown sugar, marked on the outside as enclosed Card No. 1. . . ." The whole box was to be marked so as to appear to have been shipped via Savannah.

Dr. Squibb was outraged at being asked to perpetrate fraud upon the prison keepers. Instead, he wrote to Major Scovil, commandant of the prison, asking permission to send the provisions requested, pointing out that they would be purchased with Dr. White's money and thus could actually be considered as provided by the Confederacy. "If they cannot be sent legitimately in this way," he wrote on the back of Colonel Jones's letter, "will not undertake to send them at all. Col. Jones should be as ready to offer his health and his life to his cause, as a prisoner, as he did in going into the war as an officer."

He was happy, however, to forward a box of provisions which arrived in New York a few days later, coming legitimately from Colonel Jones's brother in Augusta, Georgia, and marked: "By flag of truce—via Savannah & New York City. Care and kindness of the officers of the Army & Navy of the United States at Savannah & elsewhere."

The box contained the exact provisions in the same quantities requested of Dr. Squibb—by no coincidence, but by the enterprise and fanatic Confederate ardor of a Georgia lady unhappily stranded in New England. Miss Kate Davidson was a distant cousin of Colonel Jones and an acquaintance of Dr. Squibb. In fact, when Dr. Squibb had returned to Brooklyn after his trip to Milledgeville in 1858, he carried a package for Miss Kate which he expressed to Milford, Connecticut. Miss Kate not only had no compunction about smuggling a letter into Georgia, stating Colonel Batt Jones's needs; she considered it her duty as a daughter of the Confederacy.

In fact, Miss Kate resented very much the fact that she was in Milford at all. She had tried to correct that situation—

without success, as she told Dr. Squibb in a letter dated Aug. 16, 1864, and signed "K. M. Davidson." She wrote:

MY DEAR FRIEND,

I suppose you have long since thought me safe with my friends in Geo., but unfortunately such has not been the case.

On the 16 of April, my friend and myself attempted to cross the Potomac, but the person to whom we entrusted our fate proved traitorous to us, and gave us up to the detestable detectives who infest all the towns of Maryland, so I have been serving my time as a 'prisoner of war' at Fortress Monroe. Of all things that I dreaded was to get into Butler's Department [General B. F. Butler, commanding the Army of the James]. I was kept a prisoner in close confinement, until the 9th of July—for ten weeks we were allowed no exercise except one walk up to the Fort. After that we were allowed to walk every day with a guard. They told me I was to be tried by court martial, but my friends in the North heard it, and after a while they procured an order for my release. The only charge they had against me was 'attempting to run the blockade,' and they *supposed* that I had destroyed my letters. They have no proof, however, but certainly no papers of any kind were found on me. I had to take the 'oath of Allegiance.' I am willing to do my part in defending the constitution but nothing more. I begged them to send me South, but they said I had merited punishment by running the blockade, and they did not intend to gratify me by letting me do what I wished. . . .

I came through New York, but I was alone, and did not like to risk going by myself to Brooklyn, which accounts for my not seeing you at the time. I suppose I shall have to try to remain in New England, a prospect not at all agreeable to me.

The English lady who accompanied me is still held prisoner. She had a very disagreeable interview with Gen. Butler. He was *exceedingly* insulting to her, and she returned it. Lord Lyons [the British ambassador] has taken up the case and a great many influential persons are doing everything in their power for her. . . . I supposed when we were first taken that she would be released immediately as she was a British subject, but Butler intends to enjoy his *spite*. . . .

I am so distressed and so disappointed about not getting back home. . . . It was a foolish thing for me to have come on. If I had been alone I should have got home safely. My friends there would have put me over when I first got to Ft. Mays, but they could not manage it well with her.

Remember me to your wife. I hope her health is better than when I saw you. And how are your handsome little sons? Can you not pay us a visit? . . . The sea bathing is very good here. If you come, bring your little boys. I know they would enjoy it.

Safely back in Connecticut, Miss Kate Davidson passed on to Dr. Squibb the Milledgeville chitchat she received through her own private underground. Dr. White's family was well. . . . Lewis was severely wounded and not yet able to walk with crutches. . . .

Bessie Grieve is married to Wm. Williams, brother-in-law of Capt. Jack Jones. Dr. Talmadge is a lunatic in the asylum; had been sick for a long time before I left. His brain was affected. I think they apprehended paralysis of the brain. Is there such a disease as that? Maybe I am wrong. Clara Harris, daughter of Judge Tonson, is dead. Also Wm. Stubbs, son of Dr. White's kinsman in Midway. Mr. Flinn has returned to civil life and to charge of his flock in M. These items may not interest you, but as they were from Milledgeville, I thought you might have some recollection of the persons.

I suppose Dr. White does not quite understand how much he might say to you in his notes without compromising you. Neither does he understand your feelings towards him. This accounts for his very brief notes. I shall send a letter to him by Flag of Truce and without mentioning names shall let him know that you are unchanged toward him. . . .

Dr. Squibb was deeply grateful to Miss Kate for sending a flag of truce to Dr. White, even though the flag was more than somewhat imprinted with the Stars and Bars.

For Dr. Squibb had earmarked $10,000 to be sent to Sam

White whenever it could be done legally, once the war was over. The sum was in no way intended to be related to the damage Sherman had done to Dr. White's Georgia in his march to the sea. It was merely an honest return on an old friend's investment of faith and money in the Brooklyn laboratories of Edward R. Squibb, M.D.

IV

NOBODY COULD EVER justly accuse Dr. Squibb of trying to duck reality, yet his hurt from the fact of the Civil War was so deep that he rarely referred in writing to the great wholesale fratricide of this period. True, his journals were somewhat disorganized in the first two or three years after the Furman Street fire. It was some time before his pathetically maimed and stiffened fingers could resume the regular chronicle of his daily thoughts and actions. During the early part of the war, he was still recording his personal history—in a cramped and unfamiliar hand—in small notebooks and memorandum pads. But by the time Lee was moving toward the North and Lincoln had abandoned the volunteer system for conscription, Dr. Squibb had begun to put his house in order again, transferring many of his fragmentary notes to the classical ledgers, attempting to restore a semblance of continuity and picking up with the chronology where he had left off when the boy Michael upset the ether.

And yet the journals make no mention of any military or political aspects of the war—only the relationship between the Squibb laboratory and the Army.

The poignant exchanges involving the attempts to maintain communication with friends in the South without violating espionage laws, and the generous efforts to alleviate the suffering both of his friends and of unknown friends of friends who were prisoners of war in the North, have come to light chiefly in his correspondence and in letters from others.

There is no reaction in his journal to the Emancipation Proclamation.

There is no comment on an event which was certainly a sharp nostalgic stab, the welding of another personal link to the war, the snapping of another link with his personal past—the sinking of U. S. Frigate *Cumberland* in Hampton Roads by the Confederate ironclad *Merrimac* early in March 1862.

There is no mention of the week of terror that spattered Manhattan with blood during the suffocating early days of July 1863—the draft riots in protest against the conscription law by which Lincoln hoped to raise another 300,000 men for the Union armies, which ended in a witches' Sabbath of murder, mayhem, arson and looting. Dr. Squibb could hardly have ignored the week of mob rule in New York in which armories and police stations, provost marshal's offices and Protestant missions, dozens of homes and factories, Negro churches and the Weehawken ferry depot were burned; in which dozens of Negroes were beaten, burned, and hanged; in which property damage reached millions of dollars and casualties amounted to more than a thousand dead and four or five times as many wounded. Even Brooklyn was involved, for there were rumors that the rioters were about to move on the Navy Yard, and to thwart the mob the receiving ship *North Carolina,* the corvette *Savannah,* and the gunboats *Gertrude, Granite City, Unadilla* and *Tulip* took up positions in the East River.

Dr. Squibb's failure to mention these events may well have been due to the fact that his emotions during this period were almost completely absorbed in a series of intimate crises in his personal life.

Just when his personal and professional fortunes seemed on the rise, when his crusade for decent medicines was assuming major proportions, when his business success was such that he could decide to put down roots, become a good Brooklyn burgher, and purchase residence property on the harborside bluff he had grown to love, he made the agonizing discovery that his lovely and beloved Caroline was suffering from the dread malady of Caesar and Napoleon.

"Caroline's attacks began, as far as I can remember, in the Spring of 1861," he wrote later, "and she had two or more before we went to Oyster Bay for the summer. They continued, but with what frequency I cannot now tell, until the close of 1862, when I first commenced to note their occurrence. After having passed the summer of 1862 at Mrs. Gilbert's [in Ossining, New York], she came home, but returned for a week and then, Nov. 26, had a severe one while at Mrs. Gilbert's and by herself in the small N.E. room."

Dr. Squibb was reluctant to believe his own diagnosis. At first he tried to convince himself that the seizures were symptoms of hysteria. After all, Caroline was a high-strung, hypersensitive person. She was quick to laughter and quicker to tears. She could be gay and petulant within minutes. She would sulk for hours when she was disappointed. And hysteria could produce both tonic and clonic spasms.

The adoring husband and the scientist were here both partners and adversaries. The husband was thinking wishfully. The scientist was observing facts. But both were watching anxiously, compassionately. The husband was hoping that his beautiful wife was merely suffering from a condition that a young Frenchman named Charcot was treating in Paris (with some success) with suggestion and hypnotism. The physician was apprehensively checking all symptoms against the classic pattern which physicians since Hippocrates had pronounced practically incurable in adults.

Carefully, meticulously, pathetically, Dr. Squibb kept a detailed record of Caroline's attacks. Well schooled in differential diagnosis, he charted intervals and time of seizure. He recorded the most minute symptoms. Far ahead of his time—endocrinology was not even a gleam in the eye of those pioneers of the still-nonexistent Johns Hopkins, Drs. William Welch and William Osler—Dr. Squibb tried to equate the seizures with his beloved wife's catamenial periods.

At first the intervals read: "31 days . . . 30 days . . . 45

days . . ." Then came the hopeful "102 days . . ." But the hours were heartbreaking: "Had two, half an hour apart, at 4 a.m., at No. 43 Middagh Street, the first time she had two." . . . "At Middagh Street, at 2:30 a.m." . . . "At Mrs. Gilbert's, two, at 3 and 5 a.m." . . . "Nov. 1. Convulsion at Middagh Street between 3:30 and 4 a.m., having menstruated from Oct. 26 to 30th."

Since most of the attacks at this period occurred at night, Dr. Squibb could not make his differential diagnosis on the abruptness of the fall. Whenever there was a premonitory aura, however—"a faint spell," Caroline called it—he would lie awake all night, hoping against hope, watching for symptoms. There was no arching of the spine, which Charcot had noted. But occasionally he dozed off, and when he awakened there were telltale stains of bloody froth on the pillow, there was a sore and bitten tongue, and there was evidence of incontinence.

It did not take him long to admit the truth, once all the evidence was at hand. His darling, the mother of his children, was an epileptic.

The heartsick husband and the determined physician went to work together. Dr. Squibb spent many a sleepless night watching to prevent Caroline from injuring herself, after he had been warned by an aura. Sometimes nothing happened. Sometimes he succeeded in preventing convulsions by administering a preliminary whiff of chloroform. Once, when his ounce of prevention had failed, he thrust his fire-scarred fingers between her sleeping lips to stop the bloody laceration of her tongue during the clonic stage—and wore a bandage on his bitten hand for days afterward. It was not until many months later that he began to treat her with bromides.

Yet during all these years he maintained a detailed record of periodicity, possible causes—digestive upsets, servant troubles, irritations of every kind—in an effort to break through the riddle of epilepsy. The journals offer many pages of careful observations, testifying to many sleepless nights watching over his Caroline. We find such passages as:

"At 43 Middagh St. About 4.5 a.m. had the first one, and then between that and 7 a.m. had 3 more, 1st and 3d lying on her r. side, 2d and 4th lying on her left. This is the first time she was ever known to be attacked while lying on her l. side. . . . Interval 57 days."

And again:

"Had faint spells all day . . . being awakened by them at 6:40 a.m. and having them at intervals of an hour or so all day. From 7 to 9 in the evening had two or three bad ones approaching to convulsion, as twitching of muscles. . . . Had been in bed all day. Soon after I got to bed and she got to sleep, at 1:15 this morning she had a convulsion and a second at 6:25, having had faint spells between as could be noticed by her breathing, although she did not awake between. The convulsions were neither severe nor long; the first while lying on her r. side, the second on her left. . . . Interval, 46 days."

When in the spring of 1863 Dr. Squibb learned that his wife was with child, he was faced with fresh worries. Would Caroline's pregnancy affect her condition? Would her condition affect normal gestation? In any event, he gave Mary Fogarty full and detailed instructions on what to do in any emergency, bundled Mary, Caroline and the boys onto the Hudson River steamer, took them to Ossining and left them at Mrs. Gilbert's pension.

This was early in June. During the month he arranged to buy several pieces of land on the slope between Furman Street and Columbia Street (now Columbia Heights), planning to build stores on the lower level and his home on the street above. On July 3 he took title to the property. Caroline surprised him by coming to town for the occasion, and to be with her husband on his forty-fourth birthday.

Instead of a day of celebration, however, July Fourth was one of anguish. Caroline miscarried after ten weeks.

By November, she was again gestating.

Shortly after Christmas she had a series of severe attacks, and for six weeks it was doubtful that she would succeed in keeping her baby. However, she weathered another series of seizures in February and April and in May was able to survive the work and annoyance of moving to Manhattan. Miss Simonson was giving up her boardinghouse in Brooklyn and opening a new place at 204 West Fourteenth Street, New York, near the Academy of Music. The cornerstone of the new Squibb home on Brooklyn Heights had been laid six weeks earlier, but the house would not be finished before the end of the year, so the Squibb family went with Miss Simonson.

When Dr. Squibb took Caroline and the children to Ossining on May 30, he also took a white pony named Kit and a pony cart for the boys. The Squibbs occupied Mrs. Gilbert's "n.w. corner room and the small one adjoining, and the s.e. corner room, at $48 per week and $5 for the pony and wagon."

On the July 30 weekend, Dr. Squibb went as usual to join his family and found Caroline complaining of colicky pains. He prescribed a little brandy with ginger. However, he recorded, "About 5 o'clock in the morning, Sunday, July 31st, she awoke me saying she had more pain and had hardly slept since 12 o'clock. On her lying down beside me and calling attention to the hardness of the abdomen during the paroxysms of pain, I soon judged what might be their true character. Got up to dress myself at once but the pains were so rapid that I could only get time to get shirt, pantaloons and slippers on before the perineum needed constant support, and at about 6 o'clock, as near as I could judge from looking at the time afterward, the baby was born. . . . Gave [Caroline] some chloroform from the bottle only during the few last expulsive pains. After the cord was tied and cut, Mrs. Gilbert came and washed and dressed the baby. It was found to be a moderate sized, plump, healthy looking and quite perfect to all appearance female child, which gratified the mother very much."

Caroline wanted to name the little girl after Helen and Rosalie Hart, sisters of Mrs. Bache's late first husband.

"This I did not object to," wrote Dr. Squibb, "but pointed out what I believed would be the disadvantage to the child, should she live, of having a fanciful or sentimental name attached to that of Squibb, and reminded her of the single step from the sublime to the ridiculous. She abandoned her idea at once, and said, as I left it entirely to her, that her next choice was Mary after her sister Mary King. I acceded to this at once, although a little anxious to suggest my mother's name of Catherine H. Squibb. . . .

"May God in His wisdom bless this event in its results, and give me strength of purpose enough to do my whole duty manfully toward this new being in the full light of the almost discouraging weight of responsibility, so that in my heart I may be able to say, whether her life be short or long, happy or miserable, that I did my whole duty unflinchingly.

"I recall at this time vividly what I believe to have been my poor 'Mother's Prayer' for me her son under somewhat similar circumstances, and have now read it over again in her scrapbook where it is copied by her own hand:

"Keep, Heavenly Father, keep her heart
    Pure, humble, ardent and sincere,
Teaching the hand when to impart,
    The eye to shed the pitying tear.
With virtuous fortitude supplied
    Undazzled by the tinsel glare
Of fashion, folly and of pride,
    Oh, answer this a father's prayer."

Dr. Squibb did not record how he came into possession of his mother's scrapbook. At the time of his father's death, it will be recalled, Grandmother Squibb gave him locks of his three dead sisters' hair, with accompanying inscriptions described as "the only pieces of mother's handwriting that I possess."

It is quite likely that the scrapbook was sent to him by Cousin Martha Dodgson. Some years later it was Cousin Martha who rediscovered the location of Dr. Squibb's mother's grave, which he had lost track of, enabling him to erect a new headstone.

seven

CRUSADE

I

IRONICALLY, THE PERIOD spanned by the Civil War marked the first real progress in the crusade that was to become Dr. Squibb's whole life: the fight to regulate drug imports, manufacture and sales so that Americans could be assured of getting pure medicines of uniform strength and decent distribution.

Nothing better illustrates the amazing scope and method of Dr. Squibb's apparently limitless energy than his activity during the trying war years. Here was a man who had been maimed and disfigured for life by his own Frankenstein-like creation. While fighting his way back to health, he had recreated his own laboratories, expanded them to meet the military needs of a war that hurt him deeply, continued his scientific research and wrote about it in professional publications, adjusted himself to the tragic discovery that his cherished wife would be a semi-invalid for life, delivered their third child, and began building his own home—the first he had ever known. And on top of this, he waged his private war on quackery and adulterated drugs.

Dr. Squibb's first victory of national magnitude in his fight for dependable medicines came while he was a member of the 1860 Committee for the Revision of the U. S. Pharmacopoeia.

A pharmacopoeia is a register of approved drugs, chemicals, and medicinal preparations, combined with tests for their identification, purity, and strength, and standard formulas for achieving uniform reliability. The Egyptians had a pharmacopoeia of sorts in 1500 B.C. The voluminous writings of Galen, the Greek of Asia Minor who became a fashionable physician of second-century Rome, constituted the chief pharmacopoeia of Europe—largely erroneous—for a thousand years. In his honor, medicines prepared from either crude drugs or chemicals by physical processes, such as solutions or extracts, are still called "galenicals."

In the eighteenth century local pharmacopoeias appeared in London and in Edinburgh (prepared by the Royal College of Physicians). The first national pharmacopoeia appeared in France in 1818, and in the same year—the year before Dr. Squibb was born—Dr. Lyman Spalding of New York began the movement which was to result in the publication of the first United States Pharmacopoeia in 1820. No official national pharmacopoeia appeared in Britain until 1864.

The first U. S. Pharmacopoeia was drafted by a convention meeting in the Senate Chamber of the Capitol in Washington. The delegates were physicians chosen by regional meetings. About a score of them straggled in during the week of the convention. Travel was uncertain; the stagecoach trip from New York required from forty to fifty hours, with overnight stops at Trenton and Baltimore. However, the convention turned out a book of 272 pages containing a primary list of 217 preparations. When published in December 1820, it won the acclaim of the Surgeon General of the Army but did not receive the unqualified approval of the Navy.

The convention decreed that the U. S. Pharmacopoeia should be revised every ten years. The 1850 convention invited pharmacists and other scientists to sit with the physicians in the revision sessions. The 1860 convention named Dr. Squibb to the Committee of Revision.

Dr. Squibb was delighted with the opportunity to put his ideas about pure drugs to practical application. The meetings of the Committee of Revision were held in Philadelphia at the home of his idol, Dr. George B. Wood, collaborator of the revered Professor Franklin Bache in the *Dispensatory*. Other members included his old friend William Procter, editor of the *American Journal of Pharmacy*, and Alfred B. Taylor, a strong and articulate voice in matters pharmaceutical.

Dr. Squibb was still terribly sensitive about his disfigurement and disliked appearing in public, where he could rarely help overhearing remarks about his curiously lidless eyes and the facial scars that were still visible despite his beard. However, the prospect of working with friends in a common cause that had become the main purpose of his life was irresistible. The *American Journal of Pharmacy*, in reporting progress of the Revision Committee, noted that "the committee is meeting three times each month when the member from New York [Dr. Squibb] is almost always at his post, although it involves a trip of 100 miles."

There were many things about the Pharmacopoeia that Dr. Squibb had long been anxious to get off his chest and he lost no time in doing so. There were compounds that he thought should be dropped, formulas improved, and standards raised. Years later Professor Procter used to tell a story characteristic of Dr. Squibb's missionary zeal and direct methods.

As the titles of the Pharmacopoeia were being considered in alphabetical order, the subject of aloes came up early in the discussion. Dr. Squibb wanted to know why the Pharmacopoeia made no distinction between various grades of aloes, thus giving the pharmacist and the physician the impression that commercial aloes was pure aloes, whereas there should be a special category created for purified aloes.

Professor Taylor interrupted to say he thought commercial aloes was reasonably pure.

"Gentlemen," declared Dr. Squibb, "I give you my word that all the commercial aloes available on this market is filled with mechanical impurities of all sorts—sticks, stones, earth, goatskin, even bits of iron and lead to increase the weight."

Dr. Wood chuckled. "Dr. Squibb always was given to exaggeration," he said.

Professor Procter laughingly suggested that Dr. Squibb must be referring to commercial aloes bought in New York. Philadelphia aloes he was sure could never contain all those impurities.

"Professor Procter," declared Dr. Squibb, "I want you to go to the most reliable drug supplier in Philadelphia and buy a cask of the best grade of aloes that you can find. I'll pay you for it. Ship it to New York at my expense. The Committee will receive in return not only the result of my analysis but the component parts into which I propose to divide the cask—aloes and extraneous materials."

Next week in his laboratory Dr. Squibb melted and softened the aloes which Professor Procter sent him, dissolved out everything that was soluble in water or alcohol, strained and weighed the residue, and sent two packages to the Committee of Revision in Philadelphia—the aloes and the debris.

The Committee was profoundly surprised and impressed. The package of impurities weighed almost half as much as the purified product. Dr. Squibb had made his point dramatically: It was impossible to buy imported aloes that was not loaded with foreign matter.

Every edition of the U. S. Pharmacopoeia since the 1860 revision has retained Dr. Squibb's "Aloes Purificata."

II

NOT ALL OF Dr. Squibb's efforts were as successful.

For years he had been gathering evidence that the drug law of 1848—"An Act to prevent the importation of adulterated and spurious drugs and medicines"—was being enforced loosely if at all, because the customs officials charged with its enforcement were political appointees who knew nothing about drugs and cared less.

At the annual convention of the American Pharmaceutical Society in Philadelphia in 1862, he upbraided the society's Committee on Adulteration for inaction, and moved that the committee be dissolved, to be replaced by a five-man Committee on the Drug Market "whose duty it shall be to report annually the fluctuations in the supply and demand of drugs, the variations in quality, and adulteration and sophistication coming under their observation or reported by others. . . ."

Little, apparently, came from this resolution.

In 1860 the American Medical Association had appointed Dr. Squibb chairman of a special committee to report on the practical working of the 1848 act, but he had trouble getting together with his fellow committee members. In 1863 he was reappointed with the understanding that he would report to the 1864 convention.

However, "the procrastination of the chairman," to use his own words, left little time for the two other members of the committee to prepare a minority report, and since they disagreed with Dr. Squibb—"both objected to various parts of it as being inaccurate or improper, or without their knowledge of the truthfulness of the statements made"—he "decided to offer the materials . . . as a volunteer paper . . . with the distinct understanding that the other members of the committee . . . are not responsible in any degree."

Dr. Squibb's paper described the 1848 act as "wise and beneficent" even though it set standards for import below the strict requirements of the Pharmacopoeia.

For instance, cinchona barks, by whatever title were admitted when affording 1 per cent. of quinia, or 2 per cent. of *all* the natural alkaloids taken together, whilst really good medicinal cinchona barks should yield a larger percentage than this of the two prominently useful crystallizable alkaloids, quinia and cinchona. Again, jalap was admitted when it contained not less than 11 per cent. of resin of jalap, whilst the average yield when the drug is only of fair quality is above 12 per cent., and when of good quality often over 14 per cent. . . . Senna was admitted to entry when it afforded 28 per cent. or more of soluble matter whilst that of fair quality rarely yields less than 33 per cent. . . .

[The existence of the 1848 act] and the promulgation of its standards, tests, and penalties, was naturally of great service to the medical interests of the drug market, and when to these was added the effect of numerous rejections, the value of the law could not remain doubtful.

A little later in the history of its application, however, glaring instances of maladministration appeared to become more numerous, and political party influences took possession of the offices under the law, so that by the year 1860, when the Association's committee was first appointed, abundant evidence could be adduced to show that the law was rarely administered at all, and that its value to the medical profession consisted mainly in its existence upon the statute book. The evidences of this want of administration . . . are as follows:

Cinchona barks, so called . . . whenever purchased outside of certain narrow commercial channels to which their cost, rather than their intrinsic medicinal value, confines them, are very rarely met with of standard quality, whilst the general market is always abundantly supplied by importation with barks of little or no medicinal value.

Inferior, damaged and spurious jalap has been repeatedly seen in the general market . . . and in one instance a lot of true jalap, in quantity large enough to supply the legitimate demands for the drug in a city like New York for a year or two, from which the resin had been nearly all extracted before importation, was passed through the custom-house, sold in the market, and powdered for medicinal use.

Scammony has been repeatedly met with during the period above mentioned containing from 25 to 48 per cent. of the resin of scammony, less frequently from 55 to 60 per cent., and occasionally as low as 16 to 20 per cent., whilst the law required 70 per cent. at least, and the examiner who passes it is sworn to enforce the law.

Senna has been steadily falling off in general quality for many years, and it has been long difficult to find an original package which comes squarely up to the standard of quality, whilst most of that met with could, by the rejection of 10 to 55 per cent. of sticks, stones, and dirt, be brought up to the standard. . . .

The principal fault appears to lie in the officers appointed to execute the law, and the whole responsibility of this fault rests upon the Secretary of the Treasury who makes the appointments. It appears to matter little what particular party is in power, as the result has been the same in all.

The last Secretary of the Treasury [John A. Dix] appointed a special examiner of drugs in the New York custom-house whose administration of the law exhibited no qualifications of fitness for the office whatever; and the effects of the law upon the drug market during that administration render it probable that the appointment was made, as was asserted at the time, solely as a reward for political services rendered during the canvass for the presidential election.

The present Secretary of the Treasury [Salmon P. Chase] made a very singular appointment, which has yielded no better results, and under circumstances which deserve to be known to this Association.

Soon after the present Administration came into office, and in anticipation of the changes that were to be made in the custom-house, the entire medical and pharmaceutical organizations of the State of New York moved harmoniously upon this subject, through a joint committee of five societies headed by the Medical Society of the State, and embracing the New York Academy of Medicine and the New York College of Pharmacy. After due deliberation and discussion this large joint committee decided upon petitioning the President of the United States and the Secretary of the Treasury. . . .

These petitions were as follows:

To His Excellency Abraham Lincoln, President of the United States.

The undersigned, presiding officers of the New York State Medical Society, New York County Medical Society, Kings

County Medical Society, New York Academy of Medicine, and New York College of Pharmacy, beg leave to represent—

That by discussion in these several bodies, by committees of conference, and finally by a joint committee, these bodies are unanimously agreed to solicit your attention to the proper execution of the law known as the U. S. Drug Law, passed by Congress in 1848, "To prevent the importation of adulterated and spurious drugs and medicines."

This law, if thoroughly executed, is a great public safeguard and benefit; if administered through venality, incompetence, or carelessness, it becomes mischievous, and may increase the evils it aims to correct. Its execution in accordance with its true intent and spirit demands the highest order of integrity, and a high standard or scientific and practical knowledge of medicine, pharmacy and chemistry as applied to the quality and value of drugs and chemicals. In view therefore of the importance of selection of officers thus properly qualified, and the difficulty of deciding as to these qualifications without a critical examination, we respectfully recommend: 1st, That the candidates be graduates of a regular medical college, or a college of pharmacy; and 2d. The reference of all candidates to the Medical Boards of Examination of the army or navy, whose competency for such duty is well established, who shall report their decisions or selections to the appointing power through their respective departments. It will be remembered that these Boards meet for the examination of candidates for the Medical Corps of the Army and Navy every year, generally in March, and always in some of the large ports of entry.

We are, very respectfully,

Your obedient servants.

A similar petition was addressed to the Honorable Salmon P. Chase, Secretary of the Treasury. The petitions, with many signatures, were repeated from Boston, Baltimore, and Louisville, and slightly altered ones were sent from Philadelphia.

The official petitions from the New York Societies [Dr.

Squibb's report continues] were sent to Washington by a special messenger . . . to be presented to the President and Secretary of the Treasury. Although upon such an errand, access could not be obtained to either of these officers; the Assistant Secretary of the Treasury was seen, and the petitions were placed in his hands with the necessary explanations concerning them. The messenger was told that the Secretary, in making his appointments, would be guided only by fitness for the offices, and that the Committee might rest assured that the true interests at stake were well known to the Treasury Department, and would be protected. Some months after this, and after the Army and Navy Boards had been in session at New York and Philadelphia, the appointments were made without any regard for qualifications for the offices that could be ascertained at the time, or which have been exhibited since in the execution of the important duties, for there certainly never has been a time since the passage of the law when more bad foreign drugs have been passed through the custom-houses than during the past two or three years.

As it is not the object of the Association in making an inquiry into the working of this law, nor of the writer in endeavoring to answer this inquiry, to detail the evidences of personal disqualification in the special officers appointed, that may have been presented in the course of the investigation, all such evidences are withheld from publication, though accessible for all proper legitimate purposes. . . .

The time again draws near when these offices may possibly be changed, and the Association will judge whether, in view of past experience, it be worth while to take any action in the matter. The profession appears to be rapidly, and doubtless justly, losing much of the former reliance upon drugs, and whether this loss of confidence be due in greater or in lesser part to the bad quality of the materia medica in general use, there appears some danger that the equally pernicious opposite extreme of absolute scepticism may be as rapidly reached. One of the penalties which the operation of natural laws imposes upon undue vigor and over-stimulated activity is that of hastening from one extreme to another, and of holding rarely, and but for a short time, that middle ground in whose genial soil truth and knowledge are best cultivated.

Dr. Squibb's report was highly praised, and its author applauded.

But no action was taken.

If, however, Dr. Squibb's phrase, "The time again draws near when these offices may possibly be changed," indicated an uneasiness that President Lincoln might possibly be defeated that year by General McClellan, he must have been gratified by the election results. McClellan won only two states, with twenty-one electoral votes.

eight

THE HOUSEHOLDER

I

THE PROSPECT OF OWNING his own home, a house built to his own specifications and desires, was tremendously exciting to Dr. Squibb. During that summer and autumn of 1864, every minute he could spare from the laboratories he spent at nearby Columbia Street, watching the building take shape, assuring himself that the materials were of the quality he had selected and that the workmanship was sound. He recorded the progress of the masons and carpenters, followed the painters and plasterers from floor to floor, advised the tile man from Miller & Coates, and complained because the plumbers were behind schedule.

He went to Manhattan to Brandeis & Rhodes to select personally the washbasins, the urinal, the water closets, and the tubs for the laundry in the basement.

Caroline remained much later than usual at Ossining with Baby Mary, young Ed and Charles, and her two maids. During the week Dr. Squibb slept on a cot in his second-floor office in the Doughty Street laboratory. When Caroline came down from time to time and stayed overnight with the Kings, Dr. Squibb found it odd that she preferred to spend her afternoons shopping in New York, rather than clambering over bare joists and temporary flooring in their half-finished house.

One day in October, however, she came down to New York to sit for Brady, the photographer, for "imperials" to match the photographs of Dr. Squibb which would hang in the boys' rooms. On leaving the studio they walked to A. T. Stewart's new store to look at carpets. Stewart's had recently moved uptown to Tenth Street and Broadway, and the Squibbs were greatly impressed by the cast-iron façade and the huge, skylighted stairwell in the center of the new building. (It later became the north building of John Wanamaker's.)

They were not impressed by the carpets, however, although they bought ten pairs of blankets.

"We then walked down Broadway," Dr. Squibb recorded, "and rather casually stopped at Sloan's carpet store. We however saw carpets we both liked, and fearing the present reduction of prices would not last long with gold going up, we ordered all our carpets of Mr. Mitchel to the amount of some hundreds of yards. Paid 4$ per yard for parlor and library— 684 + 448 + 240 = 1372 square feet. . . . The upstairs carpets are of 3 ply ingrain at 2.75 per yard, probably about 310 yards of that. Thus say 816$ + 698 + 33 for making = 1546$ + 100$ more for drugget and stair crash = 1646$ and 76 yards for dining room at 2.75 = 209 + 6$ for making, 215, making a total of 1861 dollars for carpeting."

They also looked at gas fixtures and chandeliers at Ball & Black's before Caroline returned to Ossining.

Dr. Squibb continued shopping for furniture and equipment. He got beds for the third-story rooms at Brooks's and also an extension dining table. He went to Shuster's for mantels and marble slabs for the butler's pantry and furniture tops, settling on dark Lisbon marble as a top for the sideboard. He went to Marcotti's, looking for walnut tables for the kitchen, and to Ebbinghousen's for a nursery bureau for the third-floor front room ($58). Roosevelt & Son wanted

$99.20 for the "looking-glass plate" for the living room and agreed to have it cut, silvered and ready in ten days.

He went to Haughwout's for chinaware and carving knives, buying a celery stand, preserve dishes, saltcellars, a spoon holder, and chamber pots. For plated ware—and he insisted on a German silver base—he found Hiram Young's on John Street to be cheaper than Haughwout's. He had the gas laid on and engaged a bellhanger to install the doorbells.

On Monday, November 14, Dr. Squibb began moving his family and household goods down from Ossining. Young Ed was the first to move, for he was to enter Mr. Cleveland's school.

"Awoke very early, looking out for the time, and up at half past 5," the doctor wrote. "Very cold morning and roads hard frozen. Ryder [the livery-stable man who boarded Kit, the pony] came out and took 2 trunks, rocking chair and pillows, and I took Kit and the pony wagon, saddles, &c and Ed, and we all went down to meet the boat at 7. Waited until half past 7 or later, before the boat came, and did not reach home much before 12."

The following Monday Dr. Squibb "came down in the 8:08 train, bringing Ed, Chas., and Margaret [the second maid], and three trunks. Went at once to the House and commenced to get ready for living."

Dr. Squibb made arrangements for the boys to take their meals at a neighbor's, Mrs. Williams', while he interviewed a new cook who had been recommended to him, a girl named Katy Diffely. He engaged her "after a long plain talk" during which he "told her plainly that I wanted to hire a servant and not a mistress, that there was much hard work to do but that she might find a good home."

Although it was a dull, disagreeable, rainy day, he immediately took Katy to Manhattan to buy kitchen necessaries and groceries so that she could start serving meals. And since neither the furniture nor the crockery had come, he had to run around after them "in the wet, perplexed and disheartened." Furthermore, "The House was still all open and it was discovered that the front doors were two feet too short, through some mistake. . . . Then Brooks did not send the bedding altho I had been there to tell them we could not sleep without it. Thus the day passed and we yet managed to get the beds and bedsteads, and by dint of unpacking diligently all the boxes &c, we got the bedding for them, and went to bed dispirited and uneasy lest the children should get sick from the damp house. . . . Heating apparatus did not go well, the middle coils refusing. Went to bed with a bad headache and awoke a 3 a.m. with it still, after that could not sleep. Thus passed the first night in the new House."

Dr. Squibb returned to Ossining to bring down Caroline, Baby Mary, and Mary Fogarty on November 24, which was Thanksgiving Day. Caroline had had a seizure two nights before, but she seemed in good health and spirits, even though the arrival at the new house was not quite what Dr. Squibb had planned. In fact, it was quite dreary.

"Although in the place of a front door, the doorway was barricaded up with rough, dirty boards, and the front windows naked and cheerless, with rough, frozen mud in front instead of the flagging, and the street dug up for setting curbstones, yet Caroline seemed cheerful and glad to get home, and went round with me with some appearance of interest, particularly liking the dining room carpet. I had prepared her to find everything in confusion and no place whatever finished. . . . We dined at half past 2, and had a very nice dinner, for which and the comforts I hoped to enjoy I felt thankful. Though there be many more deserving than we, few have such a house, and such chances of a comfortable home."

Next day (Friday): "Caroline's birthday, 31 I think. She arose feeling pretty well and cheerful and seemed to enjoy the first sunrise as it appeared from her windows." However, Caroline's mother, her sister Mrs. King, and the two former sisters-in-law of Mrs. Bache, Helen and Rosalie Hart, dropped in to see the new house while Dr. Squibb was at the laboratories, and when he came home for dinner at midday, he found her "much changed since morning, hysterical and very much depressed, and left the table before dinner was over, crying, having eaten only a few mouthfulls."

It turned out that Saturday and not Friday was Caroline's birthday, as Dr. Squibb acknowledged next day. However, he was twice as busy as usual, trying to keep up with his laboratory work and his new chores as householder. He had to supervise while the gas-fixture man lowered the dining-room chandelier and Sloan's man measured the carpets for the servants' rooms. He crossed over to Manhattan and bought a store of preserved fruits at Kemp, Day & Co., wine, ale and spirits at Engs, olives and Worcestershire sauce at John Duncan & Sons, and he ran numerous other minor errands to put his household larder in shape.

That night Dr. and Mary King came in, bringing Caroline a butternut card basket for her birthday.

II

WHILE DR. SQUIBB was putting up the clotheslines and buying sausage meat for breakfast, "Caroline went over to Develin's . . . and ordered a coat for Chas. at the enormous price of 32$ and a suit for Edward at 36$."

Caroline's purchases were certainly magnified to the point of extravagance by Dr. Squibb's discovery that day that his municipal taxes for the ensuing year would amount to $2,610.

He made several attempts to collect money long overdue from the Army, but General Satterlee had still not received the funds from Washington. Since, in addition to paying taxes, Dr. Squibb had to purchase raw materials to keep his laboratories going with Army orders, he went to the U. S. Trust Company and mortgaged the new house for $15,000.

Early in December he made personal calls on his friends and relatives "to oppose exchanging Christmas presents." However, he and Caroline went to Stewart's to buy Christmas dresses for the servants and toys for the children. They also bought some composition bronzes at Cox Brothers and went to Tiffany's at Fifteenth Street and Union Square to buy a small bronze to ornament the parlor clock. For himself Dr. Squibb purchased a holospheric barometer which, no sooner had he installed it on the mantel, began to fall with alarming rapidity, announcing an imminent storm.

It took the gale of December 11 and 12 to convince Dr. Squibb at last that his heating system was not all it was intended to be.

"Up early to look after the fire," he wrote on Monday the twelfth, "and try to get heat enough to make us comfortable. The gale had continued all night and was blowing now as hard as I ever saw it, raising the water into clouds of drifting spray that looked like steam as they came over the bay. The wind howled and whistled and came through every crack, double sash seemed but little obstruction, and it came in icy cold. The rooms were down to 36°, 38° and 40° and although there was an excellent fire, the steam seemed sluggish and even impotent. By management I however got the workroom or nursery warm by half past 9. But the dining room was only half warm while the parlor was cold. The coils in the oriel window were frozen up and no steam could be got into it. The thermometer was down to 8° some time during the night and was about 16° at half past 9."

It took several trips to Manhattan, replacing the pressure gauge, readjusting the regulator wheel, and putting new valves on a larger boiler, before the system began to function. By this time, Caroline was not sure she liked the place. Even with the carpets all down, the sliding doors finally installed in the parlor, the storeroom in order and lime put into the wine cellar as a dehumidifier, the front parlor and the billiard room had to be shut up, still unfinished, until the following summer.

On Christmas Eve she finally spoke her mind, and Dr. Squibb was very much disturbed by her attitude. He wrote: "In the evening came home . . . and for the first time set the front doors open and lighted the vestibule light, and was much pleased with the cheerful, hospitable appearance of the entrance both from without and within. I had scarcely finished admiring the effect, and gone into the house, when Caroline came home and had the outer doors closed, saying singularly enough that they ought to be kept closed during the winter,—that nobody ever left their outer vestibule doors open till warm weather in the Spring. Where she gets this idea from I cannot tell, but I unwillingly acquiesced in her decision and allowed the vestibule to be closed up though it entirely spoils the whole design for which it was built, and renders both hall and vestibule gloomy, dark and useless, beside throwing the money away which the arrangement has cost. But . . . this must be sacrificed if she cannot see it. She seems to have a great general prejudice against the house though she does not seem aware of it, and although other housekeepers seem to like it, she sees little in it to please her, and is particularly disconcerted by the cold, saying she has not been comfortably warm since we have been in it except when she goes to one or other of her sisters. But I hope by close watchfulness and attention gradually to induce her to be contented here, since I feel that no one ever had a house that was really and intrinsically better or more convenient, and my prayer is that both she and I as well as our children may so live as to deserve such a house."

It had been a good year, 1864, all in all.

III

HAVING SUCCESSFULLY GOT Caroline through the turmoil of moving into the new house and the excitement of the holidays without even a premonitory aura, Dr. Squibb began to hope that he might effect a cure by carefully humoring her and relieving her of all responsibility.

He put both the boys in Mr. Cleveland's school. Mary Fogarty took complete charge of Baby Mary, except, of course, for her vaccination, which Dr. Squibb performed himself.

"Vaccinated Mary this morning about 9," he wrote, "with a quill of vaccine left for the purpose yesterday by Dr. Kissam. He said it came from a very healthy child with vigorous healthy parents, a half-Quaker family whose name I cannot now recall."

And five days later: "Vaccinated Mary again . . . from virus brought to me last Sunday by Dr. H. S. Smith and just taken from a healthy child in the Luquier family, the vaccination of Saturday last having failed."

The second one took.

Dr. Squibb also assumed complete charge of the household. Or so he thought. At least, as became a former caterer of the *Erie,* he organized the daily menus, bought the groceries and supplies, and paid the bills. Once a week he gave Caroline a sheaf of crisp new banknotes for clothing herself and the children, and for pin money. She did not own a checkbook as long as she lived.

Dr. Squibb paid the servants their wages and was sometimes allowed to believe that he gave them their orders, too. One day he overheard Mary Fogarty giving Caroline a sharp scolding for having invited house guests on her day off. Dr. Squibb wanted to discharge Fogy at once. After all, a man must have discipline in his own house, and to have the senior maid set a bad example to the other servants by being impertinent and arrogant to the mistress of the house could simply not be tolerated. Caroline, however, merely smiled and apologized. She refused even to think of dismissing anyone who was as clever a dressmaker as was Mary Fogarty. Fogy was indispensable.

So Fogy not only remained, but she was excluded from Dr. Squibb's plan for reorganizing his domestic staff. Calling in Margaret, the second maid, and Catherine, the cook, he told them he had reached the conclusion that their duties in the new house were excessive. To lighten their work, he proposed to engage another girl if they would absorb part of the added expense by each taking a reduction in wages of $2 a month (to $10). They agreed, and Dr. Squibb engaged another colleen named Ann McCaulden for $8 a month and found.

The augmented staff functioned as smoothly as clockwork. The routine was simple but scheduled to the minute. Breakfast was at seven sharp, and there was no excuse for not being punctual, for there was a clock in practically every room in the house. Dr. Squibb set them all himself every Sunday morning before going to church, having set his own watch the previous day in New York, either at Tiffany's or at Charley Fellows' jewelry store in Maiden Lane. Caroline was encouraged to remain in bed—Mary Fogarty carried her breakfast tray upstairs—but the two boys knew they had to be punctual and no nonsense.

Breakfast was in fact a no-nonsense meal. There were sausages or short ribs, kippers or eggs, hot cakes or waffles, fresh fruit, biscuits and coffee. The boys, however, were not allowed to drink coffee until they were grown up.

After breakfast Dr. Squibb would repair to the kitchen and write the menus for the day. At seven-forty sharp he would leave the house to walk to the laboratories. On the way he passed the house of the Reverend Henry Ward Beecher, who used to say he set his clocks by the time Dr. Squibb passed every morning, so regularly punctual was he. At eight o'clock he entered the laboratories by the 23 Vine Street entrance and, after a quick look around, went downstairs to the main offices at 36 Doughty Street to look over the orders and take the mail that had already been opened and sorted by his clerical staff.

At one o'clock he walked home to dinner.

The evening meal—tea, Dr. Squibb called it—was usually at seven, but the time was a little more flexible, in case he should be detained at the laboratory or in New York, where he frequently went for personal or business errands. When he came home at night, therefore, the moment he entered the door he drew from his vest pocket a small ivory whistle and, like a boatswain's mate piping the ship's company to mess, blew a clear, rounded, well-sustained note. Instantly the kitchen came to life. The cook and the maids sprang into action, knowing that when the doctor had freshened up and changed his "tired shoes," he would expect the scalloped oysters or the chicken salad to be on the table. A Chinese gong announced that tea was ready. When there was cold meat and green salad, Dr. Squibb always mixed the salad dressing himself at table, blending the ingredients in a soup plate. He liked his salad well loaded with Spanish onion rings, although his wife considered this inelegant. Caroline poured the tea.

They sometimes ate a late snack, too. On one occasion, when they had been in the new house only three months, they went to see Heller the Conjurer ("and were much disappointed"). On the way home they stopped at Dorlon's to eat roasted oysters—with unfortunate results.

Next morning, wrote Dr. Squibb, "just as I awaked and asked Caroline what time it was by the mantel clock, I found she was commencing one of her attacks. It proved to be very light and passed over quickly and she probably did not bite her tongue at all. I had been awakened by her during the later part of the night and watched her with anxiety till after 5. This attack came on about 6:40 a.m. Left her about as usual, but on returning to dinner found she had probably had another attack, of what severity I could not tell. . . . While I was at dinner she had a strong but not a long convulsion, much stronger than either of the two last that I saw. During the deep sleep that followed I left her. . . . This attack was . . . in all human probability brought on by my injudicious proposal to eat oysters at bed time."

Another series of attacks followed. Dr. Squibb spent many a sleepless night, watching, sometimes giving her a whiff of chloroform when he detected the warning globus, the rapid swallowing which was a prelude to a seizure, even in her sleep. He fanned her, too, during her fits of hysterical crying as she lay on the sofa in the back parlor. He tried fluidextract of valerian, but it did not seem to help.

IV

ON FEBRUARY 13, 1865, the Army's new pharmaceutical laboratory at Astoria burned to the ground.

Before the week was out, General Satterlee came over to Brooklyn to see Dr. Squibb with a large order for supplies and the news that Washington did not wish to rebuild the Astoria laboratory. Dr. Squibb recorded that Dr. Satterlee "applied to me to take the work of that Laby. which I could not do, but desired to sell my Laby. to them, or failing that, to take a portion of the work only, with a suggestion for the remainder. He thought I had better go to Washington and see the Surgeon General and I acceded."

Dr. Squibb took a 7 P.M. train for Washington and sat up all night, arriving next morning. "Arrived at Willard's Hotel about 6 o'clock," he wrote, "and went to bed till near 10. Then breakfasted and went to the Surgeon General's Office where I had a conversation first with Dr. Crane, then with the Surgeon General. I urged them to continue their Laby. policy because Dr. Satterlee desired it rather than because I really approved of it, and the purchase of my Laby. for their purposes. This they did not entertain, but said the question of continuing the policy or not would depend upon the decision of the Secy. of War. Crane however told me that for some reasons mentioned by him and others he was not at liberty to mention, he believed the Laby. here would not be continued."

The Surgeon General's office then put Dr. Squibb in the hands of Dr. J. J. Woodward, pioneer photomicrographer and one of the founders of the United States Army Medical Museum, a fabulous institution which has since grown into the Armed Forces Institute of Pathology. He spent the morning and part of the afternoon with Dr. Woodward in the museum and in his bureau of medical statistics. "On leaving him," wrote Dr. Squibb, "called on Dr. Whelan [chief of the Navy's Bureau of Medicine and Surgery], then again on Crane, and after 4 back to Willard's to dine. After a shockingly dirty bad dinner walked down to the depot and at 6 p.m. started home."

Willard's food has improved considerably in the last 90 years.

Returning from Washington, Dr. Squibb reorganized his lab staff in order to try to absorb more of the Army's orders. He had recently hired a German-trained chemist named Musgiller in whom he had great confidence as a scientist and technician. He shifted some of the responsibility for the new work to his shoulders. He also bought two lots adjoining the Vine-Doughty Street property from a Mr. Ely for $4,500 and began building an extension to the laboratories.

Then, on April 9, Lee surrendered at Appomattox and the war was over.

On April 14 Dr. Squibb's neighbor, the Reverend Henry Ward Beecher, was asked by President Lincoln to deliver the oration at Fort Sumter for the ceremonial raising of the Stars and Stripes to the staff from which they had been hauled down more than four years earlier.

The next day Dr. Squibb received the news of the President's assassination and closed the laboratory.

On Tuesday, April 25, the Lincoln funeral train reached New York and Dr. Squibb joined the Kings County Medical Society delegation marching in the funeral procession from nine-twenty in the morning until five that evening.

It was a sad closing week for a month which had begun with such promise.

V

ON THE MORNING OF June 1, 1865, Lieutenant Colonel Batt Jones of Georgia, having been released from Yankee prison, arrived in Brooklyn for a short stay at the Squibbs' new house.

"He is supplying himself with a few necessaries," wrote Dr. Squibb, "and will go home when he can. Capt. Tom White still confined, and I wrote to the War Office with Dr. Satterlee's endorsement on Friday to try to have him released."

Captain White was liberated from Fort Delaware on Sunday and appeared at Dr. Squibb's on Tuesday, sharing the guest room with Colonel Jones.

"He dined with us, and I then took him over to Develin's for clothing," Dr. Squibb recorded.

Next day the two Confederate officers went to Milford, Connecticut, to see Miss Kate Davidson, and they brought her back with them that evening.

"Found Miss Kate had come down to purchase some things for Dr. White's family," wrote Dr. Squibb. "Thursday, Friday and Saturday we were engaged in these purchases and got a large trunk and a box filled with dry goods, clothing, etc. Capt. White left on Saturday morning and Col. Jones on Saturday evening by the steamer Carolina, he taking the goods and money to Dr. White. Caroline remained in her rooms upstairs all the latter part of the week, seeing only her own family."

After 58 days of comparative health, she had had another series of attacks.

Dr. Squibb tried another remedy: twenty drops of fluid-extract of calisaya (yellow cinchona bark) in a tablespoonful of sherry wine twice a day, before breakfast and dinner, and a glass of wine and a cracker at eleven in the morning. If nothing else, it should improve her appetite. She had been losing weight lately.

VI

ALTHOUGH HE HAD long since given up any pretense at being a practicing Quaker, Dr. Squibb continued to be an intensely religious man. He was, however, a rugged individualist in church matters as he was in lay affairs. He never ceased to walk humbly before his God, but neither did he relinquish the right to view God's ministers on earth with a critical eye. He was apt to choose a church according to the sincerity, the intelligence, and the ability of the pastor. When in later years he gravitated toward the Episcopal Church, it was undoubtedly because of his deep admiration for Dr. Charles Henry Hall of Holy Trinity in Brooklyn, and for Dr. S. D. McConnell, who succeeded to the pulpit of the venerable red church at Montague and Clinton streets when Dr. Hall died.

During the Civil War years and the postwar period, Dr. Squibb was a resolute free-lance. Since Caroline was also religious, there was no question about the children being brought up as good Christians. However, Dr. Squibb assumed full responsibility for the religious education of his sons. He rarely missed a Sunday in taking them to church, but he rarely took them to the same church two Sundays in succession.

Caroline, on the other hand, was partial to Dr. Van Dyke's church—the First Church of Brooklyn (later called the Second Church) at Clinton and Remsen streets. Dr. Henry Jackson Van Dyke was one of the country's most distinguished Presbyterians. A product of the University of Pennsylvania, Yale, and Princeton Theological Seminary (class of 1845), he was a dramatic figure in the pulpit. A high, broad forehead rose above heavy, forbidding eyebrows. The fierceness of his jutting chin was softened somewhat by the fact that his beard was curly. But there was nothing soft about Dr. Van Dyke's liberal views. He was an uncompromising advocate of the revision of the Westminster Confession of Faith of 1649. "If we cannot have liberty and orthodoxy," he once thundered, "let us have liberty and go without orthodoxy."

Dr. Squibb, too, liked the Reverend Dr. Van Dyke's approach. He usually accompanied his wife to the evening services at the Presbyterian Church during this period, but while Caroline also attended morning services, Dr. Squibb took the boys on a grand sampling tour of many religions, including his own original Society of Friends.

Shortly before the end of the war he made his first visit to the Friends Meeting in Schermerhorn Street—and he took the boys. Charles at the time of Appomattox was seven, Edward twelve. And the week before Lee's surrender, Dr. Squibb made his first (and apparently his last) visit to "Mr. Robinson's church . . . and heard him pray for all except Southern people, and emphatically except all human effort from the saving effect of the atonement."

Thenceforth we find entries in the journal indicating that he took the boys to Grace Church in Hicks Street; to Trinity Church; to Dr. Canfield's church; to "Dr. Bethune's old church"; to St. Ann's in Clinton Street. And although there were many churches in Dr. Squibb's neighborhood in Brooklyn, when the weather was fine on a Sunday morning he would take the boys for a ride to Manhattan on the Fulton Ferry, dropping into whatever church might strike his fancy.

We find in the journal such entries as the following: "This morning took the boys over to the lowest church on 5th Avenue, Episcopal, and this evening went with Caroline to Mr. Vandyke's. . . ." "This morning took the boys to Dr. [Richard S.] Stoors' church [Church of the Pilgrims, Remsen and Henry Streets] and heard a characteristic sermon. . . ." "This morning took the boys over to church in 5th Avenue between 11th and 12th Sts [First Presbyterian] and in the evening Caroline and I heard Mr. Van Dyke upon David and Uriah. . . ." "This morning took the boys over to church on the corner of University Place and 10th St. and heard a curious Presbyterian sermon. . . ." "This morning took the boys over to Irving Hall where Dr. Tyng holds his services during the rebuilding of his church." [Dr. Stephen H. Tyng was rector of St. George's Protestant Episcopal Church on Stuyvesant Square at Sixteenth Street, burned in 1865.] "Took the boys to the church corner of Lafayette Place and Great Jones St. Found it to be Episcopal."

Little Mary Squibb was first introduced to religion at the age of twenty months. When Caroline's sister Sally Fellows had her third baby, Caroline took little Mary to New York and the babies were baptized together with water from the Pool of Siloam which Dr. Squibb had brought home from Jerusalem on the frigate *Cumberland* nearly twenty years before.

Dr. Squibb felt very keenly that the development of his offspring into good, useful and God-fearing citizens was very much his own responsibility. He kept close watch on the quality of both the instruction and the ethical training his children were getting, and when these failed to meet his standards he made a change. He removed both boys from Mr. Cleveland's school after he had "told him plainly the reason, namely, the lack of what I considered proper order and discipline in his school." He entered Ed in Brooklyn Polytechnic Institute, then only a dozen years old, and Charles in the Brooklyn Juvenile High School.

Dr. Squibb believed that precept and example were not the only useful instruments for shaping character. He still clung to his seafaring belief, articulately expressed in the *Philadelphia North American*, that a sound thrashing, when well earned, was good for the soul. The act of administering corporal punishment was repulsive to him, but he sincerely thought he would be shirking his duty if he failed to go through with it.

Even little Mary got hers before she was three.

"Yesterday at dinner time," he wrote, "was obliged to give poor little Mary her first regular whipping. She had a habit of screaming for what she wanted, and getting into a terrible temper which I have for some time been trying to control, but unsuccessfully. She was, however, always ready to come and tell me of her 'screaming and crying.' Having been pretty thoroughly conquered about a year ago, I trust she may not now be very difficult to control if I have the courage and determination to do it."

The usual cause for corporal punishment, however, was

lying—a capital offense in Dr. Squibb's eyes. Young Charles was eight years old when he began to feel the lash for falsehood.

"Thursday morning was obliged to give Chas. a whipping for a downright lie to avoid taking his own shoes to be mended on the morning before," his father wrote. "Then went to school with him to see his teachers in regard to him, dreading lest he should get into a habit of being untruthful. He told his mother that his school commences at ¼ past 8, and he had not time to take his shoes. It was exceedingly hard to whip a poor little frail fellow who seems to have so slight a hold on life."

Young Ed, too, took his share of lashes, but he was more amenable to discipline and by the time Charles had reached the age of accurate observation Ed seemed never to get whipped. More than thirty years after his father's death, "poor little frail" Charlie, then a robust old man of seventy-four, wrote to F. W. Nitardy, a Squibb vice-president, about his early training:

"In his office there used to be two brown iron hospital beds on which he, and I think my brother, occasionally slept. In one bookcase on top of the books was a rawhide with which he used to castigate me (I never remember my brother being punished). His navy training taught him the value of corporal punishment. I never could see it. He laid on ten cracks like a boatswain but always with tears in his eyes which hurt me as bad as the rawhide."

When he told the truth about his misdeeds, however, Charles was never punished. Once, as he roamed through the laboratory, he took a chew of tobacco from an old engineer named Robert Kinney—"a brand in a tinfoil package called Solace [that] looked and smelled so good that I asked him to let me taste it." He was sick and getting sicker by the minute when summoned to Dr. Squibb's office. When questioned, he was too ill to tell anything but the truth.

"My father simply gave me a lecture on the value of tobacco as a depressant which I still remember though as sick as a dog. His only comfort was that the effects would soon pass off," Charles recalled.

It was typical of Dr. Squibb that he should have chosen this illustrative moment to enlighten his wretched and retching young son on the physiological effects and pharmaceutical qualities of tobacco. He was a born teacher and found it difficult to resist an opportunity to pass his own knowledge on to others. His colleagues frequently took advantage of this fact, judging from his journal for November 18, 1865:

"Dr. Dalton yesterday invited me to lecture on Materia Medica and Pharmacy at the College of Physicians and Surgeons, which invitation I declined. But after thinking of the matter overnight, reconsidered my decision because it seemed selfish and churlish to refuse to supply an emergency like that now made by Dr. Smith's illness, and therefore went up to see Dr. Dalton about it this morning. Did not meet him but saw Dr. Watts and talked with him on the subject, offering to fill the vacancy."

That decision, too, was characteristic of Dr. Squibb.

So was the page of prayer and self-appraisal which he wrote in his journal on the last day of 1865:

"The pregnant new year is now here, and whether it be freighted with blessings of the last, or with sorrows and bitterness which may now be foreshadowed, I will try to accept them with a proper spirit and a grateful heart. Should it be within the future of this year to break my family circle, or to dispel the hope of my wife's improvement, or both, can I have the fortitude and courage to bear it manfully, and will my religion give me strength enough to say 'Thy will be done' with me and in my heart, and then work on with amended life till myself relieved of labor and brought to judgment. Let me try. This moment I feel fully aware of my great, yes, terrible responsibility to my family. How much of their shortcoming now and in future depends on me, their natural guide and example. God give me strength faithfully to do that work set before me in the right way, for otherwise I am very weak and frail."

VII

THE "SORROWS AND BITTERNESS" of which Dr. Squibb seemed to have a premonition on the last day of 1865 began to materialize before the new year was more than a few hours old.

Baby Mary was seized with convulsions which Dr. McClellan, who was called in, believed had been caused either by the condition of her red and swollen gums—she was teething—or by the piece of apple which her father had given her at dinner. At Dr. McClellan's suggestion, Dr. Squibb gave her an emetic and an enema, but the convulsions continued intermittently for several days.

Dr. McClellan called three times on New Year's Day, very anxious about his little patient. Caroline was "nearly laid up, feeling very badly," and the front doorbell rang thirty times to announce New Year's callers. "During these visits," wrote Dr. Squibb, "I was twice called to poor little baby in convulsion." He sat up with his daughter all night, dozing in his chair, and next day went to the laboratory only twice.

The night of January 2 she seemed better, but he determined to sit up with her anyhow. Shortly before midnight there was a frantic ringing of the doorbell. Hurrying down, he found a white-faced neighbor, Mr. Van Sindesen.

"He asked me to go to Mr. Geo. L. Sampson, who had fallen in an apoplexy," Dr. Squibb reported. "I ran to him at once and found him on the floor in front of his dressing bureau, without any discernable signs of life, though this must have been within 8 minutes of his fall. No pulsation could be found anywhere, nor sounds about the heart. Hot water, mustard, etc., were freely employed till Dr. McClellan got there, but without effect. He had doubtless been dead from the moment of his fall. After giving up all efforts to produce reaction and while waiting for the undertaker, we witnessed a scene, the impressive character of which I shall never forget. The old warm friend whom I had so loved and reverenced lying there as though asleep, and his children around him in their grief, was a sad scene for me and one which should teach me a lesson.

"He was buried on Friday afternoon after a manly, forcible, honest notice of his character by Mr. Van Dyke. His loss has depressed me greatly though so sudden that none of us can realize it yet."

Dr. Squibb missed his friend Sampson in more ways than one. The late president of the Brooklyn Savings Bank had long been a financial adviser to the doctor, whom he had regarded as economically erratic, often too cautious in small matters, too reckless in big ones. Several times the banker had counseled the doctor against getting into deep water or had rescued him when he had got beyond his depth. And in this cold, cold January of 1866, when the mercury remained below zero for days at a time, Dr. Squibb indeed needed the warm advice and help of George Sampson.

He had undertaken heavy expenses in expanding his laboratories, buying new equipment, and hiring a larger staff. The bigger plant had scarcely been opened when the war ended and Army orders practically ceased. The postwar depression began to be felt in all branches of the chemical business, and, as a contemporary wag expressed it, "drugs became a drug on the market." On January 21 Dr. Squibb wrote:

"Advertising the Laboratory for sale in all the morning papers, and had but two inquiries. Trying to make arrangements for a mortgage of 25,000.00 on the Laboratory, and have not yet succeeded. Must tomorrow do the very disagreeable thing of asking Mr. Sullivan to endorse a note for me, to pay a note due. Hardly any business doing and expenses very heavy, and no Mr. Sampson to go to."

Mr. Sullivan proved to be an unsatisfactory go-between. Two weeks later the application for a $25,000 mortgage was refused.

Dr. Squibb worried for another few weeks over the fact that laboratories, too,—even laboratories with a reputation for making pure, reliable medicines—seemed to be an unsound risk. Then his original note was renewed.

nine

FELLOWSHIP

I

DR. SQUIBB was a congenital joiner, yet he never joined any organization to which he did not expect to devote time and energy. Three or four nights of every week were taken up with meetings, most of them related to either pharmacy or medicine. He tried to avoid top responsibility, often without success. He never refused to share his knowledge and experience. He was always ready to read a paper based on his original research.

He of course belonged to the Kings County Medical Society, of which he became treasurer during 1866. He was a member of the Long Island Historical Society, the New York State Medical Society, the New York Academy of Medicine, the American Pharmaceutical Association, the U. S. Pharmacopoeia Committee of Revision, and the American Medical Association. He attended every convention he could possibly make (sometimes he was forced to remain at home by Caroline's ill health) and at most of them he made some contribution to the fund of human knowledge.

Probably his favorite society was an organization which was both professional and social—the Brooklyn Medical and Surgical Society. Dr. Squibb was decidedly a gregarious person, and he liked the monthly meetings of the Brooklyn Society, which was practically a neighborhood group—Drs. McClellan, Minor, H. S. Smith, D. A. Dodge, James Crane, B. A. Segur, J. C. Hutchison, and A. N. Bell. The membership at this time was limited to twelve, so that each of the monthly meetings could be held at the home of a different member.

The Brooklyn Society devoted two hours to the reading of papers on interesting cases which the members had come across during the past month—all duly recorded by the secretary, Dr. E. R. Squibb (and still available in the Squibb archives in New Brunswick, New Jersey). After the serious part of the meeting, the physicians retired to the dining room for a nocturnal snack and perhaps a glass or two of wine. When the society met at the Squibb home, the supper usually consisted of Baltimore terrapin, scalloped Chesapeake Bay oysters, chicken salad (compounded by a secret Squibb formula), and mince pies made as close as possible to his Aunt Mary's recipe. In any event, they were made with good cider and were redolent with French cognac.

That winter and spring he tried the therapeutic effect of travel on Caroline's malady. He insisted that she accompany him to the State Medical Society convention in Albany. Since Dr. and Mrs. McClellan also were going, they all traveled together by train.

Dr. Squibb was pleased by the fact that the convention elected his neighbor, Dr. Hutchison, president of the society for the ensuing year. He was upset by the fact that the attendance of the convention was swelled by physicians lobbying for or against the Bill then pending before the New York State legislature, proposing the creation of a State Health Commission. Dr. Squibb did not like physicians in politics, except when they were acting as a unified professional body. He did not like physicians in politics as individuals. And he had been maneuvered into lending his name to back the Health Bill by colleagues who were also suggesting his name as Health Commissioner for Brooklyn. He definitely did not like this sort of thing.

The Squibbs returned to Brooklyn on Friday, February 9, "Caroline having been very well during the trip." For that he was thankful.

On Sunday he wrote letters to every state senator and assemblyman of his area, disassociating himself from the Health Bill. Two of these he delivered in person—to Messrs. Reynolds and Pierson—"getting home at 6 o'clock and finding Caroline very nervous and irritable although I had left her 3 hours before cheerful and well. This seems very liable to happen every time I go out, except to my daily work."

The story of Dr. Squibb and the Health Bill began in mid-January when Drs. Crane and McClellan called to ask him to be the first Health Commissioner under the pending bill, which was expected to pass. Next day Judge Birdseye brought him a copy of the bill and Dr. Squibb thought it would disqualify him because he had not been actively practicing medicine for five continuous years in the district. Those sincerely interested in Dr. Squibb's appointment proposed amendments, and the amended bill passed the New York State legislature on February 17, 1866.

On February 19, Dr. I. T. Williams of Dunkirk, New York, made an appointment for Dr. Squibb to see Governor Reuben E. Fenton. Dr. Squibb told the Governor he did not wish the appointment, but Gov. Fenton asked him to withhold decision until he had returned from Washington.

"I never desired [the appointment]," wrote Dr. Squibb, "and now dread it since I cannot consistently decline it without a trial after acceding to the use of my name to many over-warm and injudicious friends."

On Monday, February 26, Dr. Squibb was summoned to the Fifth Avenue Hotel in New York by Governor Fenton.

"He commenced by telling me that he had determined to send my name to the Senate on the following day as Commissioner for Brooklyn," wrote Dr. Squibb, "but wished to talk a little on some other matters. Then said that when the Board got together he should have some names to send for some of the offices under the Board, and though he would not mention the names, thought I would have no difficulty in voting for the nominations. Said he thought it all-important that the Board should be harmonious, etc. These indirect attempts to compromise my independence in the matter were repulsive and irritating, and I told him I could not promise to harmonize with those I did not know, and that against the only member of the Board yet known to anyone, namely Dr. Swinburne, I had a strong prejudice and dislike. He replied that that altered the whole face of the matter and showed me pretty clearly that Dr. Swinburne was to manage all his interests in the Board, and he could nominate no one who could not accord with him.

"We had a longer conversation in which he gave me by inference and deduction, rather than from a plain, manly showing, that I was expected to do what I would not do, and that the reputed honesty of my character was to be his guarantee that I would do what he wanted if I took the position. It was an utterly disgusting and disgraceful interview, and was closed by my thanking him for letting me off from the position, and by my asking him to consider what I said of Dr. Swinburne as private, excepting as regard to Dr. S. himself, but that I had rather *he* should know of it than not.

"Dr. Swinburne was in Brooklyn within 3 hours after the close of the interview, looking for another name to be used in place of mine, and he ultimately succeeded in getting that of Dr. [James] Crane, who was nominated and confirmed and is now the overrun and beset Commissioner with difficulties and responsibilities not enviable."

Dr. Squibb's "strong prejudice and dislike" of Dr. John Swinburne, the Governor's pet, were based on his belief that Dr. Swinburne was more interested in politics than in the sciences of health and healing and that while he would gladly trade the Oath of Hippocrates for the oath of office, he regarded neither as a particularly solemn commitment.

Dr. Swinburne was about the same age as Dr. Squibb. He

had studied at Albany Medical College but had done nothing of importance until the Civil War, when he volunteered to serve with General McClellan's Army of the Potomac. His war service was brief but heroic. He went into action for the first time in April 1862. He was caught in the debacle at Savage's Station, ten miles east of Richmond, and when the Union forces withdrew on June 29 he remained behind to treat the wounded. He next turned up in New York two years later, no longer in the Army, to accept an appointment from Governor Horatio Seymour as Health Officer of the Port of New York.

A rather distinguished-looking man with a General Grant beard and a high forehead that continued deep into his thinning hair, Dr. Swinburne was as impressive to politicians as he was unimpressive to Dr. Squibb. He continued in the good graces of Governor Fenton, as Dr. Squibb pointed out, and made himself even more important to Fenton's successor, Governor John T. Hoffman, who gave him the job of rebuilding the quarantine station in the lower bay—a $750,-000 project which entailed creating two artificial islands about a quarter-mile off the South Beach area of Staten Island. Out of gratitude to the Governor he named one of these Hoffman's Island. The other he modestly called Swinburne Island. Both names are still in use, although the islands ceased to function as quarantine stations when Congress began restricting immigration half a century later. Hoffman's was more recently reactivated as a training center for the United States Maritime Service.

Another colleague who shared Dr. Squibb's professional disesteem at this period was Dr. Agrippa Nelson Bell, a protégé of Dr. Swinburne's. Dr. Bell was a Virginian who had attended Harvard and had secured an M. D. from Jefferson several years before Dr. Squibb. Like Dr. Squibb, he had served the Navy as assistant surgeon during the Mexican War, although it took him ten years to be promoted to passed assistant surgeon. By that time (1855) he had acquired a large and expensive family, and he resigned a few months after his promotion to seek greater financial rewards in private practice.

Dr. Bell was a rather curious-looking individual. His forehead extended to the top of his skull, and, as though to make up for the lack of hair above, he wore long, fuzzy gray sideburns, almost long enough to be called mutton-chop whiskers. His rimless oval spectacles and his crooked, thin-lipped smile gave him a humorless, pedantic mien. Try as he might to hide his emotions, he was always betrayed by the activity of a prominent Adam's apple above his gates-ajar collar and Ascot tie.

Dr. Squibb rather liked Dr. Bell personally, for he was one of the twelve members of the Brooklyn Medical and Surgical Society. He even overlooked Dr. Bell's curious theories, such as his belief that yellow fever was infectious but not personally contagious. He could tolerate Dr. Bell's repetitious boasting about how he had stopped an epidemic in his ship during the Mexican War by using steam as a disinfectant. He could understand why a man with eight children might strive to the limit of his ability to improve his economic status. But he had no sympathy with such a man—particularly a man entrusted with human life and health—who tried to overreach his capabilities.

Dr. Squibb's friendship for Dr. Bell began to cool perceptibly at the time the Health Commissionership was being discussed. He had previously been annoyed with Dr. Bell's intrigue among the staff of the Brooklyn City Hospital, angling for a high-paid appointment for which Dr. Squibb did not believe him qualified. And he was further disturbed by Dr. Bell's sycophantic dancing around Dr. Swinburne's political Maypole, seeking pressure to assure his appointment to the newly formed Health Commission.

Two days after Dr. Crane's nomination to the post Dr. Squibb had refused, Dr. Squibb reported that he "went to see Dr. Bell and had a long plain talk with him, saying I thought there was no chance for his nomination by Crane as deputy, and telling him plainly why I would not have nominated him as the probable reason why Crane would not, namely that he was not fitted for the place."

Two weeks later (April 1866), the Brooklyn Medical and Surgical Society met at Dr. Bell's house, and the growing coolness of the other colleagues toward the host was quite apparent to Dr. Squibb but not to Dr. Bell himself. Dr. Squibb therefore resolved to warn Dr. Bell that his scheming at Brooklyn City Hospital was not only alienating his friends but jeopardizing his staff position there:

"On Tuesday morning went to see Dr. Bell to advise him to resign from B.C.H. and told him plainly that if he did not do so, I believed he would be dropped again," wrote Dr. Squibb. "On Wednesday he came to see me and borrowed 200$."

The loan was not mentioned again for four years, during which time Dr. Bell entrenched himself even more deeply in Dr. Swinburne's favor, a maneuver which was to win him the position of superintendent of Hoffman's Island Hospital when Dr. Swinburne became head man of the quarantine station.

In the interim, however, Dr. Bell's genius for intrigue— instinctive, no doubt, since he did not seem aware of it himself—came close to destroying the cordiality of the intimate little Medical and Surgical Society. With his characteristic frankness, Dr. Squibb wrote to Dr. Bell suggesting that, to save the club, one or the other of them should resign.

"For several years back," Dr. Squibb finally wrote in June 1870, "there has been an increasing want of congeniality on my part between us, and this has of late grown to such an extent as to make any profession of personal friendship hypo-critical if not worse. . . . I do not aim at closing our acquaintanceship, for I have no personal enmity against you in any form . . . nor would I do you a personal disservice if I knew it or could help it. It however seems good for me to make a broad distinction between friendship and acquaint-anceship. . . . As our Society is and ought to be only held together by personal friendship . . . I feel perfectly willing to resign my membership, however valuable that may be to me. . . . But if you think, or can ascertain, that there are others in the Society who feel as I do, you yourself would desire to resign rather than render the Society still unharmonious after I should have withdrawn. . . ."

Dr. Bell did not resign, but three weeks later he sent Dr. Squibb a letter which read:

DEAR SIR:

Your note of 22 ult. duly received and would have been acknowledged before, but that I have been waiting the propitious time when I could, as I do now, inclose evidence of your apparent friendship to me four years ago. For which please send the due bill given at the time.

Your kind loan when I was in distress has been of great service to me and I sincerely thank you for it—the more since it must have cost you great sacrifice of feeling at least to have granted it.
. . .

The suggestions of your note, coming from a friend—if such a paradox can be imaginable—might have been worthy of consideration. But having opportunities probably equal to your own for an appreciation of the state of the case, at least satisfactory to myself, that the rule or ruin party of the society consisted of but three individuals, yourself being one of them and speaking for the three, it must be plain to you that I had abundant reason to think I should fare better by consulting my friends than either of those who had formally, on the face of your note, declared themselves otherwise. On any other construction of your note, it exhibits an arrogant presumption at most excusable only as applicable to your children or your servants.

Respectfully yours

A. N. Bell.

"Got a letter from Dr. Bell this week," Dr. Squibb commented in his journal, "enclosing a check for 200$ lent him in 1866, and interest on it, but the interest calculated short. Did not reply to his letter and hope now that our future association will be one of common courtesy only. Feel very glad that we now understand each other beyond reasonable chance of misconception."

The Brooklyn Medical and Surgery Society was not reorganized until November 1872, when its membership was reduced to nine. The nine did not include Dr. Bell, but it did include Dr. Minor, even though he had moved to Manhattan.

The members still exchanged medical reports on interesting cases, but the group continued to be largely social. The scalloped oysters and the terrapin seemed equally as important as the papers on prolapsed uteri or enucleation in glaucoma which preceded them. When the group met at Dr. Squibb's, Dr. Minor had to promise to walk home from the Fulton Ferry before he got a second piece of mince pie.

II

DR. SQUIBB RARELY missed an out-of-town meeting of his nonsocial statewide or national professional organizations, and during 1866 he tried taking Caroline along on his trips as a therapeutic experiment. The experiment was only partially successful.

In May the Squibbs traveled to Baltimore with Dr. and Mrs. McClellan and Dr. and Mrs. Minor for the American Medical Association convention. Dr. Squibb had prepared a paper on the treatment of the primary stages of epidemic cholera, evidently a controversial subject at that time, and one on which Dr. Bell had claimed to be an expert. Dr. Squibb had intended to present the paper in the form of a preamble and resolution, but at a session of the section on hygiene, his colleagues got into such an argument over his proposals that he "had to withdraw my preamble and resolutions on the primary management of cholera to prevent their discussion or defeat."

"The hotel was very bad," he wrote, "and we had a small uncomfortable room and bed. . . . During the night Caroline had the window opened and took cold, so that she remained in bed . . . for nearly two days after we got there, and was not well again until we reached Phila. on the way home."

At Philadelphia they stayed with Caroline's parents, who had moved across the Delaware to suburban Riverton. In town he bought some books at Lippincott's, called on Martha Dodgson, and left his paper on cholera with his friend William Procter for his *American Journal of Pharmacy*. The A.M.A. *Journal* had not even been thought of at this time. He also hired one of Professor Procter's students at the Philadelphia College of Pharmacy, Thomas J. Covell, to come and work in the Squibb laboratories.

In August Dr. Squibb took Caroline with him to the American Pharmaceutical Society convention in Detroit, a rather complicated journey which Dr. Squibb complicated even further by side trips for sight-seeing.

"On Friday the 18th," Dr. Squibb wrote, "Caroline came down from Sing Sing, and we started that evening at 5 by the Harlem train, slept that night at the Delavan House, and the next night reached the Niagara House at Niagara Falls by 10. Remained there still Sunday afternoon, seeing the American side, and then crossed to the Clifton House where we remained till 1.30 p.m. of Tuesday when we left for Detroit by the Gt. Western Road. On reaching Windsor that night had my pocket picked, losing only 17 or 18 dollars, however. Reached the Russel House, Detroit, Tuesday night about 11. Wednesday, Thursday and Friday occupied by the Association meetings [Dr. Squibb read a report on the workings of the Internal Revenue Law and a paper on improved methods for making fluidextract of Buchu, a diuretic and diaphoretic made from the leaves of an African plant, Barosma Botulina], and an excursion on the river.

"On Saturday morning started in company with Mr. and Mrs. Procter, Mr. and Mrs. Orne, Mr. and Mrs. Markoe, Mr. Lincoln and Mr. Slade, by the Grand Trunk Road, and reached Kingston the next (Sunday) morning at 3. Then took the boat Grecian and passed down the St. Lawrence to Montreal, arriving at St. Lawrence Hall at about 7.30 p.m. Left Montreal on Monday at 3.30 p.m. by Rouse's Point and Lake Champlain to Fouquet's at Plattsburg, arriving about 8 p.m. Left Plattsburg at 7.30 a.m. on Tuesday and passed down the Lake to Ticonderoga and then across to Lake George where we fell in with Mr. [George G.] Sampson and Dr. Potter, and with them reached the Fort William Henry Hotel after 8 o'clock p.m. Lodged here and started this (Wednesday) morning at 4 a.m. for Moreau station. Thence to Albany and home by the Hudson River Road, getting here by 6 p.m. . . . The trip was a pleasant one, but after the first 3 days not at all so to Caroline, as she was sick, uncomfortable, dissatisfied and unhappy all the time, and got home apparently more dead than alive."

She had, however, gone through more than half a year without a true attack. Dr. Squibb was pleased, although he was not sure which therapy should get the credit—travel, or a new sedative he was trying. Just before the war started, he had received a pamphlet from a professor at Jefferson Medical College, Dr. Roberts Bartholow, urging the use of bromides in the management of nervous afflictions. Bromides had long been known to chemists, of course, but they had never been used therapeutically in the United States. In fact, they had not appeared on the lists of reputable pharmaceutical manufacturers until 1866, when Rosengarten of Philadelphia, one of Dr. Squibb's few senior competitors, began production. It was at this time that Dr. Squibb first began trying it himself. He gave Caroline fifteen grains of potassium bromide three times a day. It seemed to help, although it interfered with her appetite.

She went to Ossining for the summer as usual, taking the children and two of the servants. Dr. Squibb did not go up weekends until July, as he was laid up with a bad case of conjunctivitis of the left eye, with ulceration of the cornea— a legacy from the Furman Street fire. Dr. McClellan kept him in a dark room for two weeks and would not let him read for a month. Dr. Noyes twice punctured the cornea.

When he resumed his weekend trips—by river steamer when he could—his gallantry once got him into trouble. "On Saturday afternoon went to Sing Sing as usual," he wrote, "but on carrying the baggage of a Miss Wagner ashore, got left at Tarrytown and had to go up by train."

"Poor Kit, the white poney" did not go to Ossining that year, for she had been "disabled now for some time past and pronounced by Pilgrim to be incurable and was growing worse so fast that I had to make up my mind to put her out of her misery. . . . The poor beast went out of this world in a gentle trot, and apparently without pain, as she had plenty of chloroform, and that the best I could give her. She had been very faithful to us."

It was not a bad summer to stay in Brooklyn. He had engaged two competent new assistants to help at the laboratory —Professor Procter's protegé, Thomas Covell, and a promising young man named John A. Dunn, who had such a good background and seemed so alert that Dr. Squibb started him at $12 a week. So he had plenty of time to work on a paper on disinfectants for the New York Academy of Medicine and for all his other extracurricular professional activities.

The house, too, was just about where he wanted it. He had acquired several new clocks—a traveler's alarm clock for his bedroom, a "little old chamber clock from Ball Black & Co.," a little laboratory alarm clock from Read & Taylor, and a French clock in a transparent case which Mr. Brandeis brought back from Europe, "plain but rich . . . an exquisite piece of workmanship." Caroline, however, immediately took a dislike to the French clock when she came to town for some shopping, and she wanted to sell it and get "an ornamental group" for the back parlor mantel.

A bowling alley and the billiard room in the basement were both finished, and Dr. Squibb's colleagues frequently came in for a game in the evenings. One Friday in September he "had Drs. McClellan, Crane, and Smith to dine and try the Missouri wines recently received from Eve Sandes, and they left about 7 o'clock. Norman Sampson came in at the end of the dinner, and after the doctors left, he and I and Chas. Sampson went over to the San Francisco Minstrels, and were entertained although the company is not a very good one."

One of his nocturnal visits to New York proved to be a serious misadventure, since for some reason Dr. Squibb was apparently an irresistible target for pickpockets. He had been to the Academy of Music in Fourteenth Street with some friends from New Brunswick to see *Les Huguenots* ("I do not find myself an admirer of Meyerbeer's music.") and was on his way back to Brooklyn, when:

"We had difficulty in getting a car and after waiting some time on the 4th Av. had to cross to the 3d and then got a very crowded car. They [Mr. and Mrs. Flash, his friends] managed to get standing room inside but I had to remain on the platform and was there crowded and jostled during the first part of the trip down. On getting into the ferry house to wait for a boat and going to look what time it was, I found my watch and chain gone, and the upper button of my vest open. They had evidently been stolen on the car, and probably most of those who had crowded the platform were a confederated gang of pickpockets. Though a very valuable watch and chain, I regretted the loss more in consequence of their being a memorial of poor grandmother. I begged Mr. and Mrs. Flash to say nothing whatever of the loss to anyone, since being quite able to bear the loss alone, I beside dislike very much being condoled with and talked about. On Wednesday morning I took my old watch, and going to Chas. Fellows got another chain as nearly as possible like the one lost, I thus escaped all observation. Then went to police headquarters and had the loss recorded, but without obtaining any satisfaction or hope of getting the watch. I next put an advertisement in the Herald, offering 150$ reward for the watch 'and no questions asked,' application to be made to Cooper and Fellows."

He did not recover the watch, but the press of business dulled his sense of loss. "On Tuesday, Kings County Medical Society, on Wednesday and Thursday evenings, Academy of Medicine; Brown-Sequard lecture on Friday. On Thursday our meeting at Crane's. This evening have to go to Mr. Wells' rooms to consult upon the Tariff."

The tariff consultations involved Dr. Squibb's research into whisky frauds and his advice on changes in the internal-revenue laws to protect the import of legitimate medicines (containing alcohol) from protective duties on liquors, and to insure the purity of imported liquors.

It is not surprising that during this period his journal entries began to be made weekly—usually on Saturday—instead of daily.

III

ON DECEMBER 4, 1866, DR. SQUIBB wrote (this, exceptionally, was a Monday): "This morning it is just one year since Caroline had her last attack of epilepsy, and whether the cure be permanent or not, it is a source of great comfort and relief to me, and I ought to be thankful for it as the very greatest blessing that could be bestowed upon me and my family by the Great Giver of all things. She has since our return from the country only taken the bromide at bedtime, and I have gradually so reduced the dose that she for a week or two past has only taken 7 or 8 grains."

Caroline did have a succession of colds that year end, but Dr. Squibb attributed this "to her going out with no head covering—the new fashionable bonnet, so called."

He bought a double magic lantern for the boys and spent Christmas Day showing them how to work it. He also tried "to show Eddy how to use and keep his new gold pen, and the differences between master's writing and that of everyday life." After dinner he played billiards with Mr. Van Sindesen, then resumed his reading of Pope's *Essay on Man*.

warmed and shut up the library at home, and while Caroline

ten

DEATH AND TAXES

I

T HE YEAR 1867 should have been a good one for Dr.
Squibb. His fourth child was born that year, he won two
significant victories in his long, running fight against fraud
and adulteration in the pharmaceutical trade, and he actually
started work on the book he had been planning for so long.
Dr. Squibb, however, was not happy. The post-Civil War
depression had developed into a real financial panic, and
business was at a standstill. The Squibb laboratories stood
idle for want of orders, even from the Army. Taxes were
heavy and Dr. Squibb went deeper into debt. He seemed to
be obsessed with thoughts of death, to the point of buying a
cemetery plot.

He devoted New Year's Day of 1867 to thanking God for
the blessings of the year past and "to the commencement of
my long thought-of project of recording my knowledge and
information in the form of a book upon Materia Medica and
Pharmacy. Having a large mass of matter already collected
and available, the labor of systematizing and arranging it
truthfully, so as to be of most use and value to others, has
long impressed me as being a very formidable and laborious
as well as most important undertaking, and for the last two

years I have shrunk from it. . . . The only real distaste beside the labor and want of time . . . is that so many of the subjects to be embraced are without the bounds of my knowledge, and must be treated second hand or from the resources of others. I have almost made up my mind to say as little as possible about what I do not personally know. I yesterday warmed and shut up the library at home, and while Caroline received her New Year's visitors in the parlors, I wrote the first article in my book, upon Acacia, and finished it before going to bed."

It was to be a long way from Acacia to Zinc Sulphate. Dr. Squibb had so many other things to do.

First of all, he had a long series of analyses to complete before he could testify on behalf of honesty and decency in the whisky-fraud trials.

Second, he wanted to go to Washington to point out the flaws in the revenue bill passed by the Senate. He reached Washington on February 14 and found that a Mr. Wells of the Treasury Department had set up a meeting of interested parties in one of the committee rooms in the Capitol.

"Mr. M. G. Rosengarten, Mr. Sailer, Dr. C. A. Lee and myself met and went over the tariff in whatever interested those present, and the result was quite unsatisfactory to me because Mr. Wells acceded to their desired alterations in the Senate Bill almost entirely and would not change the bill where I felt sure it had been changed by special-interest legislation from the recommendations I had made in his report. I was rather disheartened at the results of this meeting and felt very much like coming back home that night although he wished me to go before the Committee of Ways and Means on Friday morning."

Dr. Squibb remained, and next morning at eleven-thirty he appeared before the House committee. He noted several names—Allison, Hooper, Morehead—and seemed particularly impressed by the questions of a youngish Republican Congressman from Ohio, a man who had been a brigadier general on Rosecrans' staff at Chickamauga—James A. Garfield.

"The Committee . . . with many interruptions went through the entire [drug] list, asking my advice and information whenever changes were proposed. I was thus occupied in their room until after 4 o'clock with the result of getting through the list and changing everything back again from the Senate Bill to where I had originally placed them, with one or two exceptions which were left open. My sitting with the Committee was every way successful and most of the private-interest legislation was thus far successfully opposed."

On his way home he broke his journey at Philadelphia and called on Professor Procter. Their interview was of great importance to both Dr. Squibb and, as it turned out, American pharmacy.

Dr. Squibb told the professor that he wanted "someone about me to grow into the business with ability and education." Professor Procter produced a young man named Joseph Price Remington, who had just graduated from the Philadelphia College of Pharmacy. Dr. Squibb hired him on the spot.

II

JOSEPH REMINGTON CAME to Brooklyn on February 21, 1867. He was nineteen years old. Dr. Squibb records that he "took him down to the house to stay until he can get a good boarding place." Sixty-odd years later son Charles Squibb, who was not quite ten at the time, thought he remembered that "Pa told him there was no job but the broom, and he took the broom and went to work sweeping up the mill room in the basement." It is quite likely that Dr. Squibb handed Remington a broom as part of the education of someone he hoped would "grow into the business," but he had far greater respect for the young man's abilities. Within a few days he was already initiating him into the mysteries of making ether, showing him how to assay opium and cinchona bark, and how to put up a diarrhea mixture for Costa Rica. He also let him help on experiments with carbolic acid and perchlorate of copper for Dr. Satterlee.

Joseph Remington became part of the Squibb family. In the evenings he would go to lectures and concerts with the doctor and Caroline. Days he would let Ed and Charlie watch him in the laboratory. He was very fond of the boys —Ed was only five years his junior—and frequently took them to Central Park, the Navy Yard, or a railway station. One holiday afternoon he took the boys to see the *Great Eastern,* then the largest liner afloat, measuring 680 feet over-all, with an 83-foot beam and a registered tonnage of 19,000. And the next winter he induced Dr. Squibb to build a low retaining frame in the back yard so that it could be flooded in freezing weather and become a skating rink for the boys.

On young Edward's fourteenth birthday (for which his father gave him his first watch), Remington took the boy to Philadelphia for a visit, his first.

Joseph Remington did not fulfill Dr. Squibb's hope of growing into the business, but he did grow into one of the great figures in American pharmacy. After three years in the Squibb laboratories, he was recalled to Philadelphia by the death of his mother. He never returned to the manufacturing side of pharmacy; instead, he drifted into teaching.

He was, like Dr. Squibb, predestined to be a teacher. Charles Squibb wrote of him: "He was a born teacher. I learned more from him than from any teacher I ever had. He would . . . explain everything so clearly that I could hold it and use it."

And Joseph Remington learned much from Dr. Squibb. There is no doubt that his three years in Brooklyn had a tremendous influence upon his life. As Remington himself described it in writing of Dr. Squibb:

"Sterling honesty, and right because it was right, were his guiding principles. If an error occurred in making a preparation in the laboratory, the standing rule was to report it at once. The writer well remembers an occasion when some mistake was made in the menstruum for a lot of fluidextract of cinchona. It contained possibly 10 per cent. too much or too little alcohol. The culprit, a most worthy German pharmacist, appeared before the doctor and confessed his sin. Without a moment's hesitation the doctor said, 'That's too bad. That's too bad. Empty it all down the culvert.' And fully $500 worth of fluidextract of cinchona found its way into the East River.

"The writer had the hardihood to ask the doctor . . . why this had been done and the answer has never been forgotten. He admitted that it would be possible to make an equal lot of fluidextract of cinchona with a menstruum so altered that when the two were mixed the result would have the proper alcoholic strength. He turned almost fiercely and said, 'Such work can never be done in this laboratory. These mistakes are costly but the example and lessons to be learned are valuable, and I will not permit a patched-up fluidextract to leave this place.' He never referred again to the incident and it may well be said that mistakes of that kind were never made again."

More than twenty years later, in 1888, Joseph P. Remington published a book that was very much like the work Dr. Squibb himself had always planned to write: *The Practice of Pharmacy*.

And the year after Dr. Squibb's death, Remington was elected chairman of the Committee on Revision of the U. S. Pharmacopoeia.

III

AT THE END OF February Kate Diffely announced that she had just been married and the Squibbs had better start looking for a new cook.

A few days later Caroline, who had been enjoying comparatively good health for more than a year, had another seizure.

"On Wednesday night Caroline went to bed about as well

as usual," wrote Dr. Squibb, "but at about two minutes before 1 o'clock in the morning (28th) she awoke me in a convulsion, the first she has had since Dec. 4, 1865, when she had 3, and those the first since June 4, 1865. . . . I roused her enough to give her a dose of bromide, but about 5 a.m. she again had a paroxysm. In the morning seemed better and not so confused as I had expected. She must have had one before 11 o'clock since at that time Margaret [Mary Fogarty's sister] wiped blood from her face and there was a stain on the pillow. When I got home at half-past 2 she appeared to be just recovering from a fourth, and when I went up from dinner appeared to have had a fifth, and was very much confused and incoherent. She had two others in the afternoon, the last about 5 o'clock, and did not recover her full consciousness during the last 3 intervals, and . . . gave me very much anxiety. . . . She has taken the bromide in 15 gr. doses 3 or 4 times in the 24 hours, and last night and today every four hours. Sarah, Mary and I watched by her all night and found she had passed a very good night. . . . Used my first two fingers between her teeth and had them pretty badly bruised. Her tongue is sore and swollen and she complains much of stiffness. I very much regret that she did not resume the bromide a month ago, as she has had a warning each month for 3 months."

Two weeks later Dr. Squibb changed his source of supply, having "procured 3 lbs. of Pfizer's bromide for a uniform stock, and today made up a bottle for her to commence upon. It appears as if this was nicer and purer than that of Rosengarten which she has been taking."

Dr. Squibb had been considering not sending Caroline and the children to the country that summer, business being very slack, but the resumption of her attacks changed his mind. So when Mrs. Gilbert came down from Ossining to say she had a chance of renting the regular Squibb rooms if the doctor did not want them, he immediately reserved them at the rate of $55 a week.

Things were really bad, however. To cut down expenses

Dr. Squibb let Charles Haslen go, and he would have liked to fire Hurd and Covell, except that they had no other jobs in prospect.

His first Army order in months amounted to less than three hundred dollars. And since everything seemed to be going wrong, it was no surprise that he should fumble one of his attempts at do-it-yourself dentistry.

"In attempting to take out a decayed tooth for Ed this evening," he wrote, "I crushed it in and bungled it very much so had to take him down to Miller the dentist where he had two large roots taken out, and with much fortitude and a manliness that gratified me very much."

IV

ALTHOUGH WHEN CAROLINE left for Ossining with her children and retinue that spring she was visibly bulging with life—her fourth child would certainly be born before the leaves turned—Dr. Squibb's thoughts that summer were oriented toward death.

First of all, there was Uncle Stephen Bonsall, who died at seventy-six of hemiplegic paralysis. Dr. Squibb went to Wilmington for the funeral.

Then he received a call from an old friend and colleague, Dr. R. O. Abbott, who had served in the Army Medical Corps, asking him to come to his boardinghouse in Clinton Street to lance a boil. Dr. Squibb "was surprized to find a formidable carbuncle" which he excised, giving the patient an opiate. Since Dr. Abbott was living alone without family or close friends, Dr. Squibb brought him home to Columbia Street, where he would be more comfortable and better attended. A few days later Dr. Abbott died there "of glycosuria and carbuncle"—in a word, diabetes. Banting had not yet been born and insulin therapy was still more than half a century in the future.

Brigadier General Israel Vogdes came from Fort Hamilton

with an honor guard to escort the body to Governor's Island for a military funeral. Dr. Squibb found it "gratifying to see the unostentatious respect that was paid to the poor fellow although he had neither relative nor connection near him."

This was the year that Dr. Squibb had his last will and testament drawn up by his neighbor, Mr. Van Sindesen, and witnessed by Dr. F. H. Cotton, Joseph P. Remington, and Mr. Covell.

This was also the year which saw him shopping for a cemetery lot. Although the old Quaker cemetery had been swallowed up in the new Prospect Park development begun the previous year (1866) by James S. T. Stranahan, burials were still being made there. By this time, however, Dr. Squibb no longer considered himself actively associated with the Society of Friends. Moreover, he liked the physical aspect of nearby Greenwood with its rolling hills and its view of the upper bay from the highest point in Brooklyn. The fact that such disparate personages as DeWitt Clinton and Lola Montez were buried there did not bother him.

One hot afternoon in late July he and Dr. McClellan drove out to the cemetery in the latter's carriage and looked at burial plots. Dr. Squibb found only one that pleased him. "This one," he explained in his journal, "was quiet and retired and unostentatious, and a little off the road, and in the south portion near the south gate. The objections to it were and are, first and greatest its near proximity to S. B. Chittenden's lot, and second its size and cost. But as I could see no other, I got the refusal of it for two weeks. We then rode to Mr. Perry's place, and thence down to Dr. Whiting's house on the Narrows, coming home by moonlight. It was a most pleasant afternoon ride and I enjoyed it very much."

A week later he went back for another look. He saw "some quiet, unostentatious places on Ocean Hills, on the Eastern slope, but they were crowded and complicated and though less conspicuous than the place near South Gate, were so only by being surrounded and cut off by more conspicuous places on all sides."

So Dr. Squibb settled on the plot near South Gate, for which he was to pay $1,000.

"It was a serious though not now a sad duty, this selecting a final resting place for these mortal bodies," he mused. ". . . There is a weather-worn wooden stake in the center of that little circle, one side of which [the caretaker] whitened with his knife to put my name upon it. The name is written now, and if we but gather round that stake into that family circle toil-worn by useful labor done in the spirit of truth and honor and self-sacrificing worship to the Great Creator, that circle will always be a happy one, and we may all henceforth look forward to it without dread or fear, and as we advance, with less sadness. May God help us all approach it only by this way."

The next month, when Pierce and Sarah Hoopes and Martha Dodgson came up from Philadelphia for a visit, Dr. Squibb took them for a ride through Prospect Park and Green Wood Cemetery.

V

ON TUESDAY AFTERNOON, Aug. 23, Dr. Squibb went to New York to order some new labels for his fluidextract of Veratrum viride, a counterirritant derived from the root of the American hellebore. On returning to Brooklyn he found a telegram summoning him at once to Ossining. Caroline was in labor.

Since the telegram had been received several hours earlier, Dr. Squibb rushed back across East River. He took a hack at the Fulton Ferry house but reached the Forty-second Street depot too late for the five o'clock train. The next train (at five-fifty) got him to Mrs. Gilbert's at seven-thirty—too late. "My anxiety was very much relieved," he wrote, "at finding Caroline safely and favorably through her confinement, and a very small but plump and healthy looking boy child in the little bed over in the corner."

Dr. G. J. Fisher, a local physician, had been summoned in time and had been on hand to administer chloroform when the expulsive pains began. The baby, the first of his children that Dr. Squibb had not brought into the world personally, weighed just six pounds.

Caroline wanted to name the child after Dr. Satterlee, wrote Dr. Squibb, "but I rather objected for various reasons, but perhaps chiefly because Richard was not a good name to go with Squibb. . . . She desires to nurse the baby for a month, and this is left to Dr. Fisher."

The matter of the name was left to Dr. Squibb, and he chose George Hanson Squibb.

"The name George," he explained, "I selected in respect to the memory of my very much respected old friend George L. Sampson, and I have before and since looked at the excellent portrait of him hanging on our walls, I cannot but pray that this boy may partake of the many and manly virtues and sterling honesty of him to whom he is named. It is rare to meet with so strong and so honest a character and yet so good a one, and if this boy lives, I heartily hope he may be like him. I did not take the L. or S. from Mr. Sampson's name because I have a desire to hand down some of the family names which are connected with my own paternal name. Edward has Hamilton, which was my Grandmother Squibb's name before marriage, and this boy is named Hanson, that being my Great-grandmother Hamilton's name before she was married. She died of what must have been Fungus Haematoceles on the left temple. I remember the tumor very well. Her sister whom we knew as 'Aunt Hanson' gave me the silver pap spoon which I now frequently use."

Dr. Squibb got all obstetrical details from Dr. Fisher and learned that "the boy was born by vertex presentation at about 35 minutes past 4, and has the birth so recorded as his 1029th recorded case." Dr. Squibb presented Dr. Fisher with a copy of Wormley's *Microchemistry* in appreciation of his services.

When the baby was a month old, however, Dr. Squibb received a discouraging note from his Ossining colleague. Caroline had been forced to give up her idea of breast-feeding the baby, and the child was not thriving on formula. Dr. Fisher wrote:

Sing Sing, N.Y.
Monday Sept. 23/67.

DEAR DOCTOR

I called at Gilberts' today to see the baby, and after a careful inspection of it, I must confess that I have rather serious apprehensions as to its living long, unless some radical change is quickly adopted. I am strongly inclined to advise a wet-nurse. I fear no artificial mode of feeding will answer.

The poor baby is very feeble and does not grow. What should be done?

Yours in haste
G. J. FISHER.

"I at once telegraphed him to get a wet nurse there if he could," wrote Dr. Squibb, "and immediately set about getting one here by advertising and sending after advertisements. By Friday succeeding in getting a healthy-looking, pert, impudent girl with a large supply of milk, named Delia O'Kane. Sent her up with the boys on Friday afternoon."

Dr. Squibb brought his family back to Brooklyn early in October aboard the Hudson River steamer *Sleepy Hollow*. He started his furnace for the first time that season, put Caroline to bed, got the baby and nursery started, and went to the laboratory.

He was still writing in his journal only once a week, usually on Saturday afternoons. The following Saturday he wrote: "Since coming home, Caroline seems to have improved somewhat, and I cannot make out what is the matter with her, except it be that from shutting herself up and refusing to see anybody for nearly 6 weeks, her mind has preyed upon itself and affected her bodily condition. For the first night at home I watched her closely all night, and less closely since, fearing she might have a night attack, but she has slept well under increased doses of the bromide, notwithstanding that she has curious faint spells in the evening. I find she gets along better when I am away than when I am with her."

Dr. Squibb was home a lot evenings that fall and winter. He was writing a paper, for his friend Procter, on podophyllum resin and how the bitter resin from the root of the May apple could best be prepared for use as a cathartic and cholagogue. He was also working a lot on his books, trying to find some way to make ends meet.

Dr. Satterlee, on closing down the Army laboratory in Philadelphia, offered Dr. Squibb first choice of anything he wanted to buy there as surplus. Dr. Squibb went to Philadelphia, took one look, and decided there was nothing he wanted at any price.

And yet: "Occupied very busily all week with office duties," he wrote on November 9, "and a good deal harassed by accumulating bills and but little to pay them with. Business seems to be running behind hand all the time."

The fact that government and university economists seemed to agree with him wholeheartedly was little consolation. Although the depression of 1867 seemed to be a necessary step in the transition to greater industrialization which the United States had to go through in the post-Civil War period, it was bad news.

"Much annoyed at not being able to borrow money for the enormous bill of taxes," was his entry for December 2, "and had to let the bill go over to this month and pay the default, $3300.00 nearly."

And a week later: "Business occupations seem to increase on me and yet without increase in business, and without giving as much time and attention to [the laboratory] upstairs as I should do. Musgiller was so unfortunate this week as to break a pot with Fluid Ext. of Ergot, whereby some $1200.00 worth of it ran down the sink, a very severe and discouraging loss, in these times of heavy taxes and expenses. Sold my German collection of microscopic objects this week to Dr. West to get some money for Caroline and servants' wages etc., trying to husband all I can get here to pay the enormous bill of taxes."

And the following week: "Mills standing still a part of this week for want of work." One day with the mercury at 8° above, Mr. Norman Sampson brought around a man who might want to buy the doctor's house. "I told them I did wish to sell at a moderate price and begged them to let this be known . . . although I consider it one of the greatest misfortunes that could now happen to me. . . . Nothing of the kind could be worse, except being in debt."

A few days before Christmas he was awakened earlier than usual by a maid who reported "water coming down in the Billiard Room, and I found on examination that a wash basin pipe in the 2nd story front hall room had frozen and bursted some time in the night, and the billiard room ceiling was full of water and the table also full. Many hogsheads of water must have come down, and the whole scene looked like a wreck. . . . The cloth was spoiled but not the table and it will be an expensive work to set it right again."

Dr. Squibb spent most of Christmas Day at the office with his cashbooks. "We had not much in the way of festivities at Christmas," he wrote, "the boys being without presents this year on account of the scarcity of money."

On New Year's Day it was too cold to work in the laboratory without heat, so he brought his work home. "The new year had come in before I got to bed," he wrote, "and at half past 5 in the morning was awakened by Caroline with the repeated swallowing which always precedes her convulsions." He aroused her and got her to sit up, but not before the attack came on. It was 6 o'clock before he could get her to take 50 grains of bromide.

It had not been a very good year.

VI

THE NEW YEAR, Dr. Squibb noted in his first entry for 1868, "has commenced not very happily for me. A load of 6 or 7000 dollars, including overdue taxes, right ahead of me and don't know where to get the money to pay them. Business very small and full of petty discouraging annoyances. Incessant work, with not an hour that can be justly or safely spared day or evening and not much light ahead of any kind. Small prospect of selling either the house or the vacant lot, and no other apparent way to escape the financial difficulties. With all of this I can keep my mind thankful to my Maker for his chastening or tempering hand, and thankful for the only way which His Christianity offers to man for successfully meeting these trials. . . . If Job could have had the influences of Christianity around him he would have been less unhappy, for it is the elevating and supporting power of these divine precepts which alone can temper adversity or hold prosperity in proper check."

The doctor's patience was not immediately rewarded, for on February 1 he made this entry: "Much occupied at the Brooklyn City and Naval Hospitals in regard to Ben Bache who shot himself in a fit of jealousy in Bridge St. on Wednesday night last. He is still alive but in a hopeless condition. A sad lesson to those of us who have children to bring up." The boy died next day and Dr. Squibb was busy for days comforting the Baches, making funeral arrangements, and taking care of the hospital expenses of his former commanding officer's dead son.

Furthermore, his financial position was even worse than he had thought. When the auditor went over his books so that he could make an income-tax return, Dr. Squibb found that "all my labor of last year [went] for an absolute loss of $8000.00, that is, lost more than two thousand dollars more than the cost of living. The reflection . . . is not pleasant nor encouraging. But it does not cause me to flinch. . . ."

Things took a turn for the better in mid-February. "On Thursday," Dr. Squibb recorded, "was sent for by Dr. Satterlee to tell me that their whole next year's wants were to be anticipated and compressed into the remainder of the fiscal year, and that I must go to work and hurry everything through, of the order they were then preparing. This order came yesterday and gives us now a good deal of work, and I hardly know what to do with it, but of course must push it through."

Dr. Squibb immediately hired six new hands, and he kept the laboratories running seven days and three evenings a week.

Caroline seemed much better, playing pachisi in the evening with Mr. Remington and the boys.

Baby George, too, seemed to be thriving at last, and Dr. Squibb asked Dr. McClellan to vaccinate him.

At the end of March Dr. Squibb wrote: "A very busy week as usual, every evening and often until quite late, but with the result that today, for the first time in many months past, all the accumulated bills are paid off and closed up to this month. In another month I expect to get entirely up square and pay for the Green Wood lot."

To give himself more time in the laboratory, Dr. Squibb finally hired a bookkeeper to take care of the business routine of E. R. Squibb, M.D. He was so delighted with the capabilities of Mr. William G. Rothe and all the free time the new man gave him, that he wondered why he had not done it long ago.

He also let his fifteen-year-old son Edward work in the office for the first time, "addressing the statements of the month and then delivering them, which he seems to have done very well. He begins to write a very good hand, far better than Alfred McClellan." Alfred was Dr. McClellan's son, whom Dr. Squibb had engaged to please his friend when the boy was forced to give up his study of medicine after a siege of tuberculosis.

He decided against sending the family to Ossining that

summer. The boys spent a few days with "Aunt and Uncle" Flash at Newville Farm near New Brunswick, and Caroline went to West Point with her sister Mary King for a short visit.

There was trouble in the kitchen again. Kate Diffely Early, the Squibbs' former cook who had left to get married, was dying of tuberculosis, and her sister Maria, who had taken over her apron, was leaving to take care of the invalid. Before Dr. Squibb could find a replacement, Caroline hired a girl named Ellen—a mistake, the doctor concluded, on two counts.

First, Caroline had promised Ellen $14 a month—an affront to Mary Fogarty's seniority. Dr. Squibb had to raise Mary to $15 a month and give her a bonus of $20 to quiet her down.

And second, Ellen was not a very good cook. Caroline's first convulsions since New Year's Day Dr. Squibb attributed to her ingestion of Ellen's apple fritters.

VII

MUCH OF THE FREE TIME gained through the advent of Mr. Rothe in the counting room Dr. Squibb devoted to his never ending fight for pure drugs. The more conscientious inspectors in the New York Custom House considered him an unofficial adviser, and they frequently sent him suspect shipments to analyze, from soap to smuggled opium. Early in March of 1868 he had been asked to look at a lot of Chinese rhubarb—a casual gesture which developed into something of a *cause célèbre* that lasted well into the autumn; it also started Dr. Squibb on a series of papers on adulterated rhubarb that appeared in the *American Journal of Pharmacy* over a period of six years.

On August 22, Dr. Squibb referred to "some very disagreeable business in regard to a lot of bad Rhubarb imported by A. A. Low & Bro." Since March he had been doing a persistent detective job, trying to run down the truth of the story, interviewing one of the Lows and the firm's broker. It was August before he could reach A. A. Low to show him the draft of the paper which he intended to deliver at the American Pharmaceutical Association's convention at Philadelphia in September and later publish in the *American Journal of Pharmacy*.

The pertinent paragraphs read:

In March last Messrs. A. A. Low and Brother entered in the New York Custom House a lot of 25 cases of Chinese Rhubarb, and by sample cases in their office offered the Rhubarb for sale. The cases shown as samples presented the appearance of Rhubarb of a low grade, the lumps being dark and discolored throughout, and some of them hollow. Mr. A. A. Low accounted for these appearances by the circumstances that the ship had had a very long passage, having put back once or oftener, and that the Rhubarb not having been properly enclosed in sheet lead or tin had become damp and discolored, and that cockroaches had eaten out the interior of the lumps. The Rhubarb when purchased in China was of strictly prime quality and at a very high cost, and the dampness, discoloration, and insect damage did not interfere materially with its intrinsic value.

Within a few days, however, the examiners at the Custom House decided that the quality was such as to prevent its being legally admitted into the country. The owners did not avail themselves of their right to appeal from this decision, but sent it to London where, in their interest, Messrs. McLean Maris and Co. bought a superior lot of Rhubarb to mix with it and had the two powdered together by Messrs. Allen & Co. of London. A portion of the powder (1000 lbs.) was reshipped to this port by Messrs. McLean Maris and Co., consigned to Messrs. G. W. Dow and Sons, the well known Drug Brokers who usually sell the drugs imported by Messrs. A. A. Low and Bro.

The powdered Rhubarb passed the Custom House unsuspected and unquestioned, having an excellent appearance, and was offered for sale in this market in August with a letter from Messrs. McLean Maris and Co. giving an outline of the history of their management of the shipment. That there was no intention to do anything equivocal—much less anything wrong—in this transaction there is abundant evidence. There was not the slightest effort at concealment or secrecy in any single step of the whole affair, everything being fairly stated by both owner and broker in the open manner which might be expected from a leading mercantile house, whose senior partner is President of the Chamber of Commerce, and a man whose lead all are willing to follow and to whom a whole community look up with respect. Had the shipment been one of Tea or Silks, very few would have found any fault with it, and as it is, a large proportion of the mercantile world will sustain it as unquestionably right, and a shrewd well-managed commercial transaction, but such, and certainly Mr. Low among these, forget or overlook the fact that this substance is an important medicine which must ultimately reach the stomachs of the sick for the purpose of restoring health, and that therefore it cannot be considered as common merchandise.

When Mr. Low read the draft of these lines, written in Dr. Squibb's copperplate hand on ruled stationery with the doctor's letterhead, he exploded.

"We had a pretty stormy interview on his part," Dr. Squibb admitted, "and he insulted me several times. He desired to know what my connection with the Custom House was, that he might write to the Sec. of the Treasury [Hugh McCulloch of Indiana] who was a friend of his, to see whether the business of his house should be published, and asked again whether I was employed by the Custom House or came there to pry . . . through mere officiousness. . . . I said, Mr. Low you entirely misapprehend my position in regard to this matter. He replied quickly without allowing me to explain, 'I don't know whether I do or not. I know but little of you, and that little a long time ago and not of my own seeking.'

"This allusion to my disaster in Furman St. and to his subscribing $50.00 to assist me, upon application of Dr. Minor, was painful to me for he appeared to have forgotten I had repaid it with interest long ago. I did not remind him of this but told him I hoped I should never forget that past.

"He defended his Rhubarb adulteration scheme on the basis chiefly of the high cost of the Rhubarb in China. I could say but little to him after he had insulted me so grossly, and showed him at once my desire to terminate the interview. He is a mistaken man and I hope I may never see him again.

"He read the paper I had prepared and said it was not true they had received indemnity for the damaged Rhubarb. I replied that his brother was my authority for the statement. He then said it was a mistake; that they had only obtained indemnity upon the packages containing it 'upon a general average.' What indemnity upon the packages does not apply to the Rhubarb I did not understand. This has been a most disagreeable matter and I will take good care not to get into such another, even though it should accomplish the good which I expect."

Dr. Squibb really meant it—at the moment.

By October, however, he was already "into such another" —this time an argument with McKesson & Robbins over a matter of opium. The customs had seized a lot of smuggled opium which was bid in and sent to be powdered by the Squibb laboratory preparatory to being processed into opiates. The smuggled opium, wrote Dr. Squibb, "appeared to be a lot passed through the Custom House by my advice, having been sunk at St. Thomas' and permitted to entry to be made into morphia. It proved, however, to be a similar lot, previously rejected, which most "probably came in subsequently through Canada."

VIII

FOR MORE THAN A YEAR Dr. Squibb had been importuned by Mr. Henry E. Pierrepont, a neighbor from Clinton Street, regarding Mr. Pierrepont's pet scheme for making small parks at the harbor end of each east-west street running into Columbia Street. He had finally pushed through the necessary legislation, and the city of Brooklyn was exercising its right of eminent domain, without opposition until condemnation notice reached Dr. Squibb.

On November 7, 1868, Dr. Squibb recorded that he had been having "some trouble in regard to 'The Small Parks' on Columbia Street, the City wanting to pay me 1600 dollars for my strip of 5 feet on Clark Street, which was double the value of it, and double what I was willing to take. Although I succeeded in taking only the 800 dollars, it was with difficulty and much talk, and with the credit to myself of being considered a great fool, which I doubtless was if it be considered that I was dealing only with mankind. Why did I not take the other 800 and give it to some church or Sunday school, as some rascal would be sure to get it? My answer that I did not take it simply because it did not belong to me, was satisfactory to few and understood by few."

So Dr. Squibb won his point, although not many considered it a victory. And the Battle of the Small Parks was not yet over.

Feeling he still had a neighborly if not proprietary interest in the little park at the foot of Clark Street, Dr. Squibb had very definite ideas how the area should look, and he put them on paper. The Brooklyn city fathers, however, did not share his views.

"They do not accept my plan for it," he wrote, "but prefer one not so good, chiefly because it is like that of Mr. Pierrepont, probably."

Dr. Squibb spent Thanksgiving Day running quinia assays for the Army. Anyway, there had been a change in the kitchen the day before. Katie G., "the best cook we ever had," had been hired away by her former employers with an offer of less work and more money. "Mr. Remington ran around and found another, a Marcella Swiener, a stout, elderly woman [who] will probably not answer."

The year end was very cold, but not as dreary as the year past. Baby George walked for the first time a few days before

214

Christmas, and Dr. Squibb gave Ed and Charles as Christmas presents "memorandum books for the important events of their lives in chronological order, and trust it may tend to make Charles more careful and systematic, for he is very heedless though not intentionally bad."

eleven

BALM IN GILEAD

I

D R. SQUIBB WAS NOT only a manufacturer of anesthetics; he was an anesthesiologist. Primarily a physician, he considered his role as a manufacturing pharmacist definitely secondary to that of healer of human ills. After making ether and chloroform for fifteen years, he had been experimenting with other painkillers, which he was almost ready to put into production. But ether and chloroform were still basic.

Dr. Squibb had consistently refused to remain shut up in his laboratory, and in the late 1860s he was venturing more and more into the sickroom and operating theater to administer his own anesthetics, to watch their effect, and to study the possibilities of improving the technique of their use. He was dissatisfied with contemporary methods of producing anesthesia. He thought Dr. Morton's original inhaler was too generous in its dosage, and he found the current practice of saturating a handkerchief with chloroform both difficult to control—and therefore liable to produce cardiac symptoms—and likely to cause burns about the mouth and nose.

He had not yet made up his mind as to the relative clinical merits of ether and chloroform when he was called upon to make a decision with poignant personal implications.

216

In February 1869 one of the Whites of Milledgeville, also a physician like his close relative Dr. Sam White, came north seeking medical help for his wife. Having received a letter from his old and dear friend Sam, Dr. Squibb went over to Jersey City to meet the train from Georgia. Miss Kate Davidson and a nurse accompanied Dr. and Mrs. White, and Dr. Squibb of course took them all home to Brooklyn with him.

"Mrs. White is brought on," he explained to his journal, "in consequence of what appears to be a cancerous disease of her tongue. She looks very bad and it seems probable that she will never get home again. . . . Dr. White thinks she may get surgical relief."

Dr. Squibb brought in Dr. Hutchison and Dr. Krackowizer, a tumor specialist, to look at Mrs. White. She improved rapidly, Dr. Squibb recorded, and: "It now seems probable that the ulceration was a simple one, aggravated gravely by malarial influences, and that she will recover, though when Dr. H. first saw her and when I first saw her, I felt sure the disease was malignant. It is a very great satisfaction to me to see her improving so fast, with eight children to be cared for. But the irritation, discomfort and bad temper in which it keeps my wife to have them in the house is a serious drawback."

Two weeks later Mrs. White was still staying with the Squibbs and "continued to improve as rapidly as any invalid I ever knew, and now goes about the house. . . . Caroline very irritable and uncomfortable and unhappy. . . . Kept me awake all the early part of two nights with hysterical crying, one night till nearly 2 o'clock."

A few days later the Whites moved to a boardinghouse at 38 East Twelfth Street in New York. It was here that Dr. Hutchison summoned Dr. Squibb on Wednesday, March 3. Mrs. White's tongue had grown worse. Dr. Hutchison wanted Dr. Squibb to administer chloroform so that his specialists, Drs. Krackowizer and Beck, could make a "thorough examination of her tongue."

217

The "thorough examination" was one of the first biopsies ever performed in America.

We must remember that this was 1869. True, there was already a New York Pathological Society, whose monthly meetings Dr. Squibb attended religiously. But pathology in America was in its infancy. William Henry Welch, generally regarded as the first great American pathologist, had just finished high school in Norfolk, Connecticut. It would be ten years before Dr. Welch would bring back from Europe the new pathological doctrines of Virchow and Cohnheim and start the first pathology laboratory at Bellevue, and another fifteen years before he became first pathologist at Johns Hopkins. So the four physicians gathered in Mrs. White's room in an East Twelfth Street boardinghouse that March afternoon—Drs. Hutchison, Krackowizer, Beck, the surgeon, and Squibb—were truly pioneers in scientific diagnosis.

"Intended to have given her chloroform only from the bottle," Dr. Squibb wrote, "but the surgeons were hurried and became impatient, and a handkerchief was used. Still she was not profoundly anesthetized. The examination resulted in their recommending an operation for the removal of the diseased mass, an operation which was considered troublesome but quite safe. A small piece of the diseased tissue was taken and subsequently examined microscopically, and proved to be malignant, epithelioma. This confirmed the judgment for operation as the only chance of avoiding a rather speedy death of great suffering, and the sooner it was done the better. I concurred heartily in this judgment."

The cancer operation was scheduled for the following Saturday, and neither the patient nor the doctors involved found it incongruous that surgery should be performed in a boardinghouse bedroom rather than in a hospital. Actually the hospitals of the period offered few advantages beyond what the physician could carry in his little black satchel. Despite the precepts and example of Florence Nightingale, the first nursing school in the United States (at Bellevue) was not to be opened for another three years. And although

Joseph Lister had already expounded his theory of phenol antisepsis in England, the Lister method of spraying an operating room with carbolic-acid mist would not be tried by American surgeons until 1881 in Chicago.

"On Saturday about 12:30," wrote Dr. Squibb, "I gave [Mrs. White] chloroform, at first from a bottle, and it acted promptly but not profoundly and the surgeons being in haste and impatient, the bottle was given up and a handkerchief used. The effect was prompt but the anaesthesia still not very profound, and the operation was completed with delay and difficulty on account of the difficulty of getting the jaws sufficiently separated. I gave no chloroform during the latter stages of the operation, or for perhaps 10 minutes before it was finished, partly because the pulse had fallen off (and came up again soon after, and was good but slow), partly because the surgeons occupied the mouth and nose, but chiefly because I judged she had had enough. Her respiration was good, but obstructed by blood and ice water syringing.

"When the operation was finished and each surgeon had carefully examined to see that all the disease was removed, and when Dr. K. had passed the silk through the posterior edge of the wound to draw the parts together, she fainted, and all efforts at restoration were unavailing. She was dead."

Though shocked and dazed himself, Dr. Squibb took complete charge of things for his heartbroken friend. He went to Brooklyn for McFarland the undertaker, ordered a metal casket, secured a Board of Health permit, telegraphed Colonel Grieve in Milledgeville and Dr. Hatton in Augusta, and decided that Dr. White and Miss Kate Davidson must start south with the body at once. He escorted them to their train in Jersey City and "got home a little after 10 p.m. after a most anxious and fatiguing day and under a shock that was terrible."

Much later that year Dr. Squibb devoted himself to the problems of ether anesthesia. He had received complaints from colleagues at Bellevue that his ether was acting strangely and sometimes dangerously. On October 2 he crossed to New York to investigate and concluded that the trouble lay not with the ether but with the doctors who administered it with sponges. They were using far more than was necessary to produce complete and prolonged anesthesia.

On his way home on the Fulton Ferry, he decided to design an ether inhaler that would be doctorproof. He made sketches for Mary Fogarty, who stopped sewing on Caroline's dresses long enough to make an L-shaped cotton bag, with an opening at the top of the L big enough to fit over a patient's face. In the short leg of the L he placed a small metal cylinder lined with flannel, designed to hold no more than two or three fluid ounces of ether, which he estimated was plenty for safe anesthesia over a long enough period for most surgery. Then he let his surgeon friends know he was ready to demonstrate.

"On Wednesday [Oct. 27]," he wrote, "went with Dr. Hutchison at 2 o'clock to give ether to a Mrs. Wadsworth for an uterine operation by Dr. Sims to try the use of a new Bag for the economical use of the ether. It succeeded very well on this first trial, 2½ f℥ used."

Ten days later he wrote: "This morning went to Bellevue Hospital to try my new ether bag. They had only one case for anaesthesia and that I succeeded by the use of 1 f℥ of ether in getting a very short anaesthesia."

And his Nov. 20 entry: "Went on Wednesday afternoon to a Mrs. Freeman who had the operation of ovariotomy performed by Dr. Sims. She was fully and favorably under the influence of the anaesthetic for more than an hour, and a little less than 6 f℥ was used."

Dr. Squibb was satisfied. He set Mary Fogarty to making ether bags and Canton-flannel liners by the dozen.

He did not, however, give up his belief in chloroform as a safe and efficient anesthetic for short periods. Despite the tragic outcome of Mrs. White's operation, he did not hesitate to continue using chloroform anesthesia on his own family when he deemed it appropriate.

Dr. Squibb had always respected competence and doffed

his hat to outstanding ability. It took the arrival in New York of Dr. Thomas B. Gunning, D.D.S., to convince him that he should abandon his efforts at do-it-yourself dentistry.

Dr. Gunning was a distinguished dentist who had achieved nationwide fame at the time of the Booth conspiracy to assassinate President Lincoln. One of the conspirators, Lewis Paine, who had been assigned to kill William H. Seward, Secretary of State, had forced his way into the Seward home on the night Lincoln was shot, attacked the Secretary in his bed, swung a knife in the darkness and slashed both cheeks away. Dr. Gunning had been called to operate on Secretary Seward's wounded jaw. He had done it successfully. So when he moved from Washington to New York, Dr. Squibb deemed him capable enough to take care of his family.

On December 4 Dr. Squibb escorted Caroline and Charles to Dr. Gunning. The trip took well over an hour. They walked to the Fulton Ferry, crossed to Manhattan and walked from the New York ferry slip to City Hall Square, where they caught the Fourth Avenue horsecar northbound. They got off at Twenty-first Street and walked to Dr. Gunning's office near Gramercy Park.

"Charles had one molar out and two filled, is to have three more filled next Saturday," Dr. Squibb wrote. "Gave him a little chloroform for the extraction. Caroline is to go on Thursday."

The next week Dr. Squibb went again to the dentist's, taking both boys this time. "Gave Edward chloroform to get some roots out," he wrote.

He did not say whether or not the roots were still remnants of his last venture in dentistry.

II

THE DEATH OF MRS. WHITE was not the only heartbreak which came to the Squibb family that year.

Dr. King, husband of Caroline's sister Mary, fell dead while climbing his cellar stairs.

Dr. McClellan's wife, long in poor health, died "calmly and probably without suffering."

And, as suddenly as a thunderhead in a summer sky, the long shadow fell upon Baby George.

Dr. Squibb had been feeling greatly encouraged with little George's progress. The baby was thriving on Delia's milk (although Delia's own child had died) and was already partially weaned. Then one Saturday evening in spring when Dr. Squibb had come home from the laboratory so late that Mr. Whitlock, a neighbor, arrived for his usual weekly game of billiards before the doctor had finished his tea, Caroline told him that "little George had a smart diarrhoea with bloody discharges. . . . I, without recognizing much importance in the attack, advised his mother to give him a dose of castor oil and this was done."

Next morning, however, it seemed probable that the baby was suffering from either cholera infantum or enterocolitis. Dr. McClellan came several times and stayed until nearly midnight. Dr. Squibb went to the laboratory to prepare some Dover's powder and bismuth for the little fellow.

On Monday Dr. Crane joined the consulting staff and advised stimulants. Dr. Squibb administered brandy and cream and later rice water and brandy. The baby rallied briefly from his depression, then gradually sank again until on Wednesday afternoon the only one of his children that Dr. Squibb had not himself delivered died at the age of twenty months and one day.

"Our dear little pet," wrote the heartbroken father, "with his affectionate, mincing ways and budding intelligence had to be watched through an amount of suffering most painful to see, down to death. Of all the trials I have ever had to pass through, this was the most severe. And poor Caroline was almost crushed by the blow."

Dr. Squibb closed down the laboratories until after the funeral on Friday. He thought it "highly probable that this acute attack was brought on by something the little fellow picked up from the floor and swallowed, possibly the head of a match, or some toy book pictures colored with poisonous colors."

He went himself to Undertaker McFarland's to supervise the preservation of the body for the funeral. He took along a 2-per-cent solution of creosote, and carbolic acid. He placed 200 drops of the acid on a piece of flannel which he folded into a linen handkerchief and tucked into the coffin.

"We have today put him in the center of the Greenwood lot," Dr. Squibb wrote after the burial services, "as a point around which we shall one by one be grouped, to serve as indicating the hope and the faith that our spirits may ultimately be grouped around his pure spirit in Heaven. We left the little spring birds singing to his sleep, the green grass and springing flowers and budding trees welcoming him, and the soft breezes whispering over him. God in His providence has recalled him from us, and I hope we may be able to bow in submission to the heavy bereavement. . . . If it shall make us better, we will be happier, and little George will not have lived and suffered in vain."

When Caroline went to Ossining for the summer she weighed only 113 pounds.

III

DR. SQUIBB'S USUAL BURDEN of unpaid extracurricular activities was augmented during 1869 by his agreement to deliver a series of lectures on pharmacy and materia medica at the New York College of Pharmacy. The college was short both of funds and of a professor of materia medica, so Dr. Squibb felt that taking on the assignment was "a kind of necessity, almost a duty."

His Brooklyn Society of Physicians and Surgeons was more of a pleasure than a duty, and when his turn came to receive the group in his home, he ordered terrapin from Prosser's in Philadelphia.

His annual trip to the New York State Medical Society convention in Albany was more agreeable than usual as a result of his successful attempt to keep off all committees. Moreover, he returned to New York in one of the new compartment railway cars, eight doctors occupying the same compartment.

For his trip to the American Pharmaceutical Association convention at Chicago in September, he took Caroline and the boys along, stopping on the way to show Eddie and Charlie Niagara Falls. The trip to Buffalo via the Erie line was "a pleasant, comfortable ride . . . in a compartment of a drawing room car by ourselves."

In addition to the sight-seeing in Chicago, the art gallery, the Academy of Natural Sciences, and "an excursion upon the lake in an uncomfortable, inappropriate boat; both the boys lost their hats and had to be resupplied on their return," Dr. Squibb had a very busy convention.

First of all, there was a 48-page report on the U. S. Pharmacopoeia, in which Dr. Squibb told the convention what he thought was good and what he thought was bad about the current edition of the pharmacists' bible. It was a careful report, detailed in the usual scrupulously documented Squibb manner, recommending certain additions to the Pharmacopoeia, suggesting that some items be dropped, and eloquent in its exhortation to physicians as to methods of revising the Pharmacopoeia in 1870. The Pharmaceutical Association was not then incorporated, so the Squibb recommendations could not be adopted as official recommendations, but the paper was ordered printed and circulated and it undoubtedly made a strong impression on the Revision Committee.

Dr. Squibb's second self-appointed task was to read out of the association a pharmacist named Stearns who had concocted and was selling a product which he called "Sweet Quinia" and which Dr. Squibb called a fraud and a swindle, since it did not contain sufficient alkaloids to merit the name of quinia.

"On Wednesday morning," Dr. Squibb reported, "Mr. Stearns came into the meeting and I immediately took him aside and showed him the preamble and resolutions proposing his expulsion from the Asso. and begged him to make a voluntary statement which might relieve me from the duty of presenting them. He promised to think of it, went to his room and drew up a statement and showed it to me in the evening. I suggested some changes in his favor and he made them. The next day he seemed to be undecided at first but finally concluded not to make the statement, and so in the afternoon I did the most disagreeable duty of offering my preamble and resolutions, upon which he was expelled as recorded in the Proceedings."

Another "very disagreeable task" was Dr. Squibb's opposition to the draft of a proposed law to regulate the practice of pharmacy, framed by a committee headed by Mr. W. Wright, Jr. Although Dr. Squibb had declined the nomination for president at the 1867 convention (at his suggestion, New York pharmacist J. Milhau was chosen in his place), his leadership of the Association was very real, despite his physician's viewpoint.

"The pharmacist's vocation is entirely supplementary to the vocation of the physician," he declared, in his speech calling for the defeat of the Wright draft, "yet here is a law that ignores physicians, and does not recognize the physician's diploma as entitling him to practice pharmacy, or to register as a pharmacist, while he is the only competent authority of the pharmacist and uses the medicines which the pharmacist prepares. I am willing to admit that the pharmacist knows more about preparing and compounding medicines than the physician does—not more than he should, but more than he does; that the pharmacist is the abler of the two in his profession, but that can never change the fact that the pharmacist is naturally and properly subordinate to the physician."

The convention voted against the draft, an action which

drew critical comment from William C. Alpers in his *History of the American Pharmaceutical Association*. Although admitting that the draft had faults, Mr. Alpers thought "it showed deep thought and care . . . and would have been a good and serviceable model for the many State laws that were about to be formed and enacted in those days. It was hailed by some as the beginning of a new era, but it utterly failed of acceptance on account of the strong opposition of Dr. Squibb and a few of his friends who looked upon it from the standpoint of a physician, forgetting entirely that they were there as members of a pharmaceutical association and that the interests of the pharmacists should count first. At no other place in the proceedings was the influence that Dr. Squibb exercised in those days at the Association more pronounced that at this one. And while his remarks and his actions do not detract at all from his reputation and great recognition as a pharmacologist, it is to be regretted that the older members of the Association did not muster courage enough to oppose him in this one matter. It appears, to the historian, that the Association, in this one instance, missed its vocation . . . and instead of framing a strong and forcible model-law for the various states, weak, compromise resolutions were passed."

On their way home, Dr. Squibb and his family stopped off in Cleveland to go to church on Sunday morning ("and heard an excellent historical sermon on the division and reunion of the Presbyterian Church"). In the afternoon they took carriages with Professor Procter's family and other delegates and rode through Euclid and Prospect streets and to the Reservoir. They reached home Tuesday morning after a dusty ride on the Atlantic & Great Western and the Erie Roads.

Total cost of the eleven-day trip: $323, of which $87.50 was for three and a half excursion tickets at $25.

IV

THE YEAR 1870, THE YEAR of the Franco-Prussian War, was also the year in which Dr. Squibb began making anodynes and hypnotics in a big way.

Ten years earlier he had written a paper on liquid compound of opium, for the *American Journal of Pharmacy,* but he had never been thoroughly satisfied with the process of manufacture or the results. For ten years he had been experimenting with opium, working out a method to standardize the morphine content, on which the pain-killing power of opium depends, at the four grains per fluid ounce prescribed by the U. S. Pharmacopoeia (the 1880 Pharmacopoeia raised this to six grains per fluid ounce).

On January 8, 1870, Dr. Squibb wrote: "The new Liq. Opii Comp. has been finished and the first 34½ lbs. put up for sale, and I this afternoon cleaned up my room and put all the apparatus away. This has been a long, troublesome work, but I believe is now thoroughly well done, and therefore well inclined to be successful. The published paper [revising the formula] is also through and the whole undertaking gives me great satisfaction. It is my offering for the good of my kind for this new year 1870, and if God should bless my efforts for the relief of human suffering in this preparation, and give me wisdom to keep it as far as possible from pandering to the growing vice of opium taking, I shall be very thankful."

March, April, and May were occupied largely in experimentation for the production of chloral. Chloral is prepared by passing chlorine gas through absolute alcohol. When the liquid is saturated, it separates into two layers. The lower layer is taken off, purified with sulphuric acid, and then separated by distillation. The chloral that is distilled off is a colorless, oily liquid of pungent, irritating odor.

Dr. Squibb made the chlorine by the action of warm sulphuric acid on common table salt in the presence of manganese oxide as a catalytic agent. He had considerable trouble with his manganese oxide, "having to return two lots and assay several more and finally to take a grade as low as 60 per cent. . . . Price now down to 6.00."

He had other troubles, too—bronchial irritation from the chlorine, and defective bottles which lost him most of an entire charge. He took on more employees, two Germans named Kramer and Gebhart, two Swedes, and a Ph.D. from Connecticut.

When fighting began between France and the German states in July, the price of chloral became the subject of wild speculative fluctuation, and legitimate buyers shied away from the market. When Von Moltke's armies began their victorious march into France in August, however, Dr. Squibb wrote: "Great advance in the price of chloral and indications that it might be scarce, so we must hurry a new process started on Thursday, even taking great risks with bad bottles. Cannot get any that are better."

The last week in August he was "very busy and laboriously occupied . . . in setting up the new double apparatus for chloral, with vertical condensing tubes, and in getting new bottles and an oil bath for the present apparatus."

He needed every dollar he could lay hands on to buy alcohol to keep his chloral production going, yet when a Mrs. Vedder, a friend of the family, got word that her husband was dead in San Francisco and came to Dr. Squibb to borrow $100 for mourning clothes, he could not refuse her. He complained to his journal, however, that "she does not know that her husband left her that much, and . . . she still owes me a balance of what I loaned her to go to Japan more than a year ago. She is a good example of the tendency of the women of this country to dress beyond their station."

To make matters worse, Sally and Charley Fellows returned from Europe with a lace shawl that Caroline had ordered. Sally had "bought it at a cost of ninety dollars for an article worth twice as much. But of course Sally smuggled the shawl and Caroline knows how much I dislike and disapprove of this. She also knows that I am much embarrassed for money and am carrying a load of borrowed money all the time, and that I am constantly refusing to give to the church and other things on the excuse of poverty, and knows that the excuse is just, but she does not know that I have undertaken to lecture for the College of Pharmacy next winter for $500 to help defray the expenses for her going in the country this summer. None of the rest of us need the country but she does and must have it and now more than ever. . . . She was much pleased by the lace shawl but I think fears to wear it lest people will say that my excuses of poverty and embarrassment are not true, or that she by extravagance in dress is adding to them."

But when Caroline went up to Ossining on the paddle-wheeler *General Sedgwick,* Dr. Squibb gave her "a new watch which she very much wanted but which I could very ill afford at this time."

V

AFTER HAVING MADE such a long and detailed appraisal of the U. S. Pharmacopoeia for the pharmacists' convention, Dr. Squibb of course went to Washington for the decennial Pharmacopoeial convention in 1870. He was not happy, however, with the way the sessions were dominated by the pharmacists whom Dr. Squibb called "the Philadelphia crowd."

The convention, he reported, "proved a failure for want of a proper representation from the medical profession, the pharmaceutical being in preponderance and with clear indication that everything must go Philadelphia way. I was very much disgusted from first to last and came home sadly disappointed.

"Seeing how it was to go, I declined to serve on the Committee on Revision but had to talk very plainly to prevent being forced upon it.

"This convention, however, was not so great a failure as

the American Medical Association which had a very useless and quarrelsome session."

Although he refused to serve as a member of the committee, he did let the revisionists have the benefit of his many very positive ideas for change.

VI

LATE IN OCTOBER OF 1870 Caroline Squibb had her first seizure in almost a year. Before going to bed at ten o'clock she had eaten a supper of cold beef and bread and butter, with a wine sangaree, but Dr. Squibb did not attribute the attack to indigestion.

"The troubles and difficulties among her family in regard to Mrs. Cook and Mrs. Cook's condition," he wrote, "have had a very bad effect upon her lately, and are perhaps the cause of this attack."

Mrs. Cook was lying ill of pneumonia at the home of one of her daughters, Mary King, who had decided to put her into a nursing home as soon as she could be moved.

"Mrs. King is determined to get her out of the house at every cost," wrote Dr. Squibb. "This most unnatural proposition seems to be endorsed by Mrs. Bache, but on the part of my wife I objected to it at once."

Neither Sally Fellows nor her brothers seemed eager to care for their mother, either, "so I told Caroline to go at once up there this afternoon," Dr. Squibb continued, "and tell Mary King and her mother that as soon as she could be moved she must come to our house and remain as long as she lives."

Mrs. Cook, however, was seventy-four and her days were numbered.

"Poor Mrs. Cook has been growing worse and now lies moribund," wrote Dr. Squibb just before Thanksgiving. "A new difficulty has now arisen with Mrs. King, who will not submit to have a post mortem examination, while the others desire it. This difficulty I think might have been deferred until after Mrs. Cook's death."

As though to prove them all wrong, Mrs. Cook took a turn for the better, sat up for a week, then got up and dressed. "She will soon be well enough to be moved to our house," Dr. Squibb commented.

On Monday, December 12, however, "Mrs. Cook, still at Mrs. King's, was taken with dizziness and vomiting after eating pigs feet, and in spite of all that could be done, had paraplegia and coma and died of uremic poisoning on Wednesday afternoon about half past 5. . . . Most of her sufferings of late were due to want of self control. . . . And the moral effect of having been refused a home by nearly all her children seemed to have less effect upon her than the restraint put upon her appetites by her illness. She was a remarkable example of a good woman in a religious and moral point of view without *the* lesson of life—namely, self control and moral training."

twelve

LIGHTNING STRIKES THRICE

I

THE OLD TWIN SPECTERS of explosion and fire which had been haunting Dr. Squibb ever since the Furman Street disaster were to be materialized several times during the early 1870s.

Since the doctor pictured himself as something of a modern Job, he could be philosophical about his major catastrophes; they only served to put into proper perspective the minor misfortunes that seemed to swarm about him like botflies after a deer. And in 1871 he was to have his usual share of annoyances and near-misses.

When he went to Albany in February of 1871 to deliver a paper on anesthesia before the New York State Medical Society, the carriage in which he and Dr. Hutchison were rushing for the Forty-second Street depot was blocked by an evening traffic jam in Canal Street, and they had to sprint after the six o'clock train. Luckily they caught it, for the next one —the eight o'clock train—was wrecked at a bridge near New Hamburg in Dutchess County, with a loss of twenty-two lives.

In May Dr. Squibb got word that Dr. James Minor and his wife, who had been living in Europe for nearly five years, were sailing from Liverpool in the S.S. *England*. In a way this was good news for Dr. Squibb, who without compensation had been managing his colleague's affairs—a matter of more than $20,000 a year—and was glad to relinquish his power of attorney. However, since the Minors were to live with the Squibbs until they found a house, it meant refurnishing the third-floor guest room, which was then meant only for overnight occupancy.

A crisis arose when Caroline decided to move her own bedroom furniture upstairs and buy an expensive suite for herself. She wanted no more "common furniture" in the house, she declared; only the best. "This I cannot afford to do," wrote Dr. Squibb, "and so told her and explained the difficulty of keeping up with our expenses. All this she appeared to recognize but still adhered to her plan."

Caroline was so miserable during the next few days that Dr. Squibb resumed her dosage of bromides, which he had recently discontinued because he thought he had detected symptoms of bromism.

He also bought "a moderate-price bedstead." Whereupon Caroline would eat no dinner and all next day lay on her bed, crying.

Dr. Squibb spent all of June 10 at the Barge Office before he learned that the Minors were not aboard the *England* but would arrive next day in the *Helvetia*. They seemed quite happy in the moderately furnished guest room, and since Caroline was going to spend the summer at Ossining anyhow, Dr. Squibb urged them to stay on and take their time about getting settled permanently.

It was not to be a very happy summer. On August 14, 1871, Dr. Squibb wrote in his journal:

"The past week was chiefly concerned with experiments and examinations in regard to the Blistering Liquid for the Army and with the distillation of carbolic acid upstairs. On Thursday evening James Hayes ran down to my room to tell me that the man Ernest Masterer had broken the receiving flask of one of the carbolic acid retorts and had scalded himself and fainted.

"When I got up to him he was semi-conscious and like a relaxed drunken man, held up by two men who were trying to get his pantaloons off. I gave him brandy both by the mouth and by the rectum, but to no purpose for he died prostrate within half an hour after the accident. We kept up artificial respiration for some time but all without good effect.

"James Hayes was assisting him when he broke the flask and received a comparatively slight burn. He most likely inhaled the hot vapor and died of its anaesthetic and irritant effect. He leaves a wife and three children from 1½ to 7 years old.

"This is by far the saddest accident of my business life, and although resulting from accidental mismanagement on his part, is none the less sad and deplorable. Both Edward and I changed these flasks frequently and safely, but we never allowed them to become as full as he did, and he had been cautioned not to do so.

"The Coroner's investigation of the case had been satisfactory and all was in progress of speedy arrangement without difficulty or loss of time when Dr. Minor came into the Coroner's office and urged a post-mortem examination. To this the Coroner acceded and arranged it for Saturday. On Saturday morning Dr. Minor went to ascertain the hour and came back to take me to the undertaker McFarland's to see it. We there found he had mistaken McFarland and that it was the inquest that was appointed for that hour.

"We then went to Dr. Sheppard's, still in pursuit of the post mortem, and then to the Coroner's office and to Dr. Segur's office, and were coming down Fulton Street when we met Edward, who told us the laboratory was on fire.

"When Edward and I got in by the Vine Street door, the building was in possession of the Fire and Police Departments and the flames were coming out the windows of the elevator tower in large volumes. John Dunn had got the vapors of a broken carbolic acid retort on fire in some way and the fire had communicated to the roof. This was about half past 10 a.m. and it continued to burn fiercely for nearly an hour and burned a large proportion of the roof below the tin, leaving the tin nearly intact.

"The large volumes of water put out by the steam fire apparatus soon put the fire out, however, and it then became difficult to control the water. This was done without damage, however, and there was no theft."

The Brooklyn *Eagle* for August 12, 1871, reported the fire in excited prose and typography that made a subhead of every twentieth phrase without stopping the narrative flow:

A FIRE IN THE REAR
DR. SQUIBB'S LABORATORY ON FIRE
EXCITEMENT OF THE DENSELY POPULATED
NEIGHBORHOOD

About a quarter past ten this morning Mr. Cleveland, a clerk in the establishment of E. R. Squibb, manufacturer of medicines at No. 36 Doughty Street, came hastily to the counting room of the EAGLE office and desired that

AN ALARM OF FIRE

should immediately be sounded from the instrument stationed there, as a fire had broken out in Squibb's factory located right in the rear of the EAGLE office, which had gotten beyond the control of those employed in the building. The alarm was immediately given and it was not five minutes before the corner of Hicks and Fulton Streets and the corner of Fulton and Columbia presented very animated scenes. Fire engines and hose carts were rolling rapidly to Doughty Street and citizens rushing in crowds to see what was the matter.

NUMBER SIX ENGINE

in its haste to get to the spot, was overturned at the corner of Fulton and Hicks Streets and somewhat "soiled" but not essentially damaged. Doughty is a narrow street running from Hicks to Furman Streets. Dr. Squibb's laboratory and general depot is

No. 36 but covers much more space than an ordinary number. It is a brick building four or five stories in height and seventy-five feet or more frontage extending through to Vine Street. Having been

BURNED OUT ONCE

Dr. Squibb, in the construction of the present building, spared no pains to render it fireproof. Every floor except the second which is used for packing, is of stone, and the partitions and walls are of solid brick or ironwork.

THE EXPLOSION OF A RETORT

of carbolic acid in the laboratory proper on the highest floor of the building was the cause of the fire this morning. So far as could be ascertained, the room was occupied by only four workmen with one of whom the accident occurred, caused, it is believed, by defective glass in the retort.

It is only two days ago that Ernest Musterer [sic], another employee, lost his life by a similar circumstance. The inhalation of this gas

IS DEATH

and with this sad experience before them, the hands have been more than usually careful.

DENSE VOLUMES OF SMOKE

filled with many pungent odors escaped from the fireproof apartment and about a quarter to eleven flames burst out through the roof.

Dr. Squibb is fully insured in the Pacific, Williamsburgh City, Humboldt, American, Merchants' and Traders', and the Phoenix of this city.

This factory and the one in the East District owned and managed by Mayor Kalbfleisch,* are the only two chemical factories in this city.

---

* Martin Kalbfleisch, who was mayor of Brooklyn from 1861 to 1863 and again from 1868 to 1871, was a pioneer in American industrial chemistry. A Hollander who had studied at the Sorbonne, he came to this country in the 1820s to work for the New York Chemical Manufacturing Company, which occupied the old Rapelje farm extending from the Hudson River to Tenth Avenue between Thirty-second and Thirty-

Dr. Squibb found that the fire damage "was limited entirely to the upper story and the elevator, but the apparatus in the loft, the chloral apparatus, and the roof were all destroyed and a damage of 6 to 7000$ incurred, without estimating the interruption and delay. But there is great cause for thankfulness that it was not more disastrous. It was not nearly as bad as the terrible accident to Ernest—and this accident, and secondly my absence with Dr. Minor were probably the ultimate and proximate causes, for the men who were there seem to have had but little presence of mind."

Dr. Squibb called on the Widow Masterer to present his sympathy, gave her twenty dollars for current expenses, and told her he would take care of all funeral costs and would continue to pay her husband's weekly salary to her for a year. He was surprised, therefore, to receive a letter "from a German Centre Street lawyer," asking him to "secure the claims of the heirs of Ernest Masterer, and I suppose this means a lawsuit." However, Dr. Squibb recorded, he still intended to pay the widow her husband's salary for the year, "lawsuit or not, and I suppose she will pay her lawyer out of this instead of saving it for her children, for she can have no other money and these Tombs lawyers do not work for nothing."

The doctor was also having trouble with the insurance companies. A week after the fire he wrote: "Only yesterday the companies finished higgling about the losses and having cut them down all they could, are now ready to pay provided I take off 60 days interest. I told Mr. Lockwood that if they would pay me back my premiums with interest on them it

---

fourth streets, Manhattan. In 1831 he struck out for himself in a barn on the Harlem River, then moved to Bridgeport, Connecticut, and later, in 1840, started making sulphuric acid in the Greenpoint district of Brooklyn. Still later he moved to Bushwick Avenue. In 1869 he took his sons Albert, Charles, and Franklin into the business and opened branch plants in Bayonne, New Jersey, and Buffalo. Dr. Squibb bought acid from him for years and once referred to him in his journal in these words: "a man from Williamsburgh whose name in German means veal came to see me regarding some nitric acid which he manufactures."

would amount to more than the 6000.00 they are to pay, and yet they deduct 60.00 interest or not pay me for 60 days."

It took nearly six weeks to clear away the top-floor wreckage, replace the roof, rebuild the charred walls, and repair the chloral and carbolic-acid apparatus. Although the laboratory building was full of charred debris and charcoal dust, carpenters and masons, Dr. Squibb managed to finish his Blistering Liquid experiments for the Army, started some vinegar assays, and found time to tidy up eight technical papers for the Pharmaceutical Society convention. He decided, however, that he could not spare the time to travel to St. Louis and so sent the papers to Professor Procter to read.

Five weeks after the fire, while taking an inventory of his absolute alcohol preparatory to resuming chloral production, Dr. Squibb made a shocking discovery. The indirect cause of both the fire and the carbolic-acid accident appeared to be the same: inebriation on the job.

"Discovered this week," he wrote, "that James Hayes, Kramer, and the man Ernest who died, have been long in the habit of drinking alcohol made into drinks, and I shall this afternoon pay off and discharge James and Kramer, Ernest having discharged himself by death. I hear no more from the threatening 'Tombs lawyer' in regard to paying for Ernest's life, and go on each week paying his wages to his widow."

The Minors found a house at 3 Gramercy Park in Manhattan and moved out of the Squibb guest room on October 10, just before Caroline returned from the country.

Caroline got home in the morning, "looking pretty well. By dinner time, however, she was much depressed and looked and felt badly. She had been round the house and found carpets, etc., much worn. She has always complained unjustly that the house was not half finished and the furniture poor and mean and now it was not fit to live in. I promised her 100$ to repair damages with and on Tuesday gave her 300$, 200$ for her own clothing etc. for winter and for little Mary. This was evidently not enough, though more than I ought to

have spent, but it put her in good spirits, and she at once set
to work to get a new stair carpet. . . .

"Must look on in silence and hand out the money, since a
very little in the way of opposition makes her sick . . . but
to supply her with enough money to keep her contented is
quite beyond my power, for even borrowing money of Dr.
Minor must soon come to an end. May God help us, and have
mercy upon us."

The irritations of worn carpets and unexpected expenses
were soon put into their proper perspective, however, for
Mrs. O'Leary's incendiary cow had just kicked over the no-
torious lantern, and the magnitude of the Chicago disaster
was beginning to be realized in the East.

"Great excitement this week," wrote Dr. Squibb on October 14, 1871, "in supplying Chicago with food, clothing
and money to prevent some of the suffering by the great fire.
I was called on to subscribe over in New York as a druggist,
and again last night at the Kings County Medical Society as
a doctor. Should have responded better to both had I been
able to afford it, for I well know what fire is."

II

THE YEAR OF THE FIRE Dr. Squibb thought he had at last
found a way to throw off his perpetual debt. A German chemical engineer by the name of Schwartz had come to George
G. Sampson, one of the two sons of the doctor's late financial
adviser, with a scheme for distilling acetic acid from wood,
and Sampson had brought the man to Dr. Squibb.

Dr. Squibb was impressed. He called in Drs. Minor, Hutchison and McClellan, and they all agreed to put money into
a stock company to be called the National Chemical Wood
Treatment Co. As Dr. Squibb put up his first installment of
$1,000, he remarked: "This is the first stock speculation of
my life."

The Schwartz process called for heating wood to a point

just below the temperature of carbonization, when it would yield both acetic acid and a wood spirit high in methyl acetate, leaving a by-product of brown charcoal which was also marketable.

The company was slow getting into production. A building at Twenty-eighth Street and Eleventh Avenue in Manhattan was converted into a plant, while Dr. Squibb conducted experiments on the fractional distillation of pyroligneous acid and the purification of wood alcohol. The original $20,000 subscribed by the stockholders soon ran out, and the three investing physicians were reluctant to put up more. They finally agreed, however, on condition that Dr. Squibb take over personal management of the plant construction.

When the panic of 1873 came along, closing the New York Stock Exchange for ten days, Dr. Squibb was in better shape personally than he had been in years. His sales were up 45 per cent, possibly due to a new policy of allowing a 10-percent discount on all orders for more than $100 in a single month. Army orders had increased by $10,000 for the year. Yet the panic hit the National Chemical Wood Treatment Co. indirectly. George Sampson's brother Norman absconded with some of George's funds.

"We have had a terrible shock this week," wrote Dr. Squibb in September of 1873, "by the running away of Norman D. Sampson. He had been engaged in gold speculations on the bull side and lost heavily, but this is not the worst, although he degraded himself here by borrowing money and drawing checks without funds and lying to his brother and others. This is not the worst, for he has been foully unfaithful to his wife and family by a criminal association with a widow woman in New York named Kane."

The stockholders met at Dr. Squibb's house to consider repaying George Sampson, "now that he is in trouble," but Drs. Hutchison and Minor and a man named Cox would put up no money unless they received stock in return at 50 cents on the dollar. When Dr. Squibb sent a check for $2,500 and Dr. Hutchison one for $1,500, however, Dr. Minor changed his mind and two weeks later the stockholders voted to assess themselves, not only to repay George Sampson, but to send Schwartz to Europe for two months. If the inventor could be kept out of Dr. Squibb's hair, there was a chance that the doctor might get production started.

Dr. Squibb spent days combing Long Island for wood, from Sag Harbor to Port Jefferson. He traveled up the Hudson as far as Poughkeepsie and along the Connecticut shore as far as Lyme before he got the supplies of wood he considered proper—oak, hickory and dogwood. In most cases he found that "the man had misrepresented the quality." He missed dinner on two days because he had taken a boat across Raritan Bay to Keyport and Matawan in New Jersey, still looking for wood. When he finally found it he stayed up all night to watch the first burning. He decided the design of the ovens was wrong and was in the process of rebuilding them when, on June 13, 1874, he wrote:

"Last night about 1.20 roused by violent ringing at the door, and received a telegram from Mr. Wilson [the acetic-acid-works foreman]: 'Factory burned down.' Caroline would not allow me to go over at once so waited with her until daylight and went at half past 4. Found an almost total destruction of the entire works, and a most disheartening wreck. My third serious fire. I have been heartily sick of the acetic acid business for months past and now it culminates in this destruction of all my time and labor, and yet I cannot see that it was by any fault, omission or mismanagement of mine."

To add insult to injury, the Fire Marshal and Internal Revenue agents descended upon the ruins and kept out company personnel until they had completed their investigation as to whether or not the plant had been making whisky, and if the fire had been of incendiary origin. "Somebody," wrote Dr. Squibb, "probably some of the Insurance Companies, have been putting these officers upon us to try and get out of paying the insurance."

The stockholders decided to rebuild, but, when the landlord would not participate in building costs, they voted to move to Brooklyn. They took an option on property belonging to Mr. C. A. Coe at the foot of Gold Street, just two blocks from the Brooklyn Navy Yard. They agreed to reorganize and enlisted the services of Messrs. Case & Joyce to sell new stock.

There is no doubt that the decisions of the stockholders were based on confidence in the scientific ability and personal integrity of Edward Robinson Squibb. Although he did not welcome the responsibility, Dr. Squibb's deep sense of duty, to say nothing of the depth of his own financial involvement, drove him to make the new plant succeed.

Within five years the plant was making acetic acid, from a commercial grade of about 80 per cent to glacial acetic acid, which, since it was "clean" and measured 99.5 per cent in purity, was entitled to be called "absolute." Dr. Squibb immediately began experimenting with this pure acetic acid as a menstruum for fluidextracts.

Five years later the company was selling $33,000 worth of acid annually, $1,700 worth of wood alcohol, and more than $37,000 worth of by-products—"tinder wood." Total assets were $129,918, par value of the stock was $272,600, indebtedness to E. R. Squibb was $33,739, and net earnings for 1879 were $10,571.50.

The report of E. R. Squibb, Superintendent and Treasurer, predicted "that the earning for 1880 may pay off the debt of $8,726.22 to T. F. Rowland, and 5 per cent. interest on $33,739.00, or $1,686.95 debt to E. R. Squibb."

thirteen

FATHER SQUIBB

I

The Gothic sense of duty which drove Dr. Squibb to attack fraud and dishonesty whenever it appeared professionally also made it imperative for him to inculcate a sense of right and wrong into his children.

Caroline, he once noted, "does not agree with me in the way of bringing up children, and thinks my harsh measures make them afraid of me, but without good effect. They certainly do not fear her, neither can I see that she has much influence over them to deter them from wrong. And as they fear no one else—neither God nor man—and are not controlled without my corrections, it seems plain to me that they must be made to fear me."

This comment followed a severe whipping he had forced himself to give Charles "for a series of downright lies [to his principal] implicating two boys named Cox and Baldwin. The testimony of these boys cleared them and convicted him, and when the lies were proved on him he broke down and acknowledged them but pleaded that he could not help it. . . . How much Mr. Van Dyke's late preaching upon the ineffectualness and uselessness of goodness may have to do with this boy's mind I cannot tell. But his doctrines on this subject bring the blood to my face in shame and indignation for him. He last Sunday said the maxim that An honest man is the noblest work of God, was an 'almost infidel maxim.' If Charles has made up his mind that Mr. Van Dyke is right and that it is of no use to be good, the inference would fairly be that it is of no use to try, and the only way in which I must expect to counteract this influence is by cruelly whipping the boy, a course that costs me as much as it does him."

Dr. Squibb continued to attend Dr. Van Dyke's church, where he had taken a pew because Caroline liked the minister, but he had declined to serve as trustee. Two years later he definitely cast his lot with the Episcopalians. Dr. Charles Henry Hall, who in 1870 had taken over the pulpit at Holy Trinity, corner of Clinton and Montague streets, took Dr. Squibb's fancy by his forthright manner, his spiritual approach, and his intelligent sermons. In October 1871, Dr. Squibb took Pew 4 in Dr. Hall's church.

But the training of his children was still not left to the professionals. Father made periodic checkups with their professors and on the physical plant of their schools. When he found the classrooms ill ventilated and physical education neglected, he enrolled the boys in Mr. Burnham's gymnasium. When another boy in the gymnasium class spat water in Charlie's face, he withdrew both boys from the gymnasium until he had received an apology from Mr. Burnham and the water-spouting boy's parents. When he entered little Mary in Packer Institute, he accompanied her there and concluded it was not the ideal school and "She will need more care and attention from me now."

He made periodic appraisal of their character development.

"The children have all improved," he wrote on New Year's Eve, 1871. "Edward and Mary have improved more than Chas. in most respects, though I think he improves slowly. He still bids fair to be a generous good fellow liked by all but of no great use to himself or anybody else, with just enough weight to keep out of absolute vice."

The next year he found "Edward developing a cold, oyster-like selfishness and self-sufficiency and a sour or surly way at home which gives me much uneasiness, and I have tried to correct it by precept and example, indulging him freely and trying to do it generously yet thus far without good effect, for this week it culminated in his declining to make a drawing of a percolator for me at school. When I suggested his doing it instead of ornamental title pages and plans of houses, almost any boy would have replied that he would try to do anything I wanted, but not so he." And a month later: "Edward gives me much trouble by a snarling, dissatisfied manner and an amount of selfishness that seems to be growing. Today at table he contradicted his mother flatly and in a most offensive tone and manner, not unlike her own to me very often."

When Dr. Squibb found Edward cutting the first curly down of his adolescent beard with a pair of scissors, he "bought the boy shaving apparatus."

That summer Edward volunteered to make drawings for his father.

When little Mary came home crying with a headache, Dr. Squibb threatened "to withdraw her from that miserable Packer Institute and send her there no more unless the trustees provide better ventilated rooms."

Next fall, "Finding the Packer unimproved and Mr. Crittenden as great a humbug as ever, went to look elsewhere and finally decided to send her to the Misses Rees in State Street near Henry. Neither the school nor the rooms suit me, but it seems to be the best I can do for the present."

The Misses Rees's French and English School for Young Ladies was also attended by the children of the Reverend Noah H. Schenck, D.D., pastor of Saint Ann's Episcopal Church in Clinton Street, who had recently moved into the Squibb neighborhood. The Schenck children, in fact, played with Mary in the vacant lot next to the Squibb house and Dr. Squibb was not entirely happy over the association. The Schenck boy had once slapped Mary Squibb, and although his father had made him apologize next day, Dr. Squibb could not quite accept the lad as a little gentleman, a feeling which he did not disguise in his description of the Misses Rees's School commencement in June of 1873.

"The whole affair was a French-Schenck piece of humbug, of the grossest kind," he wrote, "and I was thoroughly disgusted with it. The prizes given far outnumbered the pupils, the two Schenck children getting 7 each. Mary probably only earned one and that was for punctuality, but this she did not get. Thinks she was awarded 5 prizes, but only got two. She however has improved rapidly and very much, and without much effort, and is now nearly through in a good physical condition, thanks to Burnham."

Mary was not spared the parental rod as she grew up, however, for in the Squibb code there was no other possible remedy for falsehood than corporal punishment, regardless of sex. There was no doubt that it was a dreaded duty for a loving father. Once when he found that Mary had lied to him about the price she had paid for a scrapbook—she added 50 cents to the net—he debated with himself for three days before finally deciding he must whip her. Then he went out immediately and bought her a muff she had been admiring in a store window.

If Mary bore any grudge against her father for his stern measures, it faded with the years. When she was a septuagenarian, reminiscing with F. W. Nitardy, Squibb vice-president, she remembered that it was her mother she had resented.

"Mother used to think I was a very homely girl when I was a child," she said, "and used to tell me so. In fact, she considered me so homely that I could not very well wear the same kind of hats and clothes that other girls wore and it used to be a real ordeal when twice a year she would take me to Balch & Price to buy a new hat. She probably never realized to what extent it made me self-conscious to always be told that I was homely and not like the others."

It was Mary Fogarty who catered to the child's desire for conformity. When she saw a girl at little Mary's church or school wearing a new coat or a stylish dress, she would tell her mistress what material to buy at Develin's or Stewart's, and by next morning her deft needle would have produced a garment that to all outward appearance was a duplicate of the other girl's.

Dr. Squibb, on the other hand, was an embittered enemy of outward appearances. One day little Mary reported her unbounded admiration for a new gold-and-coral brooch a classmate had been wearing to school. Next morning her father walked her to school and on the way stopped to look in the window of Hart's the Brooklyn jeweler who was supposed to have furnished the brooch. He went inside for a closer look, saw that the coral was imitation and the gold merely plate, and shook his head. Mary burst into tears.

A week later, however, she found on her dinner plate a reproduction of the coveted brooch in true coral and solid gold. Dr. Squibb would admit no reasonable facsimiles to his home.

More than half a century later, Mary remembered a similar case.

"I did not graduate from Packer," she recalled, "because Father did not approve of one of the subjects which were compulsory in the last year. As we did not entertain socially at home, my girlhood years were rather lonesome, especially after I had left school. When I was with Father, it was different. He seemed to understand me, and I was more natural. I used to go to New York with Father when he bought his drugs and called on some of the large drug stores and wholesale houses. . . . On one of these trips we got on the Fourth Avenue car to go up town. I asked Father where we were going, and he said 'Tiffany's.'

"When we arrived there he asked to see some stones. We were ushered into a little room and sat down. Mr. [George F.] Kuntz, who was then a young man, brought some sapphires wrapped in tissue paper for us to look at. Father looked them over very carefully but was not satisfied with any of them. Mr. Kuntz came back with more sapphires and father chose one of these and had it put into a ring which he gave me. This was to compensate me because at that time my class at Packer was getting its class ring and class pin prior to graduation. Father realized I felt badly because I was not one of them. In those days children did not go contrary to the slightest wish of their parents. Father had said that he preferred me to leave school without graduating and that was enough, but he had the sense of justice to make up to me what I had lost."

As the children grew up, their carefully chosen names seemed to drop by the wayside. Mary became "Bab." Charles called Edward "Adie." Dr. Squibb called Charles "John." And Charles called his father "Mr. Johnson."

II

CAROLINE MADE UP her mind that she would not return to Ossining for the summer of 1873. Mrs. Gilbert's food had fallen off considerably. What's more, friends of hers were going to Elizabethtown, New York, to escape the heat. Before giving his assent, Dr. Squibb took off alone for the Adirondacks in May to look over the ground.

He had a look at the Mansion House, surveyed the surroundings, then left for Westport on Lake Champlain, where he took a boat for Port Henry and the Vermont shore. Taking a train to Brandon, he made his way to Lake Dunmore in the Green Mountains. Some of *his* friends were going to Breadloaf Inn in the Green Mountains that summer, and Dr. Squibb wanted to compare.

He fell in love with Lake Dunmore, a scrap of blue nestling against the dramatic backdrop of a tall, almost sheer bluff and the massif of Mount Moosalamoo. He also liked the hotel. "There is no doubt in my judgment," he wrote in his journal, "but that the Lake Dunmore House is the best place for them to go, but Caroline desires to be with the Blakes and Mrs. Haskel, and I think will therefore prefer the poor shadeless place at Elizabethtown."

Nevertheless the doctor got prices on the southeast corner rooms in the third story of Lake Dunmore House: "50$ per week, and Edward and myself at 2$ a day each in addition during the time we may be there. This will be 64$ a week when Edward is there and 78$ a week when I am there. Washing will be about 6$ a week, and boat 5$, making a total of 89$ a week which with gratuities to servants and other extras will make at least 90$ a week, or about 30$ a week more than we ever paid before, but as I shall not be there much, will really be about 16$ a week."

Caroline Squibb was indeed unhappy over the suggestion that they go to Vermont, but, inasmuch as she did not have an attack, the doctor wrote to E. P. Hitchcock, proprietor of Lake Dunmore House, reserving the rooms he had seen. And on Wednesday morning, June 25, 1873, he drove his sizable group to the Forty-second Street depot and loaded Caroline and her hoops, the three children, Mary Fogarty, and Sarah Kenyon, the second maid, into the eight o'clock train. They reached Brandon, Vermont, at eight that night and were met by the Lake Dunmore House coach, and Mr. J. W. Porter, the hotel manager.

"Caroline was much disappointed with the rooms I had taken," Dr. Squibb wrote, "from the manifest impracticability of getting her four trunks and the two trunks of the girls into the rooms. After sleeping there one night without unpacking anything, we had a consultation with Mr. Hitchcock and Mr. Porter, and being the first boarders of the season they offered to exchange our rooms for a set of three rooms in the N.E. corner of the 2nd story. These being larger and they promising to put a large wardrobe and another bureau into them, we took them. . . . We then were to pay 80.00 per week while I remained, then 70.00 while Edward was there but I away, and when he left 65.00. . . .

"The locality seems to be a very pleasant and salubrious one, and I know not where they could be better placed if the management of the house should be successful as far as we are concerned—and the proprietors are very accommodating. I hired a safe boat by the week for the boys and we rigged it up with an awning which could be used for a sail. I remained there two weeks or until July 9th, more than twice the longest time I have been absent from my work for over 16 years, but as I should probably not see them again all summer, I judged it necessary to stay long enough to get them fairly started under some little discipline which I might try to establish. Beside that, I enjoyed my stay very much. There being no boarders in the house at first, and but few during my stay, Caroline was satisfied to allow me to dress and conduct myself pretty much as I pleased. This made the place so attractive to me, and the rest and change so beneficial, that I remained two days longer than I had originally intended. Leaving there about 10:45 a.m. on Wednesday morning the 9th, Mr. H. brought me to Leicester Junction of the Rutland Rail Road to get onto the train at 12:01 p.m. whence I had a pleasant ride home, reaching the house about 10:30 p.m."

The next summer Dr. Squibb was too busy with the acetic-acid works to return to Vermont, but he sent Caroline, the children and maids. Ed stayed only a month, coming back to work in the laboratory, learning to make reagents.

From that time on, however, Mr. E. P. Hitchcock, proprietor of Lake Dunmore House, considered the Squibbs permanent members of his summer family. During the winter he came down to Brooklyn to borrow $500 from Dr. Squibb. Instead of a loan, the doctor advanced him $300 against the next summer's board.

This year (1875) Dr. Squibb had his own catboat built by Isaac Loper and shipped to Vermont. An old Navy man, he reasoned, should certainly own his own boat and teach his sons how to sail. He named the boat *Mary King*.

The Squibbs went to Lake Dunmore on Saturday, June 26. "Found ourselves the first boarders in the house," Dr. Squibb wrote, "but everything clean and healthful looking. The boat had got there safely and on Monday the 28th we unpacked and launched her with Mary in her. Sailed about and found her all right and everything we could reasonably expect."

The next day, however, was gusty and squally, with a brisk wind that raised whitecaps on the lake and even challenged the seamanship of a salty old seagoing assistant surgeon. While explaining to his boys the difference between tacking —which means to come about *into* the wind—and wearing— which means to come about *away* from the wind—the way it was done on the U. S. Brig *Perry*, Dr. Squibb capsized the *Mary King*.

"The next time we went out," he reported, "there was a stiff northerly breeze, and by mismanagement we upset her and tumbled ourselves into the lake near Kelsey's. I had left watch, wallet, etc., at the house, as it had been my intention at some time to upset her if possible. But unfortunately I had not told Ed to leave his, and his watch was injured and I had to bring it home with me. After the accident, however, we sailed all right during the remainder of my stay, and all learned a good deal about boatsailing of which I am more fond than the boys. Ed seems to be timid about it and hardly half likes it. Charles will like it better and I hope the boat will prove a source of manly amusement to them all summer and that they may have no serious accident."

After Dr. Squibb went back to Brooklyn, Ed wrote that the centerboard began to stick and had to be taken out and planed down. There was also a small leak which Mr. Hitchcock repaired by putting iron clamps on two strakes that had warped.

Charles, however, wrote his father that the boat "is perfectly elegant and works like a charm." He was now seventeen and using the *Mary King* to impress Margie and Susie Dodge, daughters of Dr. D. A. Dodge, a member of Dr. Squibb's Brooklyn Society of Physicians and Surgeons, who were summering at Lake Dunmore with their mother. "Ed does not like to have me wear while there is anybody with me in the boat," Charles wrote his father, "but I have to have someone in for ballast; so what shall I do? Wear or Not? Mr. H. says you may wear 99 times out of a hundred with safety, but when you wear the 100th, you are over. Mr. H. and Ed were displeased when I wore one time with Margie and Susie in the boat. Please give me your opinion about it."

That summer in Brooklyn Dr. Squibb received a shock of a different kind. When his colleague Dr. Bates had gone to Europe with his wife, Caroline had apparently given Mrs. Bates some money she had saved out of her allowance to buy some diamond earrings. Mrs. Bates had assumed—as what woman would not?—that Caroline would rather not pay duty on them, so she gave them to a ship's captain to deliver next time his ship reached New York. It was just Caroline's luck that when Captain Truxton brought the diamonds to Brooklyn she was still at Lake Dunmore, and it was Dr. Squibb who received them.

Horrified at the idea of receiving smuggled goods, Dr. Squibb hurried to the Fulton Ferry and rushed to New York with the diamonds.

"I at once took them to the Custom House," he wrote, "and had them seized on an application to have them released on payment of duty and shall probably get them back next week."

Next week he reported that the diamonds "were appraised at 120.80 gold, and I paid 12.10 duty on them, and was treated very civilly about it. Neither the cost nor the trouble are at all proportionate to the shame and indignity—if not the dishonor—I should have felt in seeing her wear them and remembering they were deliberately smuggled. When she will wear them I don't know, for she never goes into any dress society from year's end to year's end, and there is hardly any worse taste than wearing such 'loud' things in the street."

In the summer of 1876 Dr. Squibb spent only a week at the lake with his family to get them "settled." He mediated a dispute between the boys and their mother over the question of privacy and decided that Ed and Charlie were now old enough to have independent sleeping quarters and not be obliged to cross their mother's room when they went to bed every night. Their father arranged that they should have a room for themselves "over Mori's cottage."

Mr. Hitchcock—who had got into Dr. Squibb for another $200 advance that spring, making a total (with interest) of $712 prepaid board and lodging at Lake Dunmore House—had hired a new manager, a Warren Gilmore, to replace Mr. Porter.

The Dodges again went to the lake in August, and Dr. Squibb sent a Smith & Wesson revolver to the boys by Dr. Dodge. They already had a Navy Colt to practice with in the pine woods, but Dr. Squibb thought it too large. "It seems very necessary that all boys should learn the use and handling of such arms," was his comment.

The following year Dr. Squibb prepared as though Lake Dunmore was to be his summer place for life. He bought a black pony and individual saddles for each of the three children. Charles went up a few days ahead of the family, taking the pony on the river steamer as far as Troy, shipping him by railway to Rutland, and then riding him the rest of the way to the lake. Dr. Squibb planned to go up in August for a fortnight's rest, but his old evil star was still blazing brightly to thwart his best-laid plans.

"This evening while home to tea," he wrote on July 14, 1877, "received a startling telegram from Ed, saying 'House burned to the ground. Cottage, property and persons all safe. Mother will write.' Then spent the evening in going to the telegraph offices, trying to learn more, in vain. All I could get was that the message had reached Dey Street about 6.30 p.m. and I infer that the house burned today."

Caroline's letter a few days later reported that all their belongings had been saved, and that they were settled down in makeshift quarters, "determined to remain and make the best of it."

So the doctor stayed home and had the plumbing renovated, as he had found it becoming "foul and offensive." He installed a new water tank in the attic and had it connected to "Two new Jennings water closets and Bidets, new soil pipe throughout with entire rearrangement of the water pipes and a large steam pipe for the dressing rooms. Parlor wall cut out for larger passage for pipes and arranged so as to be more easily got at. Heating apparatus altered somewhat and cleaned out and tested. Refrigerator enlarged and rearranged. Laundry ceiled with yellow pine after the falling plaster wall all knocked off."

He also built a gymnasium on top of the Furman Street stores, as Mr. Burnham had failed and his growing children must have their daily exercise.

Since the rebuilt Lake Dunmore House—the one that still graces the lakeside—did not open for business until 1879, the Squibbs in the summer of 1878 went to Cooperstown in the Adirondacks, where Dr. Squibb rented a house from a Dr. Johnston for $475 for the season.

III

DURING THE 1870s Dr. Squibb was greatly interested in the use of toxic botanical alkaloids to relax muscles in spasmodic afflictions.

On Monday evening, November 16, 1874, he "went by special invitation to the New York Neurological Society to hear about 'curare.' " This South American Indian-arrow poison was already being used experimentally in neurotherapy, and although Dr. Squibb assayed aqueous solutions of the woody vine called Strychnos Toxifera, he considered it too dangerous for general use and never manufactured it commercially. At that time curare had not yet been broken down into its component alkaloids of curarine ($C_{19}H_{26}N_2O$), which paralyzes the terminal nerves in striated-cell muscles; and curine ($C_{18}H_{19}NO_3$) which paralyzes the heart muscles. Today, of course, curare is widely used to relax muscles in major surgery.

Dr. Squibb did, however, make fluidextract of conium, a narcotic and sedative prepared from the dried, unripe fruit of the poison hemlock, which could, he found, prove equally dangerous—in fact, fatal. On April 3, 1875, a Brooklyn professor named Dr. Frederick W. Walker, of 300 State Street, took conium extract manufactured and sold by Dr. Squibb and died shortly afterward.

The resulting coroner's inquest at Kings County Court House was a sensation, and the *New York Times* devoted three columns to the last day, which included Dr. Squibb's testimony. The coroner's jury consisted of three physicians and four laymen, with Dr. Henry C. Simms, M.D., the Coroner, presiding. The physicians included Dr. Squibb's friends, Dr. Albert Vickers and Dr. B. A. Segur, and his ex-friend, Dr. A. N. Bell. The laymen were D. D. Whitney, S. W. Moore, William P. Libby, and Alderman William Richardson.

Dr. J. C. Shaw, who performed the autopsy, gave a technical description of his findings, notably that there was much venous congestion in the brain, that the arachnoid and pia mater were very much thickened, and that the right cerebral artery, "much longer than usual, had undergone calcareous and atheromatous degeneration." The *Times* reporter remarked: "The extraordinary size of the brain (fifty-seven ounces) excited considerable surprise."

When Dr. Squibb took the stand, he was not at all on the defensive and although he was examined at great length, according to the *Times,* he "delivered his testimony, impressions, and ideas fluently and exhaustively."

Dr. Squibb's testimony gives a well-rounded picture of the case. He testified:

"The first and only time I saw the deceased was about 2:30 o'clock on Saturday afternoon, April 3, 1875; he told me his name was Walker, and that he had been sent to me by Drs. Agnew and Webster with a written prescription, and with special instructions to see me personally and trust his message with no one else; he presented the written prescription to me, and I saw that it called for one ounce of fluid extract of conium; he then told me that he had been long affected with involuntary contractions about the face and eyes, had tried unsuccessfully many plans of treatment, and that he now, at the suggestion of Drs. Agnew and Webster, wanted to try the use of conium. He said that Dr. Webster had given him a fluid extract of conium in Dr. Agnew's office so as to watch the effect. He had given him four doses at intervals of about half an hour; the first three doses consisted of forty drops each, and the last dose of sixty drops, making 180 drops in all. This he told me had been taken without any sensible effect upon him in any way, and that Dr. Agnew and Webster had attributed its want of effect to bad quality of the medicine. He told me they had sent him to me to try to get some of better quality which might be stronger, and therefore directed him to take particular instructions from me in person as to how much to take and how often to repeat the dose, and to follow my instructions closely.

"He then drew my attention to his eyes, and remarked that I also appeared to have some affection of the face and eyes. And this is the substance of all I can recall of his part of our brief interview. . . .

"I then gave him verbally the directions to take fifty minims of this fluid extract of conium-seed every half hour until he should feel some effect from it. I told him that the effect to be watched for was a kind of intoxication; that this was usually commenced by dizziness and muscular weakness and relaxation, and that when he felt this way or any other change in his condition after taking the medicine, he should stop taking it.

"In reply to his remarks regarding my own deformity of face and eyes, I said we all had our troubles of one kind or another. The matter then passed from my mind entirely, until on the following day, Sunday, I was called out of church to see Dr. Webster, who told me that Dr. Walker died near 7 o'clock on Saturday evening. . . ."

Dr. Walker had taken three doses of fifty minims each at half-hour intervals and died an hour and a half after taking the third dose.

"I am acquainted with the use of conium within the past ten years for overcoming muscular spasm, and considered Dr. Walker's condition to be one well adapted to realize its good effect, and was not at all surprised that Drs. Agnew and Webster wished to use it in his case. . . . I knew well that I was dealing with a potent medicine but one which I did not then and do not now consider very deadly nor very dangerous. From the fact that the deceased had taken a moderate quantity of the medicine dispensed under the same name and which should have been of the same strength, I inferred that he was not very sensitive to the action of the drug and attributed its want of effect to insufficiency of dose as well as to inferiority of quality. This induced me to increase the dose from the uncertain quantity of forty drops to the more definite quantity of fifty minims. . . . Minims and drops are not the same thing. The minim is a definite fixed measure, namely the 480th part of a fluid ounce, while a drop varies in quantity with the size and shape of the vial from which it is dropped and with the thinness and thickness of the liquid.

. . . Physicians can never be practically accurate in prescribing by dropping. . . . Minim measures are commonly inaccurate though far less so than measuring by drops. They are inaccurate for want of skill in making. They cannot always be distinguished from the accurate ones by inspection. There are laws regarding weights and measures but they are not often enforced."

Dr. Squibb pointed out that Dr. John Harley of London, authority on conium therapy, prescribed an average dose half again as strong as that absorbed by the late Professor Walker. In one case of Dr. Harley's, said Dr. Squibb, "a child eight years old took fifty minims of this same preparation made by me, and within thirty minutes . . . the effect was so moderate that sixty minims more were given. . . . A prisoner in Sing Sing prison took a tablespoonful or more than 240 minims without serious effect. . . .

"It is a well-known characteristic of this medicine that it does not disturb the intellect and it is plain from [Dr. Walker's] detailed account of himself while under its influence that it did not disturb his intelligence so that his bad judgment or bad theory in continuing the medicine against all his positive instructions must have been a natural quality of his judgment and not the result of the action of the medicine on his brain. . . .

"These circumstances make it doubtful to my mind whether Mr. Walker died from the effects of conium alone. The testimony of his wife in regard to the manner of his death convinces me that he died from what is called cardiac syncope or heart-fainting. Although I have no doubt that conium caused this heart-fainting, I have some doubt whether this quantity of conium could have produced heart-fainting in a healthy heart in any other way than as a pure accident which could have no more been foreseen than the accident by which he nearly lost his life when run over by a truck."

Turning to Dr. Bell of the jury, Dr. Squibb explained, with the patient forbearance of a father helping a backward child with his homework, what the hemlock plant was like and how proper conium extract was made from hemlock seeds, while that originally administered by Drs. Agnew and Webster was made from the leaves. Then he put in his perennial plea for decent medicines:

"Any properly-educated person can make fluid extract of conium-seed by directions given in the Pharmacopoeia. There is no secrecy nor any great difficulty about it, nor does it require very much knowledge or skill. This and other medicines are variable less from want of skill and knowledge than from want of common honesty in buying materials to make them. A cheap and inefficient drug when made into a fluid extract which shall fairly represent it in the official standard of minim for grains, will only be so much the more dangerous in its liquid form, because the landmarks for judging of quality are, as with powdered drugs, mainly removed."

The coroner's jury brought in a verdict which exonerated the three doctors of all blame for Dr. Walker's death, but appended was a line which Dr. Squibb found objectionable.

"Moreover," the verdict concluded, "we find that from some inappreciable cause to us, the medicine acted with extraordinary potency."

Inasmuch as the potency of his fluidextract was strictly in accordance with the Pharmacopoeia, and inasmuch as the evidence indicated that Professor Walker had, according to his widow's testimony, disregarded instructions by continuing to take the conium after he had experienced the warning symptoms described by Dr. Squibb, it is not surprising that the doctor found the verdict "not at all what it should have been."

IV

ED WAS GRADUATED from Brooklyn Polytechnic in 1875 and immediately the subject of his higher education became the deep concern of his father. All that summer there was a lengthy exchange of correspondence between Ed at Lake Dunmore and Dr. Squibb in Brooklyn. The boy wanted to go into pharmacy and medicine immediately, while his father believed he should have more mathematics and knowledge of the classics.

Dr. Squibb thought he should have a few years at Princeton, but he "had a long talk with Prof. G. A. Barker and Dr. Woodward on the subject of colleges, and both urge Harvard. Their judgments are better founded than mine, and I fear I shall have to give way in my prejudice against New England character and New England for forming character."

Dr. Squibb succeeded, however, in persuading Ed that he should first spend a year at the University of Virginia, which he did reluctantly and not very happily.

When the time came for Ed to enter Harvard in July of 1876, Dr. Squibb went along to get him settled in a room at the private house of a Mrs. Cate, 22 Concord Avenue, Cambridge, and to straighten out his academic status. He wrote: "Ed and I were confused by the conflicting statements of the Dean and Prof. Wadsworth of the L. S. School in regard to his examination but with the net result fairly stated that his examination for preliminary matter was not necessary and so he was not examined. . . . Had written to President [Charles W.] Eliot on Friday last about these examinations but got no reply. Met him in University Hall, and got a lame apology. The whole college concern strikes me as wanting in common civility and common honesty."

The following year Charles joined his brother at Harvard, sharing rooms. Before the term was out, however, the different temperaments of the two brothers pointed to an inevitable separation of quarters.

"Letter from Ed today," wrote Dr. Squibb on February 16, 1878, "gives me some uneasiness on account of Charles, who seems from Ed's account to be disturbed in his studies by the girls in the house, not through any fault of theirs but by his own inclination for their society rather than for study. I have frequently cautioned him to control himself in this, and must stick to it. Ed thinks he would be better in the college dormitories."

Ed got his Bachelor of Science degree, *magna cum laude,* in June of that year. Dr. Squibb, of course, came to Cambridge for the commencement. It was a distinguished class. Among the A.B.s were Ogden Mills, who became Herbert Hoover's Secretary of the Treasury; Henry Osborne Taylor, who was to write *The Medieval Mind;* and Paul Shorey, the historian and classicist. Psychologist Granville Stanley Hall received his Ph.D. on a thesis entitled "The Perception of Space" and Charles Sedgwick Minot, who was to become a noted embryologist and inventor of the rotary microtome, became Doctor of Science on his thesis, "The Physiology of Muscular Contraction."

After Ed Squibb had spent a year at Harvard Medical School, his father's old misgivings about New England education began to revive. Early in December of 1879 Dr. Squibb went to Cambridge for a few days. "Attended all the lectures and recitations I could at the Medical School," he reported, "in order to compare them with some attended at the College of Physicians and Surgeons in New York. Found they compared very unfavorably with the N. Y. school. Indeed, it seemed a very good place to study because the study was not confused by much instruction. But much of the instruction offered was imperfect and bad. As a result I concluded, with Ed, that it would be better for him to go to a N. Y. school next year. Next helped select a room in Beck Hall for Charles where he wants to chum with 'Dad' Wade next year."

Ed entered P. and S. in 1880 but disappointed his father by refusing to live at home in Brooklyn.

"Ed wants to live in New York so took rooms for him at 104 E. 23rd Street directly opposite the college. . . . If I were in his place I would certainly live at home this winter even at a little discomfort rather than cost sixty or seventy dollars a month," he wrote. And a week later: "Ed was disappointed with his rooms at 104 E. 23rd. When he went to take possession on Monday he found the price $25 per week instead of per month, so I advised him to give them up and sent him to look at a place 261 Fourth Av., below 21st St., Eschback. Here he found two 4th story front rooms for 10$ a week. I went with him to see them and he took them, and was so anxious to get into them at once that I came over and sent his baggage over that (Wednesday) afternoon. . . . It is now probable that he will never want to live at home again."

Ed became Dr. Edward Hamilton Squibb on May 13, 1881, receiving his diploma at the hands of Dr. Alonzo Clark, president of the College of Physicians and Surgeons, the medical department of Columbia University. The commencement—the seventy-fourth for P. and S.—was held at Steinway Hall in Manhattan. The Reverend William M. Taylor addressed the 120 graduates. Dr. Edward Robinson Squibb was present, of course, as were Caroline and Mary Squibb and Margie and Susie Dodge.

The following month Charles got his A.B. at Harvard. He did not graduate *magna cum laude,* like his brother, but he had been captain of the varsity lacrosse team and received honorable mention for his natural-history work. His father was very much relieved that he graduated at all, he wrote, "for he has not worked up to his ability and I feared he might not get through. He has not been either lazy, idle, or dissolute but simply too full of other occupations."

Dr. Squibb sent both boys to Europe in the Cunarder *Parthia.* "Sketched an ideal route for them with my reasons for it, but left them entirely free from instructions and errands, telling them simply to do as they pleased and go where they pleased, and may God help them. . . . Both have less knowledge of the value of time and money than any two young men I ever knew with such opportunities. . . . Far from wishing them strength through adversity, I yet sometimes doubt if they will get strength and breadth in any other way. Had no time to lecture them on the subject, and perhaps it was as well not to."

They returned on the steamer *Bothnia* in mid-October and were immediately put to work in Dr. Squibb's laboratory at $10 a week.

fourteen

THE BATTLE FOR
PURE DRUGS

I

THE LATE 1870s WERE important years for Dr. Squibb
and for unborn generations of Americans. They were
years that saw the first partial victories in the long Squibb
battle for pure-food-and-drug legislation; a crisis and a tacti-
cal defeat in the Squibb fight over the Pharmacopoeia; and
the first meeting between Dr. Squibb and the young chemist
who was to become a convert to the Squibb crusade for pure
drugs and who would carry on the fight to ultimate victory
after Dr. Squibb’s death—Dr. Harvey W. Wiley.

The year 1876, it will be remembered, saw General George
Custer lead the Seventh U. S. Cavalry to extinction at Little
Big Horn and thus snuff out almost as many lives as the 289
lost in the Brooklyn theater fire the same year. The year also
saw many scientific landmarks established: A young inventor
named Edison opened his laboratory at Menlo Park, New
Jersey. The crowds at the Philadelphia Centennial marveled
at the new electrical device by which Dr. Alexander Graham

Bell miraculously made the human voice travel along a wire. Johns Hopkins University opened its doors in Baltimore. And the American Chemical Society was founded, with Dr. John W. Draper as president. To Dr. Squibb, who was to serve twice as its vice-president, the Chemical Society was to mean more than just another to be added to his long list of scientific organizations; it was here that he was to pass on the torch to Dr. Harvey Wiley, who later became president of the society.

The year 1876 also saw a crisis in Dr. Squibb's long and bitter fight over the Pharmacopoeia. Ever since his maiden address to the American Pharmaceutical Society in 1858, the Pharmacopoeia had been one of his major interests. The start of the 1876 crisis dates back to January, 1873, when the 1870 revision of the U. S. Pharmacopoeia was published.

Dr. Squibb had promised to review the new volume for the 1873 convention of the New York State Medical Society in Albany, and on February 1 he wrote that "on looking it over [it] so disappointed me that I hesitated whether to say anything about it, laying the greatest possible stress upon the features that seemed wise and commendable. My report will be a pretty severe criticism upon the Committee and must therefore be most carefully considered and written."

Dr. Squibb blamed the Revision Committee for failing to adopt his suggestion, endorsed by the Pharmacopoeia Convention in 1870, that proportions be indicated in "parts by weight." He also found the book little more than a catalogue, requiring a dispensatory to be used intelligently, although the Wood-Bache *Dispensatory* had not been revised for many years.

His report bore some fruit, for in September 1874 Dr. Squibb received a request from D. Appleton & Company, publishers, to collaborate with a Dr. Flint in "writing a book for them of similar character to Wood and Bache's Dispensatory, promising liberal payment." He replied that he had been working at such a book for some time "so as not to take with me out of this life the knowledge I have accumulated," and said that while he was ready to resume work, he would not at this time sign a contract. "Have this week continued the preparation of this Herculean task, so far as to think much about design, etc., and to get paper, pencils, etc., and arrange to have my Journals of past 3 years bound for better reference."

Although he wrote enough to fill a score of volumes, Dr. Squibb was never to complete his Dispensatory.

He never let up in his fight to make the Pharmacopoeia a better book. After his disappointment with the 1870 revision, he decided that there would never be real improvement in the Pharmacopoeia as long as it was run by "the Philadelphia crowd." He had great respect for the Philadelphia College of Pharmacy, founded when he was two years old, despite the fact that his idols George Wood and Franklin Bache were both dead. He admired, however grudgingly, the skill and enterprise of the two Philadelphia pioneering firms of manufacturing pharmacists, Rosengarten and Powers & Weightman, who still dominated the American drug market. But the man who had never patented a formula or a design, whose every discovery automatically belonged to the world, had a deep and lasting contempt for the patent-medicine profiteers who lived in the protective shadow of the ethical giants. The pseudo chemists who were actually alchemists, distilling gold from a trusting public with nostrums which Dr. Squibb declared had little or no therapeutic value, had too much voice in the management of the vade mecum of all American apothecaries.

Therefore, since Dr. Squibb had always considered pharmacy to be the handmaiden to medicine, he opened a serious campaign to hand over control of the U. S. Pharmacopoeia to U. S. physicians. As a start, he placed his "preamble and resolutions" before the 1876 convention of the American Medical Association, held at Philadelphia in June. To present and explain his proposals, he went to Philadelphia each morning and returned to Brooklyn each evening for three days. His proposals were tabled for consideration "next year."

Immediately the battle of the pamphleteers erupted. Dr. Squibb himself opened hostilities by outlining his plan before the Kings County Medical Society and the New York College of Pharmacy. His arguments thus presented were combined in a pamphlet which was to be broadcast to the medical and pharmaceutical profession. Dr. Squibb finished his editorial job in December of 1876 and on the next-to-last day of the year wrote: "Pharmacopoeia pamphlet finished on Thursday. Got one estimate for it from the 'Eagle' office, 500 for $265.00 and now await another from Sherman & Co."

The Squibb plan was simple enough. He proposed to abolish the "Pharmacopoeial Convention" which Dr. Lyman Spalding had devised to launch the first U. S. Pharmacopoeia of 1820. In many ways Dr. Squibb was reverting to the founder's original idea. In 1817, Dr. Spalding placed his original proposal before the New York County Medical Society. The Society appointed a committee which met at Dr. Spalding's New York home in March 1818—a year before Dr. Squibb was born—and drafted an invitation to medical societies and schools, asking them to send delegates to regional conventions scheduled during 1819 in Boston, Philadelphia, and Columbia, South Carolina, and in Lexington, Kentucky, the "Western" region. The Southern and Western regions sent no official delegates, although a few Southerners drifted in to the first convention in the Senate chamber of the Capitol in Washington the first week of January 1820. They were all physicians.

The Philadelphia College of Pharmacy was invited to review the 1830 Pharmacopoeia and make suggestions. The Boston and New York Colleges of Pharmacy joined Philadelphia in the 1840 revision, and in 1850 the pharmacists seemed firmly entrenched. Dr. Squibb proposed to give the book back to the M.D.s.

The Squibb plan would transfer control from the Pharmacopoeial Convention to the American Medical Association. The A.M.A. would set up a "Pharmacopoeial Council" consisting of five members—a chairman to be appointed by the A.M.A., one member chosen by the Surgeon General of the Army, another named by the Surgeon General of the Navy, and two by the American Pharmaceutical Association. Thus, although the pharmacists would have two appointments on the Council, to one by the A.M.A., they would be outvoted by the physicians. Moreover, control and ownership of the Pharmacopoeia would rest with the A.M.A.

The Squibb plan also envisaged publication of a monthly or quarterly supplement to keep physicians and pharmacists abreast of current developments and remedies in the field of medicine and pharmaceutics.

The Squibb proposals were like a kick at a hornets' nest. Swarms of pamphlets attacking the plan flew into the mails. (The International Postal Union was less than two years old.) The most important attacks called for "rejoinders." Some rejoinders required answers. Printers were having a field day.

The pharmacists, long docile followers of Dr. Squibb, at last closed ranks and ganged up against him. He suddenly realized the great professional as well as personal loss that had been his with the death in 1874 of his good friends and loyal champions, William Procter of the *American Journal of Pharmacy* and John Milhau, the New York apothecary whom the Squibb influence had made president of the Pharmaceutical Association. He was politically naked now. Interest was replacing friendship and admiration.

Dr. Horatio C. Wood wrote and distributed a pamphlet in defense of the current method of revision and publication of the Pharmacopoeia. Professor Alfred B. Taylor wrote another reply to Dr. Squibb, pointing out that the present owners of the Pharmacopoeia, the National Pharmacopoeial Convention, represented not only the medical profession (to which the Squibb plan would turn over control) but the four skills needed for publication—medical, botanical, chemical, and pharmaceutical.

On May 9, 1877, the Philadelphia County Medical Society held a special meeting to instruct its delegates to the A.M.A. convention which would consider the Squibb proposals. It was an extraordinary meeting indeed, completely overrun by pharmacists who were not members of the society. Professor Taylor appeared in person to read pertinent passages from his pamphlet. Professor John M. Maisch of the Philadelphia College of Pharmacy added his word of condemnation against the Squibb plan. Somebody else read a letter from Dr. W. S. W. Ruschenberger, medical director of the United States Navy, also opposing Dr. Squibb. Even Dr. Squibb's protegé, Joseph P. Remington, managed to crash the meeting of the Medical Society, to which he did not belong, and attacked the Squibb plan.

When the physicians regained the floor, Dr. Andrew Nebinger apologetically admitted that the Pharmacopoeia needed reform, but insisted that the Squibb proposals constituted not reform but revolution, and all revolution was destructive. Dr. Albert Frické, and Dr. Albert H. Smith, president of the local society, moved that the Philadelphia delegation to the A.M.A. convention be instructed to vote against the Squibb plan. And Dr. Richard A. Cleeman moved that a transcript of the Philadelphia proceedings be printed, and that 500 copies be distributed among all A.M.A. delegates.

Dr. Squibb girded himself for the decisive battle at the A.M.A. convention in Chicago the following month. He left for Chicago on Sunday evening, June 3, 1877, via the New York Central and Great Western lines. The outlook was not favorable. The coalescence of the pharmacists along strictly professional lines had not induced a similar party-line reaction among the physicians. They were confused. And the deck seemed stacked against the Squibb plan.

When Dr. Squibb discovered he had been allotted only an hour to read his "rejoinder," which he insisted would take two hours to present properly, he fumed. And when the previous speaker slopped over twenty minutes into his allotted hour, he exploded. The convention voted to allow him extra time next day, but after listening for half an hour President Bowditch cut him off and entertained a motion to table the Squibb plan for transfer of the Pharmacopoeia to the A.M.A.

"My entire subject of the Pharmacopoeia was indefinitely postponed without hearing the whole of my paper," Dr. Squibb complained to his journal, "and thus I was sat down upon very hard, and must try to take my punishment in as manly a way as I can. Time will show who was sat down upon beside me, and who is worsted in this controversy."

Dr Squibb went home via the Pittsburg, Fort Wayne & Chicago Railroad and the Pennsylvania Central Road. He left for Albany again by the Hudson River night boat on June 18 for the New York Medical Society convention. He reported the meeting to be "very satisfactory, though it was pretty hard work for me, as being president I had to be prompt and punctual and on a continuous strain."

He had swallowed his disappointment over his failure at Chicago, and he kept the three-day session at Albany interested in such papers as "Hydrophobia—Rabies Canina" by Dr. John W. Greene of New York (this was nine years before Pasteur announced his antirabies inoculations), "Climatic Influence in the Production of Nervous Disease" by Dr. A. McLean Hamilton of New York, "The Feasibility of Removing the Thyroid Gland" by Dr. Julius F. Miner of Buffalo, "Morbid Conditions of the Prostate Gland" by Dr. Frederick Hyde of Cortland, "Typhoid Infection of Drinking Water" by Dr. E. V. Stoddard of Rochester (four years before the isolation of the typhoid bacillus), and "Convulsive Disorder without Convulsion" by Dr. Mary Putnam Jocobi of New York.

II

AFTER THE CHICAGO CONVENTION Dr. Squibb lost his faith in the A.M.A., and more and more he used the New York Society as his sounding board. The following year he became spokesman for a joint committee composed of New York state groups studying possible legislation to guarantee the honesty and purity of medicines. The committee included representatives of the New York Academy of Sciences, the New York Academy of Medicine, the New York County Medical Society, the Therapeutical Society, the New York College of Pharmacy, and the New York Medico-Legal Society. Representatives of two national organizations, the Public Health Association and the American Chemical Society, were also included. The last-named is significant, because the joint committee's work was certainly the foundation of the first national pure-food-and-drug laws, and the work was finally translated into national action nearly thirty years later by an enthusiastic official of the American Chemical Society, then the state chemist of Indiana, Dr. Harvey W. Wiley.

The report of the committee was submitted to the 1879 Convention of the New York State Medical Society under the signature of Dr. Squibb, who entitled it "Rough Draft of a Proposed Law to Prevent the Adulteration of Food and Medicine and to Create a State Board of Health."

Great Britain had already enacted a "Sale of Food and Drugs Act" in 1875, and Dr. Squibb pointed out that his draft aimed to avoid some of the defects in the British law by, first, carefully defining adulteration in its various forms and giving examples, and, second, bypassing the question of intent to defraud because a "very large proportion of the adulterations practiced are not attempts at fraud, nor designed to damage health, but are straining efforts to make money. And these efforts are so earnest and so intense, energetic, and absorbing as to leave all other considerations in the background. That the public is hurt and cheated is but an accident rather than a malicious intention." And third, to avoid making it the duty of an injured consumer to prosecute, he proposed using only the inspectors as witnesses, "because very few persons have either the inclination, time or money to give to such prosecutions; and that it is much cheaper for individuals to suffer than to prosecute."

Dr. Squibb's draft set as standard the formulas given in the Pharmacopoeia of the United States or other countries. Otherwise ingredients must be stated on the label, or, in the case of secret or proprietary formulas, presented in testimony by the proprietors.

The draft proposed banning "any compound which contains any poisonous or hurtful ingredients not publicly stated and professed by the label," such as alum in baking powder, lead in cosmetics, and powerful drugs in patent medicines; the adding of substances to lower the "strength, purity, quality, or true value" of a compound, such as corn meal in flour, chicory in coffee, terra alba in cream of tartar, or foreign substances in powdered opium; the substitution of one substance for another to deceive the public, such as artificial wines and liquors, artificial mustard seed and the use of potato starch for arrow root, dead oil for carbolic acid; the use of misleading coloring, damaged flour mixed with good flour and garden rhubarb with medicinal rhubarb; and of diluted substances.

Dr. Squibb proposed that the law be administered by a State Board of Health consisting of five men chosen by the Governor from among eight nominees of the Medical Society, Columbia University, Cornell University, the New York Bar Association, and the New York Medico-Legal Society. The five would include two physicians, one chemist and physicist, and one lawyer; the Governor himself would choose a business member, preferably a manufacturer. The board would select competent inspectors by competitive examination.

Board members would receive $2,000 a year but would forfeit a month's pay for every meeting missed. The chairman of the board would receive $3,000. (The New York State Commissioner of Health today receives $18,500 a year.)

Dr. E. M. Moore of Rochester criticized Dr. Squibb's proposal as incomplete, declaring that "Dr. Squibb has not rendered justice to himself in omitting to make a more extended reference to the duties and prerogatives of such a board."

Dr. Squibb replied that "it was believed to be unwise to embrace too much in the proposed law, for by so doing it might be defeated altogether. If we can get a State Board of Health, there will be no difficulty whatever in referring all questions of Hygiene to that board at any time."

The proposed state pure-food-and-drug law attracted so much attention in the press, largely favorable, that G. P. Putnam's Sons offered to publish it as a pamphlet in its Economic Series. "Wrote a preface for it," Dr. Squibb noted on February 15, 1879, "and a reply to criticisms by the press, and added the British law and some comments on it. Finished this and took it to them this morning."

The Squibb bill was enacted into law by both the New York and New Jersey legislatures, with a few minor changes to which Dr. Squibb of course objected.

And the text of the New York law was introduced practically intact as Senate Bill 649, "A Bill to Prevent the Adulteration of Food and Drugs," on December 20, 1881, Forty-seventh Congress of the United States, first session. Sponsored by Senator Miller of New York, the bill was referred to the Committee on Commerce.

The Proprietary Association of America had been organized that year, a rich group of highly prosperous manufacturers of patent medicines, men who hated Dr. Squibb because he was not content merely to despise them but fought them violently at every opportunity. There is no evidence that the Proprietary Association lobbied against the Squibb-

Miller pure-food-and-drug bill. It may have been pure coincidence that the bill died in committee.

By 1884, however, the Proprietary Association was a full-fledged lobby, strong enough to kill a House bill introduced that year proposing to bar the mails to "noxious and dangerous medicines."

Realization of Dr. Squibb's dream of a Federal pure-food-and-drug law was still twenty-two years in the future.

III

DR. SQUIBB'S OLD FRIEND Dr. Minor died of pneumonia in the spring of 1879. His death was followed a few weeks later by that of his wife, also from pneumonia. "She seemed from the first to be determined to die, and wished to die," wrote Dr. Squibb, who kept vigil over both in their last hours. He supposed he was to be executor of the Minor estate, which was considerable, but he was unable to find a will, and Dr. Minor's affairs were in a state of confusion. While he was in Europe, Dr. Squibb had kept them in order, but now . . .

In any event he tried to straighten things out and he was certainly going to look after the Minor children, Lucy and Pierrepont. He would take them along with his family for the summer.

For summer headquarters this year he chose Lake Waramaug, in northwestern Connecticut. He took a train to New Preston to meet Mr. George C. Hopkins, who had an inn at the lake, a beautiful L-shaped stretch of limpid coolness lying among the green foothills of the Berkshires. Dr. Squibb liked the place, even though it lacked proper swimming and riding facilities for the large summer colony he intended to bring up. He took rooms at Mr. Hopkins' for the Squibbs and the Dodges, and he made arrangements for the Minor children to stay with the Beemans, who were neighbors.

Returning to Brooklyn, he set two of his carpenters to

work building a bathing float and bought four tents, having partitions made so that they could serve as dressing rooms. He sent two of his men to Lake Waramaug to pitch the tents and get the float into the water. He also bought two horses, which he sent by Sound steamer to Bridgeport, where they were met by Mr. Hopkins and led overland for the forty-odd miles to the lake.

The Squibb party was quite a formidable caravan. There were of course the doctor and Caroline, Edward, Charles and Mary Squibb, the faithful Mary Fogarty, and the Minor children. There were also Dan Dodge and Mary Duane, a girl from Bergen Point whom Dr. Squibb was grooming to be a daughter-in-law. Later he would bring up Virginia Henderson, also daughter-in-law material, Mary Duane's brother Frank, and the two Dodge girls, Susie and Marge.

"All very much pleased with the place," Dr. Squibb reported, "except Caroline, and she very much dissatisfied with the diet. The food is very plain and wholesome and plenty of it, but not nicely cooked, and with her every meal is an irritation. . . . The children enjoyed themselves very much indeed, and Mary Duane, with her splendid character and disposition, and her thorough enjoyment of everything, is a very great acquisition to our party. She is indeed a splendid girl, and much like Virginia in some things, and much her superior in others."

The doctor was not very subtle in his role of matchmaker. He named his two horses Molly and John—Molly was for Mary Duane, and John was his nickname for Charles Squibb. Virginia Henderson, a distant relative who had inherited a small fortune and was something of a ward of Dr. Squibb's, was evidently destined for Edward.

Nothing came of either romance that summer, but Dr. Squibb unexpectedly discovered that little Mary, age fifteen, had been secretly exchanging letters with Frank Duane. "When I spoke to her about the impropriety of it unless I saw them," wrote Dr. Squibb, "she did not behave well about it, and has not shown them to me. Her association with older girls has led her to think that she should guide herself."

Two weeks later he wrote: "Mary still sticks out, and will not show me her letters from Frank Duane, although I have spoken to her in regard to it again. She evidently intends not to do it, as I have given her every chance. She grows more 'fast' and forward all the time. No becoming modesty or gentleness of promise for the future, but only an idea that she is now as big as anybody." And finally: "Could not get Mary to show me the letters she receives from Frank Duane, so had to tell her she must show them. If she would not trust me, she must show them to her mother. This she says she has now done. Don't know how much farther my duty extends in the matter, but her behavior hurts me very much."

However annoying Mary's behavior may have been, it was neither as startling nor as serious as the telegram Dr. Squibb received in Brooklyn that summer from Lucy Minor at Lake Waramaug, saying: "Brother very ill. Come immediately." Curiously, Dr. Hutchison at the same time received a wire from Lucy's brother which explained his "illness." It seems that Pierrepont Minor had accidentally shot one of Mr. Beeman's sons, and Dr. Hutchison went up to investigate.

Next day Dr. Squibb received a detailed letter from Ed, reporting that Pierrepont Minor "mistook Eddy Beeman for a woodchuck and fired at him and hit him, the ball entering the anterior lower part of the thigh, passing up longitudinally and out at the upper part into the groin, passing over the crest of the illium and out at the back, making four wounds, and the fear was that it had passed through the ascending colon. . . . Pierrepont is such an unfortunate ass that there is no knowing what he will do."

Dr. Squibb went to the lake a few days later, found Eddie Beeman recovering nicely, sent Pierrepont home to Brooklyn, and opened negotiations with Mr. Beeman regarding damages, finally settling for $500.

Dr. Squibb was pleased with Lake Waramaug and tried to make a deal with Mr. Hopkins to reserve the whole house for his family and friends for the following summer. He sent his men up in the late spring to build a private dock. He bought new sails for the catboat *Mary King*. But his attempts to play Cupid were a dismal failure.

"Had a pleasant but not very gay visit," he recorded early in August 1880, on returning to Brooklyn from the lake, "my satisfaction hoped for, being spoiled by Charles' bad success with Mary [Duane]. I had the heart-ache all the time both for myself and for him."

He brought Mary Duane and her sister Anne down with him, as they were going to Southampton for three weeks. Dr. Squibb suggested that they stay there for the rest of the season, and as soon as he told her it was on Charles's account Mary agreed. "We talked the matter over freely and frankly on both sides and I found her at all times throughout the straightforward, good girl that I always supposed her to be . . . but found her more mistaken than I supposed in her notions of life, and a wider difference between her ideal and the realities of life than I had expected. Knew well enough that her experience of mankind must be very small, and that her experience of life in modern novels was far larger, and that the aggregate of the two placed her in a very false position and in great danger of mistakes that might be fatal to her happiness."

Virginia Henderson did not take to Edward any more enthusiastically than Mary Duane had taken to Charles, but this Dr. Squibb did not regret when he learned that Virginia was determined to learn acting and go on the stage. While he loved the theater as a spectator, he knew that becoming a professional actress would be a "grave mistake."

Little Mary, whom Dr. Squibb considered still much too young even to dream of marriage, was the only one of the Squibb children who had already picked a mate at this time. Her father, of course, did not know it. Neither did the prospective groom. Mary was only fifteen, but she had recently achieved physiological womanhood. ("Very sorry this could not have been postponed, as I had hoped it might have been, for a year or two longer," was her father's comment when he learned of the event.) And when she first laid eyes on the young man her brother brought home she knew instantly what she wanted.

The young man was John C. Munro, a classmate of Charles's at Harvard, a premedical student from Lexington, Massachusetts. Charles Squibb had frequently been a week-end guest at the Munro home, and for Christmas vacation in 1879 he brought young Munro home to Brooklyn.

Dr. Squibb gave a party in his gymnasium over the Furman Street stores and, besides the Squibbs and John Munro, invited Margie, Sue and Dan Dodge, the Duanes, Jenny Bache, Minnie and Helen Fellows—some eighteen or twenty in all.

"I had procured a piano and a man to play in the Gym," reported Dr. Squibb, "and at 5 o'clock or soon after, they began their dance. . . . They danced till about 7, then had some refreshments which I had ordered from Delmonico, chiefly Boned Turkey and Chicken Salad, with Oysters (scalloped) and rolls. No ice cream nor wine. After supper they danced again till about 10, then broke up, and the guests leaving, got to bed about 11. This is the first of a series of common sense parties. . . . The gym was airy and cool, and not filled with either bad air or carpet dust, nor products of body or gas combustion, so that they danced easily and freely and had a good romp. No fine clothes nor gloves. They enjoyed themselves very much, ate nothing to disturb their sleep after such exercise, and then slept solidly through until near 8 this morning. . . . after which they were fresh for a good skate this morning after a good breakfast."

Mary Squibb had danced a good part of the evening with John Munro. She had shared the "good breakfast"—the Philadelphia scrapple, the eggs, hot breads and fruit, but no coffee; she was not allowed coffee until she was "grown up." She had skated with the young man on the pond in the yard. And she had decided she liked him. From that moment on, the boy from Lexington hadn't a chance. Mary did not rush things. She waited patiently while he finished medical school. She did suggest to her father that a man like John Munro might be useful around the laboratory during vacations, and Dr. Squibb, trying him out on several occasions, found him more of a help than Charles. But she waited until he had begun to practice before she decided that he should ask her father for her hand—in a letter which surprised and delighted Dr. Squibb. They were married some seven years after the "common sense party" and made their home in Boston.

Dr. Squibb was also surprised when in 1884 Edward announced that he was about to marry Jane Graves Sampson, daughter of Dr. Squibb's associate in the acetic-acid factory and granddaughter of the late banker George L. Sampson. Dr. Squibb was surprised that Graves (as she was called) had accepted him. A man could not ask for a better wife, but . . . well, the doctor wondered if Ed could make her happy.

Charles Squibb didn't get married until 1887—to Margie Dodge, the girl he almost swept overboard with the boom of the catboat *Mary King* while "wearing" on Lake Dunmore twelve years earlier. Charles did manage to keep "Mr. Johnson" from making the arrangements for his honeymoon. "He did not tell me where they would go until after they had decided and made the arrangements," wrote Dr. Squibb, "and then on asking him I found they were going to the West Point Hotel, and probably to occupy the same room that Caroline and I went to on the day we were married."

IV

ALTHOUGH DR. SQUIBB failed in his attempt to deliver the Pharmacopoeia into the control of the physicians, his fight was not without results. The controversy had brought to light obvious defects in the Pharmacopoeia which the pharmacists themselves could not deny. Moreover, a new influence was making itself felt in the American Pharmaceutical Association in the persons of two brilliant young German apothecaries who had recently come to live in America, Dr. Frederick Hoffmann and Dr. Charles Rice, pharmacist at New York's Bellevue Hospital.

Drs. Hoffmann and Rice were thoroughly trained in the scientific methods then reaching a new high in Germany of the period. This was the era of Virchow and Cohnheim, of Klebs and Koch and Ehrlich. Drs. Hoffmann and Rice thought the new German Pharmacopoeia, with its advanced ideas on standardization, was the answer to many of Dr. Squibb's criticisms.

Dr. Hoffmann proposed that the American Pharmaceutical Association create a new Committee on the Pharmacopoeia to study the needs of the 1880 revision and submit a revised text for the whole volume. The proposal was adopted and Dr. Charles Rice was made chairman of the committee, which also included Dr. Hoffmann, P. W. Bedford, John M. Maisch, Joseph P. Remington, Charles Bullock, George F. H. Markoe, Samuel A. D. Sheppard, Louis Dohme, Ezekiel H. Sargent, C. Lewis Diehl, John Uri Lloyd, William H. Crawford, Charles Mohr, Emlen Painter, and William Saunders.

Dr. Squibb traveled to Washington in May for the 1880 Pharmacopoeia convention—the sixth decennial convention, held at the National Medical College on H Street. Although he was not a delegate, he was admitted by special vote of the convention after the delegates had been seated. He was not very happy with the proceedings, although he approved generally of the outcome.

"Kept myself from taking any active part whatever," he wrote, "and accomplished my determination of coming home without any work. The general drift of the convention I did not like. Gas and Buncombe seemed to rule, and of course brought such men as Amory and Bedford into high places. But it is perhaps better than to have the whole thing go bodily again into the Dispensatory interest in Philadelphia. Phila. got badly defeated throughout and they are apparently very much disgusted."

His determination to stay out of the Pharmacopoeia controversy, however, was shortlived. He had not been home three weeks before he noted that he had "acceded to Charles Rice's urgent solicitation to serve on the Committee of Final Revision and Publication."

fifteen

THE CORNER TURNED

I

THE 1880S MARKED ANOTHER turning point in the financial fortunes of the Squibb laboratories. Prosperity, which had been periodically peeping from around the corner ever since the Civil War, at last stepped out into the open. There were still no Squibb salesmen on the road and no showrooms in Manhattan, but the world had found that Dr. Squibb was making superior mousetraps on Brooklyn Heights and was beating a path to his door.

The acetic-acid works, too, was prospering at last. The National Chemical Wood Treatment Co. had built its own bulkhead and pier at the foot of Gold Street, and spur tracks ran into the factory.

Orders for Squibb products were coming in from all over the world—from Mexico and South America, from Japan and India, from a medical mission at Tientsin, China. Some orders came via the recently established International Postal Union, but some still were delivered by a sea captain or the purser of an ocean liner who also brought a bank draft or gold for payment. The price list, the original of which Dr. Squibb had addressed by hand for some 300-odd physicians

and pharmacists in New York and Brooklyn, was now broadcast by the thousands to four continents. The 69 items on the
original list had grown to 324 by 1883, the first year in which
the sixteen-page list became a bound pamphlet in terra-cotta-
colored covers, the color of the cover to be changed every six
months to distinguish old lists from new.

The list ranged from Acetic Acid, Glacial, 99.5 per cent. at
75 cents a pound, glass-stoppered bottle included, to Zinc Sulphate, "purified for medicinal uses," at 25 cents a pound tin.
Ether for anesthesia sold for $1.10 a pound if purchased in
three-pound glass-stoppered bottles, or $1.16 a pound if pur-
chased in quarter-pound tins. True scammony (powdered)
brought $12 per pound tin, and powdered opium (percentage
of morphine stated on the label) $8.50 a pound. Also listed
were a few miscellaneous items such as roller bandages and
litmus paper.

The list was well annotated as to strength, dosage, and
method of manufacture, and although the cover specified
that the "Standard of Strength and Quality Adopted for
These Preparations is the United States Pharmacopoeia," the
notes sometimes took a sideswipe at the Pharmacopoeia when
it differed from what Dr. Squibb considered correct. The
note on "Fluid Extracts," for instance, read as follows:

"These Fluid Extracts are not strictly officinal because they
are not made in accordance with the officinal process. The
object of the processes of the Pharmacopoeia is to obtain
preparations which represent the drug from which they are
made in the proportion of minim for grain. The processes of
the Pharmacopoeia do not accomplish the object in the best
or most economical way, and therefore a departure from
them may be justifiable. And it is believed that the preparations here offered are more in accordance with the object of
the Pharmacopoeia—that is, better represent the drugs in proportion of minim for grain—than any that can be made by the
officinal process. The method of repercolation by which they

are made is published in the Proceedings of the American Pharmaceutical Association for several successive years.

"By this process, and also perhaps by other processes, it is now no longer difficult to make fluid extracts . . . without the use of heat. But to obtain good drugs even at high prices from which to prepare the fluid extract becomes more and more difficult, while the quality of the drug used is always hidden in the extract or fluid extract."

The 1883 list restated terms of payment. There was still a discount of 10 per cent on monthly purchases of more than $100, but there was no discount for cash. On the other hand: "All accounts are due and payable during the last half of the month succeeding that in which the indebtedness was incurred, and all accounts remaining unpaid when due, without acceptable excuse offered, will be charged with interest at the rate of six per cent. until paid."

And still another instance of Squibb independence: "Although orders are thankfully received, and buyers served as faithfully as possible, yet no one is ever solicited to buy, either directly or indirectly, but all are left to be guided by their own judgment of their interests; therefore, no goods are ever taken back or exchanged except for complaints of bad quality."

The 1883 list also inaugurated a new policy of including the bottle or tin in the price quoted—reluctantly, Dr. Squibb noted in his apologetic explanation: "In this new plan of including packages, no deception is intended;—no one is asked to believe that he gets a package, the absolute price of which varies between 3.6 cents and 23 cents, for nothing,—but it is only so included now that the buyer can never know the cost except by inference, and the manufacturer may, if he chooses, use this element of uncertainty to the buyer to skillfully increase his profits a little. It is therefore a bad plan. . . . but as there is no violation of principle involved to those who choose to apply it honestly, it is reluctantly adopted in this list, though less in compliance with the popular clamor for it, than to get rid of putting up articles in paper which never should be put in paper. The main object, however, is to secure as far as is possible the identity of articles which are supplied by this manufacturer against fraudulent imitations which are so much more easily perpetrated by paper parcels. Hence the rule of this list now is that no article will be sent out in paper parcels, and this rule will be adhered to.

"Imitations of the articles of this manufacturer are constantly increasing, and his empty bottles, tins and labels are largely used for fraudulent refilling, and the responsibility of buying supplies liable to this fraud must necessarily be placed upon the buyer. But in cutting off the paper parcel business, the opportunities for such practices are much diminished."

Although terribly jealous of his name as a synonym for honest manufacture, Dr. Squibb never took personal advantage of the law of 1870 which first authorized the registration of trade-marks by the United States Patent Office. In fact, he resented the fact that, since "Squibb" was becoming a household word in the drug business, some people looked upon Squibb products as patent medicines. He said so publicly at the New York Medical Society's 1882 convention in Albany, after Dr. E. C. Seguin, in reading a paper on "Efficient Dosage of Certain Remedies," referred to "Dr. Squibb's fluid extract of conium."

Dr. Squibb protested: "There is somewhat of a proprietary flavor in the expression 'Squibb's fluid extract' employed by Dr. Seguin, which I do not like, as the preparation is simply the fluid extract of conium made according to the U. S. Pharmacopoeia of 1880, to which the profession is quite as much indebted for the quality of the preparation as to myself. Of course, it is good to have good material with which to work, and the preparation should be made in the proper way. The Secretary, Dr. Smith, has collected most of the conium I have used, and it has been cured in the most careful and efficient manner."

Dr. Seguin replied apologetically that he certainly had not

meant to imply that the preparation was in any way proprietary, and that when interrupted by the Business Committee he was about to refer to the essay written by Dr. Squibb in 1867 describing the process of gathering and saving the conium as practiced by Dr. Manlius Smith.

Protest though he did, the name of Squibb became an asset, even though he refused to list it as such on his balance sheet. And although his business and residence properties continued to be encumbered by substantial mortgages, the pressure to meet current obligations eased considerably. And he finally felt free to indulge an expensive fancy he had been incubating for years: a plan to build a house for each of "the boys" on the vacant lots adjoining his own home on Columbia Heights. His own home was No. 152. The boys' houses would be Nos. 148 and 150. The estimate which had long made him hesitate was $46,000 for the two houses. In 1883 he gave the order to begin excavating.

He also increased his patronage of the theater, of which he had always been an indiscriminate admirer. He attended all sorts of performances on both sides of the East River. He was a regular at Wallack's Theater, even before the theater moved uptown from Chambers Street to Thirteenth and Broadway, where the auditorium was perfumed three times a week. He saw William H. Gillette playing in his own "Farcical comedy," *The Professor,* at Daniel Frohman's new Madison Square Theater, and John Drew in Augustin Daly's *The Big Bonanza* at Daly's Fifth Avenue Theater. He saw Joseph Jefferson repeatedly in *Rip Van Winkle* and caught him with Mrs. John Drew in Sheridan's *The Rivals.* He admired E. H. Sothern in *Lord Chumley,* by Henry C. DeMille and David Belasco, at Frohman's Lyceum and went to see Coquelin in French repertory at the Palmer, when theaters began to be lighted with electricity and ice water was provided in the smoking rooms.

He was passionately devoted to the opera and took family and friends to several performances a week of Colonel Mapleson's season ("Her Majesty's Opera Company in America") both at the New York Academy of Music in Fourteenth Street and the Brooklyn Academy. Colonel Mapleson's company was built around such stalwarts as Campanini, Del Puente, Alwina Valleria, Marie Roze, Anna Louise Cary, and Etelka Gerster, all of whom attacked Verdi, Rossini, Mozart, or Wagner with equal gusto. He was particularly fond of Etelka Gerster, sister of a New York physician, a friend of his. Miss Gerster had an incredible repertoire—Rosina in *The Barber,* Marguerite in *Faust,* Violetta in *La Traviata,* Marta, Lucia, Linda di Chamounix, and Elsa in *Lohengrin,* among others.

Dr. Squibb did not care for *Lohengrin.* After hearing it, he wrote: "I never again want to hear any 'music of the future.' It has for me only loud noises and loud dresses. Every reality in Wagner that others seem to get, goes over my head." And he could not condone a libretto that was not clean and wholesome. He found *Faust* to be "a dirty, disagreeable thing, though having some fine music in it." And his comment on Donizetti's *La Favorita* was that he "enjoyed the music very much but as usual the uncleanness of the plot of the opera marred it much for me."

Caroline rarely accompanied her husband to the theater. Occasionally she would go to a concert or to a conjuring exhibition by Hermann the Great. When Adelina Patti came through on one of her farewell tours, Caroline went to New York with Dr. Squibb to hear the great diva in *La Traviata* and *Lucia di Lammermoor.* As a rule, however, she looked upon the theater as vulgar and boisterous.

Consequently, whenever Dr. Squibb took his children or friends to theater or opera, he always handed his wife the price of a ticket—$2.50 for a parquet seat at the Brooklyn Academy, $3.50 in New York. With this money Caroline created what she called her "theater fund," with which she bought a set of Golden Butterfly and Chinese medallion china. When she had accumulated enough of the colored dishes, she used them on holidays and for company in place of the severely simple fine white china which had been Dr. Squibb's choice of tableware.

Dr. Squibb was also able at last to indulge in a few private charities and to establish his own personal social-security system. He set up a private pharmacy for the Little Sisters of the Poor and stocked it annually. He donated a portable dispensary to St. John's Hospital and kept it supplied with medicines. He subscribed $500 to the building fund of the Brooklyn Eye and Ear Hospital (whereupon Caroline immediately ordered $476 worth of new hangings for the front parlor). And he "established a savings fund for my older employees," he wrote, "putting away in the tin box in an endorsed envelope for Fanny Bartlett two one-hundred-dollar U. S. bonds 4½ p.c. and for Mr. Rothe one one-hundred-dollar bond. Gave him besides this $100 in money that he wanted foolishly to spend on minerals for his cabinet though I advised him not to do so."

Dr. Squibb also paid a bill for $215 presented by Charles to pay for a violoncello that John Munro had found for him "cheap" in Lexington. Dr. Squibb, who did not approve of his younger son's ambition to play the cello, was "shocked and disappointed . . . for I supposed that in deference to the strong expression of my wishes and my reasons for them, he had given the matter up. But not he."

Dr. Squibb mused that Charles seemed destined to be a consumer for life and would never be much of a producer. He wondered if he had made a mistake in sending him to Harvard where "he had acquired a set of tastes and habits, gentlemanly enough in themselves," but "had acquired no appetite for any work that would ever enable him to gratify them."

However, Father wrote the check for $215. He also deposited $215 each to the account of Mary and Edward in the Brooklyn Savings Bank. He insisted on treating all of his children equally.

II

CAROLINE WAS IN BETTER HEALTH than she had been in a very long time. Nearly two years went by without a seizure. Dr. Squibb attributed this partly to her approach to the climacteric, for he was convinced of the relationship between her convulsions and catamenia; partly to the use of bromides, carefully spaced to avoid the mental and muscular symptoms of bromism; and partly to his great care in guarding her from the slightest emotional frustration, for he had noted that her attacks frequently followed psychic disturbances.

Giving in to his wife on one score caused Dr. Squibb considerable unhappiness. He was decidedly a gregarious person, while Caroline disliked having anybody come into the house except her own family. A periodic source of trouble between them was Dr. Squibb's oldest and dearest friend and distant cousin, Martha Dodgson, of Darby and Philadelphia.

"Caroline has been very irritable and unhappy all week," he once wrote. "I think an expected visit from Martha Dodgson is hanging over her very heavily, and I fear I shall have to write to Martha and ask her not to come. When a man marries, he marries into his wife's family, but marries out of his own family. It has always been a terrible drag upon my poor wife to have my relatives come to see us, and now not one of them has been in my house for five years . . . and now the thought of Martha's coming makes her sick, though she is not aware of it herself."

Instead of calling off the visit, however, Dr. Squibb increased Caroline's dose of sodium bromide and went over to Jersey City to meet Martha's train. She stayed a week.

"Her visit not only renewed the pleasant association of old times," Dr. Squibb wrote, "but gave me a good opportunity of enquiring about all my other relatives whom I never see and rarely hear from. Martha looks very well and seems to take good care of herself. Caroline did not stand the visit very well, and by the time it was over she felt and looked sick enough. Now however she is better again. Left off the bromide . . . except twice at bed time."

Martha Dodgson came almost every year after that, although her arrival was always preceded by some such notations as: "Letter from Martha Dodgson promising her long-expected visit for next Wednesday. But this got me in trouble at home, for this visit was so disagreeable to Caroline that she said some things about it that were very bitter to me. . . . Caroline has been miserable as well as irritable all week."

The kitchen was also a source of friction between husband and wife. Dr. Squibb had always considered this his domain, believing that Caroline's role as mistress of the house was adequately performed in presiding over the tall silver tea urn at Sunday supper. However, Caroline had her own tastes and would make life miserable for any cook who did not suit her in every respect. Anne, for instance, whom Dr. Squibb adored for her curried chicken and brandied peaches, made bread and rolls that Caroline declared unfit for human consumption.

"In order to try to retain her and satisfy Caroline," wrote Dr. Squibb, "I went yesterday to the Vienna Bakery and got them to serve us, and Caroline ate more bread this morning than for a long time. But how long it will last I can't tell."

It lasted nearly three years, and Anne's successor, Maggie, almost immediately caused another near-crisis, which Dr. Squibb managed to avert.

"The new cook Maggie," he wrote early in 1883, "became quite intoxicated last Thursday and Friday week, and was sore-headed afterward so that I have not spoken to her about it yet. She probably began upon the brandy for mince pies, and then brought the remainder into the house. She is an excellent cook, the best we ever had, and I must try to reclaim her. Caroline fortunately has not found it out."

The case of Mary Ann Covey, waitress in the Squibb household for ten years, was a more tragic one. On Christmas, 1880, she went to bed with "indications of some gouty abdominal pains with that kind of kidney irritation as indicated by the urine. . . . decomposed expression of face, red centre tongue, feeble and rapid pulse, and high temperature. I went at once for Dr. McClellan," wrote Dr. Squibb, "and he at once recognized some form of peritonitis, and gave her opium in full quantities. The pain was relieved and she passed a better night, but . . . suffered much from nausea, retching and vomiting from the opium. She then gradually sunk until 3.20 to 3.30 on Friday morning when she died quietly."

Those who today shake their heads and smile sadly at the diagnosis and treatment must remember that this was six years before Dr. Reginald Fitz, pathologist at Massachusetts General Hospital, first differentiated acute appendicitis from peritonitis.

"To lose her seems very much like losing one of the family," wrote Dr. Squibb. ". . . The matter upset Caroline very much of course, and but for her I should have had Mary Ann buried from our house as one of the family."

Under the circumstances, however, Dr. Squibb went to Undertaker James Harper to select a coffin and had Mary Ann taken to her married sister's house in Newark.

Two years later Caroline herself developed similar symptoms—great nausea, "tenderness over the lower abdomen on deep pressure, especially on the right side, but no evidence of inflammatory action, temperature a degree below normal and pulse good." The management of the case by Drs. Squibb and McClellan would raise the hackles of a modern physician, for Dr. Fitz had not yet made his contribution to the literature, and surgery in such cases had not yet been dreamed of. They gave her alternately rhubarb pills, calomel, and a capsule containing colocynth and hyoscyamus. For days she could keep nothing on her stomach, "not even a little red champagne," and Dr. Squibb was frantic.

"If she does not get some nourishment," he wrote, "she must die." He and Dr. McClellan decided that the only way to save her life was to feed her rectally. On the fifth day of her illness he "went to town for a syringe and at 4.30 gave her four fluid ounces of good soup containing half a fluid ounce of brandy."

Dr. Squibb continued the process every four hours, day and night, for a week, "occasionally adding a little opiate to relieve colicky pains, and on this she has lived up to yesterday when for the first time she would take a bird or a chop and a little roasted potato. Today she has taken still more, but is in no condition to abandon the enemata. She is still very feeble."

It was in fact weeks before she was definitely on the road to recovery and Dr. Squibb could resume his normal sleeping and working schedule.

Although he apparently was no better diagnostician than most of his generation of physicians, Dr. Squibb was far ahead of his time in his approach to psychosomatic medicine. At the 1881 convention of the Medical Society of the State of New York, following a paper on "Epithelioma of the Cervix Uteri" by Dr. William Warren Potter of Buffalo, Dr. Squibb arose to deliver one of his usual diatribes against quack remedies. In addition to attacking so-called "cures" for cancer, Dr. Squibb made an excellent case for psychotherapy.

"I think it proper to allude here," said Dr. Squibb, "to a medical cure of these cancerous diseases of the uterus very much in vogue, and . . . that is by the internal administration of Chian turpentine. Dr. Clay of Birmingham, England, advises the use of Chian turpentine in a particular form as a specific cure for cancerous diseases of the uterus and its appendages. The subject attracted universal attention from the character of the authority recommending it, and all the Chian turpentine lying around in the shops of London was brought forth and used, and was used vigorously and with close observation. The whole upshot has been . . . on quite as good authority as that of the originator of the treatment, it was soon found to be useless. Lately very decisive action was taken by the Middlesex Hospital. A resolution . . . was passed by the faculty that no more of this vaunted turpentine should be used because it had been proved worthless. I say this to save our members from trying it; they might as well use Condurango, Mississquoi water, or mud.

"It is only necessary to get up an excitement in the treatment of cancer to allow anything to be tried. Anyone with a hopeless disease is willing to try anything. Dr. Clay still considers he cures cases. The hospital people say they get the cases after he gets through with them.

"Now let us investigate this success of Dr. Clay, and compare it with Condurango [the bark of a South American vine], Mississquoi water, and mud, and all other cancerous cures. It is very easily explained. Dr. Clay has a case of cancerous disease in a hopeless condition, and he promises the patient that he has a specific cure. The moral effect is that he gives the patient hope, and any patient having this hope placed in her will be better for the time being. The cancerous woman will do better, eat better, sleep better, after having this hope put in her, and the Chian turpentine seems to act simply by giving hope to the hopeless.

"This Chian turpentine* has a remarkable history. No real Chian turpentine ever reached this country; there wasn't enough of it. And therefore the successful results in this country must have been from a spurious article. The inference is that a spurious article is just as good as the real, if we base its use on the ground of giving hope to the hopeless."

* Chian turpentine, originally from the Greek island of Chios, is made from a tree of the sumac family (Pistacia Terebinthus), while United States turpentine comes largely from Georgia pine, Canadian from balsam fir, and various European turpentines from larches and other conifers.

III

THE YEARS BEGAN TO crowd in upon Dr. Squibb. As he advanced into his sixties, the associates of his early career were dropping off, one by one. Dr. Satterlee died in his eighty-third year, after he "had become burdensome to himself and friends." Dr. Benjamin Franklin Bache, retired from the Navy as a commodore ten years earlier, died in 1881 at the age of eighty, "ending a long life full of vicissitudes and by no means so fertile of good as it should have been, with his rare ability and genius," Dr. Squibb remarked. "He should have been a very great man but was only an able man."

The same year saw the death by an assassin's bullet of the former Ohio Congressman who had rewritten the Senate tariff bill in accordance with Dr. Squibb's ideas after the Civil War and who had just become President of the United States—James A. Garfield.

By 1883 there were only five members left of the original dozen who had made up the Brooklyn Medical and Surgical Society.

Dr. Squibb's own health was holding up pretty well, although he was beginning to feel his age. His beard was white now, and his poor mutilated eyes were giving him more and more trouble. Occasionally he had to sit in the dark for an hour or so to rest them. His scarred hands often pained him, especially the left one. He suffered from varicose veins which sometimes became so inflamed that he had to bind up his legs. Yet he spent longer hours at the laboratory than his employees, working through weekends and holidays. And he never stopped walking for exercise.

When the Brooklyn Bridge was under construction, he and daughter Mary walked on the footbridge at sunset, admired the view, but found the great height "a severe nervous strain." He was invited to the opening ceremonies of the bridge, which was practically in his backyard, on May 24, 1883, but the crowd come to gawk at President Chester A.

Arthur, Governor Grover Cleveland of New York, Mayor Seth Low of Brooklyn and Mayor Franklin Edson of New York City was so dense that Dr. Squibb went back to work in the laboratory. He did not go to the reception given by his neighbor Colonel Washington A. Roebling, chief engineer of the bridge project, because he considered it "a model of bad taste and splurge." He stayed home and watched the fireworks display from his windows.

Once the bridge was opened, Dr. Squibb frequently walked across to Manhattan instead of taking the Fulton Ferry. Sometimes he walked over and back merely for the exercise. On one occasion, while getting off an omnibus near the Manhattan approach to the bridge, he was run over by a horse and wagon.

"On getting out of one stage and passing behind another on Broadway at Park Row," he reported, "was knocked down by a horse and run over by a grocer's wagon. Somehow managed to clear the horse's feet and also the wheels by a hard scramble, but the hind wheel came so near going over me between the pelvis and the ribs that I was pretty severely pinched and bruised before I got out from in front of the wheel. I was bruised in a good many places, but that one much the worst, and the bruises have nearly disabled me ever since.

"It was all done in an instant and I don't know how I escaped serious injury, but I attribute it to the muscular activity and the sixth sense or instinct. The street was covered with a mortar-like mud, and I was badly smeared, but on taking off my overcoat got home pretty well and cleaned myself up, so that I was able to say nothing about the matter to anyone. Several persons passing happened to know me but luckily they were far-off outsiders, and therefore no fuss has been made."

Even though he was aging, Dr. Squibb was not one to fuss over such trifles as a narrow escape from being trampled to death.

sixteen

AN EPHEMERIS

I

WHEN THE SQUIBB PLAN for the U. S. Pharmacopoeia was defeated at the 1877 convention of the American Medical Association, the American medical and pharmaceutical professions were served by a number of professional journals, none of them very authoritative except the *American Journal of Pharmacy* and one or two others. The proceedings of the Philadelphia Medical Society meeting opposing the Squibb plan were ordered distributed to such publications as *Druggists' Circular, Chicago Pharmacist, Medical News, Philadelphia Medical Times, Medical and Surgical Reporter, New York Medical Record, New Remedies,* and of course the *Journal of Pharmacy.*

The *Journal of the American Medical Association* had not even been thought of—except by Dr. Squibb—and was not to appear for another half-dozen years. Part of the Squibb plan, it will be recalled, envisaged a monthly or quarterly supplement to the Pharmacopoeia to let doctors and apothecaries in on the latest discoveries in medicine and pharmacy. When the A.M.A. rejected his plan, Dr. Squibb determined at least to carry out his idea of an up-to-date publication, even if he had to do it on his own.

Nearly four years passed before he got around to it, but once started it moved rapidly.

On New Year's Eve, 1881, Dr. Squibb wrote: "A very busy week, but not so much with usual occupations as preparing to issue a pamphlet or Journal which has been long in contemplation, and which is intended and chiefly undertaken in order to introduce Ed and Charles to that part of the public from whom they must expect to make their living. I propose to call it An Ephemeris of the Materia Medica, Pharmacy, Therapeutics, and collateral information by E.R.S., E.H.S., and C.F.S. In the first number for the middle of January I want to have the subjects of Standard Opium, Opium Assaying, and a criticism on the Adulteration Law now before Congress, and during the week I have done some work on all these heads and written a portion out. Ed and Chas. went to Lexington on Wednesday morning to return on Tuesday next, and having all this work of theirs on hand, I employed a girl, M. O. Glover, for whom I have been looking for a place, to come these last 3 days to help me, and she has given me very efficient help and would make an excellent assistant. She is a graduate first of Vassar College and then of the Boston Institute of Technology. She does twice as much work as Ed, does it well, and is always in want of more."

A week later he wrote: "Monday being a holiday, I thought I should have a good solid day to work on the first number [of *An Ephemeris*], begun in earnest a week or more ago. But about 2 o'clock the Bakery in Doughty Street commenced to burn and by evening burned up. This caused me some anxiety and occupied much of the remainder of the day."

However, copy got to the printer by mid-January and Volume I, No. 1 of *An Ephemeris* was out by the end of the month, thirty-two pages bearing the by-lines of Edward R. Squibb, M.D., Edward H. Squibb, S.B., M.D., and Charles

F. Squibb, A.B. Father Squibb seems to have done almost all the work, although he said that Ed helped with the article on morphia assays. Charles did nothing.

The first issue carried the following announcement:

An apology may be due those to whom this pamphlet is sent, for even this very feeble attempt at starting a new journal, when the field of journalism is already so well filled. But a promise is made to the readers that if this new journal—undertaken with much hesitation and diffidence—should prove at any time to have no reason to be, it shall at once cease. As being a mere ephemeral waif, it will be sent gratuitously to all. No subscribers are solicited nor any subscription list kept, nor any exchanges with other journals asked for. It may be issued bi-monthly or quarterly, or irregularly, or not at all, as the occupations of an otherwise very busy life may determine; and its chief object is, in an informal way, to note down, from time to time, the results of a long experience and observation and the deductions therefrom, together with occasional original work, as time and opportunity may serve. The contents should be accepted, if at all, as information—not as knowledge;—as material which may be of value only for the moment, or which may mature and come to be added to the common stock of knowledge. Ephemerides are things of short life . . . yet they may not be valueless nor be unimportant as elements in the growth of permanent knowledge. . . . An ephemeris of materia medica, pharmacy and therapeutics seems to be a very pretentious, ostentatious title, but the subjects are so inseparably related as to form really but one intelligent idea, and that one still incomplete at both extremities. When such a collective subject has been the business of one lifetime and becomes the expectancy of two other commencing lives educated with special reference to the subject, it does not seem irrational to hope that information may be given which may be interesting and useful to the medical and pharmaceutical professions, since the subject is the very foundation upon which the utility of these professions to mankind depends. The younger associates in this undertaking may, perhaps, at first do but little of the writing, but they will do much of the work upon which the writing is to be based.

To the professions of Medicine and Pharmacy, then, whatever may be here offered is respectfully dedicated by the writer and his two sons.

EDWARD R. SQUIBB.

BROOKLYN, January, 1882.

An Ephemeris was like a one-man consumer-research report which bore the unmistakable stamp of a rugged idealist, an independent thinker, and a fearless, uncompromising crusader. It discussed new remedies, gave practical instructions for laboratory tests and assays, attacked medical politicians and quack preparations, and began a serial criticism of the 1880 Pharmacopoeia, title by title.

Later the same year Dr. Charles Rice launched an annual publication called *A Digest of Criticisms of the Pharmacopoeia.*

Publication of the A.M.A. *Journal* did not begin until 1883.

II

An Ephemeris CONTINUED TO APPEAR every two months for many years. Volume I (which stretched though 1883), contained such varied papers as "A Discussion on Medical Ethics"; "Testing Urine for Glucose by Fehling's Solution"; an article on treatment of psoriasis inveterata by Dr. W. C. Reiter of Philadelphia; "The Elixir Nuisance and the New Pharmacopoeia"; and notes on clinical thermometers, artificial quinia and factitious jalap.

Every article was strongly impregnated with the personality of Dr. Squibb—his personal experiences, research, and philosophy. When he discussed the "urinometer," a small hydrometer to determine the specific gravity of urine, he pointed out that while such an instrument should be of importance to the physician "second only to the thermometer," most of the urinometers then sold were "so faulty and so unmanageable as to be almost useless." Wrote Dr. Squibb, "The specific gravity bottle is the only accurate urinometer," and he proceeded to give seven pages of instructions for using it.

He attacked patent medicines with unflagging vigor and great gusto. He found something called "St. Jacob's Oil" which by the expenditure of $400,000 in advertising had achieved sales of $40,000 a week, "a very respectable item in the interest account of the national debt to the patent medicine business. . . . 'St. Jacob's Oil' appears to be a feeble and badly made aconite liniment, and it consists mainly of water, ether, alcohol, turpentines, and a small proportion of aconite with red coloring matter. Its whole function is to make money for the enterprising merchants who own it, and in this it is by no means a delusion and a snare. . . . Its enormous sale is not only of great service in helping the poor to stay poor, but it also relieves a great many people of their money, who are not poor in anything but common sense and who take their medicines as they do most of their other deceptions, namely by being advertised into them. . . ."

He was just as ready to open fire on his ethical-pharmaceutical colleagues when they mislabeled their product or used impure or substandard ingredients. But he also followed through and recanted when they later improved their drugs, as may be noted in the following from *An Ephemeris* for September 1883:

DUQUESNEL'S "ACONITINE."

In No. 4 of this series of pamphlets, at page 167, there appears a short article under the above mentioned title showing that the substance sold by H. Duquesnel of Paris as "Aconitine Crystallisée" was not the alkaloid as it appeared by the label, but was really a nitrate of aconitine, and the evidence that such was the case was given in the paper.

This statement, made in November, 1882, was based upon two purchases from Duquesnel's agents here, made at not wide intervals. At the writer's request Duquesnel's attention was drawn to the facts and the paper was sent him. He emphatically denied the truth of the statement, and wrote vigorously on the subject. But all this did not rapidly change the condition of affairs, for in five subsequent purchases, under the same label, the nitrate was still found to predominate, although each purchase, excepting one, contained more of the uncombined alkaloid than the purchase before it, until by the time of one of the later purchases the proportion of uncombined alkaloid reached 32 p.c. of the whole yield, 53 p.c. being combined as nitrate.

But now a very recent purchase yields 90 p.c. of the uncombined alkaloid and 5 p.c. of the combined alkaloid, and the presence of nitric acid still very distinct. . . .

The substance, therefore, now is in much better accord with the label and it is but fair and just to the maker to state the improvement. . . . It is, however, confidently hoped that this justly celebrated maker of some of these delicate alkaloids will do better than this in the future.

In discussing "Treatment for Tapeworm," Dr. Squibb harked back to his experience in the frigate *Cumberland*. He recalled that "when in the eastern part of the Mediterranean, where uncooked sausages are largely eaten, the writer and others became affected with tapeworm, and he had good opportunities for observation, and was confirmed in the belief that the location of the head had much to do with the resistance of all obstinate cases, and that when the treatment was carefully directed by this consideration it was almost always successful, and that one parasiticide was about as good as another when well managed. Further experience at that time seemed to show that pumpkin seed and oleoresin of male fern were the best agents to use and that there was but little choice between them."

More than a century after the *Cumberland* left the eastern Mediterranean, pumpkin seed and oleoresin of male fern are still being prescribed for tapeworm.

Occasionally Dr. Squibb used *An Ephemeris* to strike back at some of his personal critics. In the September 1882 issue he wrote the following:

COPYRIGHT AND TRADE MARK ON MEDICINES

In the discussion of this subject, which has been going on in the journals for some time past, the writer, E. R. Squibb, has occasionally seen it stated that he held copyrights or trade marks for medicinal preparations. It was supposed that this misstatement grew out of the fact that some five or six years ago the writer did patent certain apparatus for the manufacture of acetic acid for the arts, by the distillation of wood. It was not thought worth while to correct this misstatement or to expose its slight foundation. But the slander does not die out, and like others gains strength by repetition, for it now appears again in a very definite form. In an advertising periodical of Messrs. Tilden & Co. called "The Journal of Materia Medica," edited by Drs. X. T. Bates and A. N. Allen, for July, 1882, page 215, this sentence occurs: "Thus Squibb copyrights his own name and thereby guarantees the purity of any of his preparations." This statement is entirely untrue in every sense, for Squibb never did copyright, trade mark, or patent any medicine or preparation of any kind, nor any bottle, label, wrapper or cover of any kind, nor any name or device of any kind. Neither did he ever claim any proprietorship in any process or medicine, nor had any secret or proprietary formula or process for anything. On the contrary, he has always been an uncompromising opponent of all proprietorship in medicinal articles, and never has, and probably never will cease from earnestly opposing all forms of copyright and trade mark and patent from the mildest form of the manufacturer of coated pills* up to the aggravated abominations of the patent medicine market. Physicians may lend themselves to such things if they choose to do so, but as they do, and when they do, they should cease to complain of their patients for doing so and thus avoiding or ignoring the physician. . . .

Nearly 10 per cent of the space in the first two years of *An Ephemeris* was devoted to a great internal fight in the Medical Society of the State of New York. Since the battle concerned the Code of Medical Ethics, Dr. Squibb was an active and passionate partisan, reported the fight blow by blow in his *Ephemeris,* and argued hotly against the proposed changes.

A committee brought a proposed revision to the 1882 state convention which accorded with what Dr. Squibb considered right and proper: No advertising, no endorsement of patent medicines, no holding of patents or copyrights; consultation with only legally qualified practitioners of medicine; regulations of fees, etc.

The report was not considered radical enough by Dr. D. B. St. John Roosa of New York City, who offered a substitute motion of a dozen lines, declaring that "a larger amount of discretion and liberty in individual action, and the abolition of detailed and specific rules, will elevate the ethics of the profession" and that the only ethical offenses "are those comprehended under the commission of acts unworthy of a physician and a gentleman."

Dr. Squibb was furious. The recommendations of Dr. Roosa, he insisted, would let down the bars to quacks. All year long he stormed and argued in the columns of *An*

---

* Dr. Squibb considered coating pills a form of adulteration. His 1883 price list noted: "This manufacturer neither makes nor deals in sugar-coated pills, nor in pills covered or coated with any other substance. . . . The aim of the physicians is that the pills they give should dissolve promptly in the upper part of the alimentary canal, and an attempt is made to secure this result in the pills of this list by avoiding all coating. . . ."

Ephemeris, but when the matter came to a vote in Albany again in 1883 he was defeated by 105 votes to 99.

In the next issue of *An Ephemeris,* Dr. Squibb put every doctor on record, together with his home town, as voting for or against letting in quacks as consultants. He noted that New York and Albany counties voted almost as a bloc. And he recorded sadly that his good friends Dr. William Manlius Smith, Dr. Walter Chase of Brooklyn, and Dr. Arpad Gerster, brother of the prima donna, had voted against him. A switch of their votes would have changed the outcome.

Still Dr. Squibb did not give up. He continued his fight all year in his *Ephemeris,* and succeeded in having the code brought to the floor again for consideration at the 1884 convention. This time he was defeated by 124 votes to 105.

"The effort," Dr. Squibb wrote in the next issue of *An Ephemeris,* "was therefore shown to have been hopeless, but not useless, for it has placed on record another earnest effort, throughout two years, for justice, sound morals, and fair play. To have abandoned the contest earlier would have been unmanly. To continue it any longer would be as unwise as it would be useless, and as the issue is one of fundamental principle and law, the true meaning of the action can only be a separation of the interests involved, for the future."

The separation took place immediately when the Central Organization to Uphold the National Code of Ethics canvassed the 5,002 physicians of New York State and got 3,860 replies. Of those replying, 2,547 physicians, or nearly 66 per cent, voted for the old code, only 1,040 (27 per cent) for the new code, the rest undecided. The vote in the convention, therefore, far from representing the sentiment of the membership, as Dr. Squibb pointed out editorially, merely showed "that an active, vigilant, unsparing minority is stronger than a supine, inactive body of twice their number; and that this large majority has allowed its central organization to be captured and held, on a grave moral issue, and has either surrendered with its defences or fled to the woods of disorganization."

The pro-Squibb faction formed an independent New York State Medical Association with Dr. H. D. Didima of Syracuse as president, Dr. Caleb Green of Cortland as recording secretary, Dr. E. D. Ferguson of Troy as corresponding secretary, and Dr. John H. Hinton of New York City as treasurer.

The new association subscribed to the A.M.A. Code of Ethics which had been rejected by Dr. St. John Roosa's substitute resolution.

The old society muddled along without a code.

Years later, when the schism was healed, the reunited New York State Medical Society had a Code of Ethics.

III

DR. SQUIBB WAS TIRED. Being a one-man publisher-editor-writer-proofreader of a bimonthly magazine was proving to be a real burden on top of his other full-time activities. He was, after all, still the one-man management of a thriving pharmaceutical laboratory and an acetic-acid factory. In addition to the many scientific societies and journals to which he had been contributing papers, he now promised to address the first meeting of the newly formed New York State Medical Association at the Murray Hill Hotel in Manhattan. And he was not getting the help he had hoped for from his two sons.

Shortly after his return from the 1884 convention in Albany he remarked that "the only time for Ephemeris work has been on Sunday afternoon and all the evenings. These, however, have enabled me to make fair progress, and I hope next week to finish the writing for this month's number. But it is getting very laborious for me to write in the evenings after busy days. Brain works badly, and the work is inferior and unsatisfactory. Have gained much this week by not going home to tea, thus making a solid day of 12½ hours work from 8 till 9:30 with an hour out for dinner."

He found he could save some time by hiring a secretary who would not only write shorthand but who could operate one of the new writing machines. "Miss Leary takes my dictation very fairly," he wrote, "and I get along better than I expected with the dictations. . . . She has now got the Remington Type Writer and is getting rapidly accustomed to the use of it, and already makes very good work with it."

He was still experimenting with possible additions to his list, and, feeling that he had succeeded in making a satisfactory cocaine, he began production and found that it would "sell freely."

He was delighted with the way Miss Glover, the Vassar-M.I.T. graduate, was handling his assays. He was deeply disappointed when she left after a year to get married.

He was disappointed, too, when Ed refused to take over the assay work. Ed was a pretty good worker if left to his own devices, but he disliked being bossed. Furthermore, he did "no more work than any $15 man," Dr. Squibb noted.

As for Charles, after being reprimanded for taking too many four-day weekends off, he announced that he was going to Spain and Morocco to make his fortune. All he wanted was his steamer fare and his weekly $10 allowance for a year. Reluctantly Dr. Squibb gave in, and Charles took off for Gibraltar with a $500 letter of credit and a rowing machine. He was back in a few months with a load of paintings, including spurious Old Masters, on which Dr. Squibb paid $150 duty, although the customs appraiser said the pictures were not worth a fraction of their declared value.

That was the last straw. Dr. Squibb determined he would go abroad himself, just for the rest, as soon as his first grandchild was born.

Ed and Graves (Dr. and Mrs. E. H. Squibb) were living in the parental home on Brooklyn Heights until their own house next door would be finished. At half past two on the morning of January 21, 1885, Ed awakened his father to ask for something to relieve Graves's "colicky pain which she thought came from having eaten mince pie and pickles for dinner." Dr. Squibb advised an emetic of mustard and water because Ed, although his bride was within a week of her calculated time of accouchement, was certain the pains were from indigestion.

When Ed came back an hour later to say the pain was no better, Dr. Squibb inquired again about the character of the pain, but they still thought it to be indigestion. "About 5 o'clock, however, the character became evident and about 5 Ed went for Dr. Lloyd and then for Miss Snyder, the nurse. Both came promptly while Caroline and I took charge of Graves. By 6 o'clock the second stage was fairly advanced, and expulsive pains sharp but not long. Dr. L. was there for the third stage and about 8.30 . . . the baby was born while Mary and I were at breakfast. The baby proved to be a healthy well-formed girl."*

Six months after he became a grandfather, Dr. Squibb made the break. He had prepared enough material for several issues of *An Ephemeris* ahead. He gave his power of attorney to his son Ed and to William G. Rothe, whose many years as head bookkeeper had made him virtually business manager of the laboratories. He left the professional affairs of the laboratories in the hands of his brilliant head chemist, John A. Dunn, whose technical knowledge, combined with his twenty years of training in the Squibb tradition, made him eminently fitted to keep the ether and chloroform stills producing at standard purity and of carrying on all other routine matters. Dr. John Cujven, a Norwegian chemist who had helped Dr. Squibb with his months of cocaine experiments, seemed quite competent of carrying on production on a commercial scale. Dr. Squibb was surprised to find that

---

* As this book was written, "the baby," Dr. Squibb's first grandchild, Caroline Squibb Sutphin (Mrs. Henry H. Sutphin), was living at Harwich Port, Mass., on Cape Cod.

Charles actually seemed to like working in the acetic-acid factory, so he left him there with Andrew Macauley, the plant foreman, to see if he could settle down.

Then he bundled his daughter Mary into the Cunarder *Etruria* and set sail for Europe. For good measure he took Charlie's fiancée, Margie Dodge, along—to give Charlie a chance to prove his stability in her absence.

Charlie—and John Munro—came to the pier to see them off. Caroline remained with Mrs. Dodge at Mohawk, New York, where they were spending the summer.

"It is a pretty serious experiment to try how the concern will get along without me," Dr. Squibb wrote on July 31, 1885, the night before the *Etruria* sailed, "and I can form no idea at all of where we shall go or when we shall return."

The September issue of *An Ephemeris* was characteristically devoted to an account of his long experiments with cocaine, including sources of supply, markets, detailed description of the manufacture of the hydrochlorate, and a report from Dr. Gunning that cocaine was only partially successful in deadening dental pain.

The November issue, however, carried the following notice:

The readers of the EPHEMERIS will observe . . . that the principal writer of this pamphlet is abroad on a tour of recreation and inspection for a longer or a shorter time, as circumstances must determine. His errand is also intimately connected with the business of his past life, inasmuch as a better knowledge of how and where to obtain the best qualities of the commercial articles of the materia medica is a prominent object of this journey. To know the markets of the world, and their availability for supplying the commodities required is undoubtedly among the most important of the interests of manufacturers,— and to know them one must see them,—or at least to see how they are made up, and to become familiar with the relations of supply and demand, and, if possible, to establish good channels of supply. For many years past the need of more definite and intimate knowledge of this kind has been felt by the writer, and now the opportunity of trying to obtain it has been made.

Under these circumstances the publication of this series of pamphlets is now, with regret, abandoned, and this number will be the last to be distributed. Whether the publication and distribution will ever be resumed will depend upon circumstances which cannot be forejudged at the writer's time of life.

The last issue contained twenty pages of travel notes. The first portion was devoted to a description of the S. S. *Etruria*, ("a magnificent ship"), from her construction, her seaworthiness, and the efficacy of her plumbing system and water supply to the conversation of steamer-chair habitués: "At one time pet dogs, of which there were several aboard, had to be caressed and discussed and absent ones described. Their virtues and their ailments never seemed to get tiresome, and one of them took Appolinaris water after meals."

After discussing the various remedies for seasickness, Dr. Squibb concluded: "What will temporarily settle one person's stomach will often make another worse. . . . A toddy of brandy at night, or a glass or two of iced champagne occasionally through the day, seem useful to many persons by alleviating the nausea and supporting the powers of endurance until the sea habit is established."

He went through the British Isles, Germany and Scandinavia, assessing public hygiene, counting apothecary signs, examining the inside of pharmacies, and philosophizing upon the economic status of the European physician. He told his *Ephemeris* readers of his observations in terms like the following:

On walking through the streets of three of the principal cities of Ireland, some remarkable contrasts with American cities are noticeable. Cork, with a population of say 80,000, has clean well-kept streets and very dirty people of the lower classes. In a walk of an hour through streets of all kinds only five pharmacists could be counted, and not over ten physicians' and surgeons' signs. In Dublin and Belfast the proportion was scarcely greater. No occupations involving the necessities of life were found in so small numbers. . . . In any similar examination in the United States the number would pretty certainly be twice as great. Not one was seen with any sign of a drinking fountain, or with tobacco or cigars, but patent medicine signs were quite common. . . . Now as the physicians in Ireland are known by their schools and by their writings to be fairly educated therapeutists, and as there must be, of course, enough of them to supply the necessities for their skill, it would seem to follow that in the United States there are far too many, and that this overcrowding of the two professions must be very hurtful, not only to the best interests of the professions, but to the community at large. . . .

More pharmacies were noticed in Edinburgh than in the other cities which have been mentioned. . . . No drinking fountains nor tobacco were seen in any store, and the number of those which paraded nostrums was small. . . . In Stockton [-on-Tees] the number of stores which sold exclusively fresh fruit,—not counting the street stands,—was greater than the number of pharmacies, while the number of flower stores was only one short. . . .

In Germany . . . the effect of legal limitation in the number of pharmacies is conspicuously seen, and the character and appearance of the establishments are very much changed; and this change is maintained in Copenhagen and Christiania. . . .

In Germany Dr. Squibb made a side trip to Darmstadt to see the famed laboratories of Merck & Company, one of the world's oldest and most respected drug manufacturers. The Merck family had been in the business since 1668, when Friedrich J. Merck opened an apothecary shop in Darmstadt called "At the Sign of the Angel." In 1818 the Mercks began manufacturing, at first specializing in opiates. Merck started making morphine in 1827 and codeine in 1836. Dr. Squibb, who had just begun his manufacture of cocaine, was anxious to see how it was made by the Mercks, who had been at it since 1862.

George Merck, Sr., current head of the firm, had made a trip to America two years earlier and had called on Dr. Squibb in Brooklyn. Dr. Squibb had devoted a whole day to him, taking him on the grand tour of the laboratories. He had given Dr. Merck blueprints of the now-famous Squibb steam ether still, and reprints of various technical articles he had written on ether and related subjects. He had taken Dr. Merck home for a dinner of scalloped oysters and mince pie and then returned to the laboratory for more tables and figures. Dr. Squibb thought he should return the courtesy of Dr. Merck's visit, and he wrote from Berlin saying he was coming to Darmstadt.

Dr. Merck received Dr. Squibb and his young lady companions politely but with great German reserve. He was an icy-eyed, balding man, with a close-trimmed mustache shading his solemn, no-nonsense mouth. He wore bow ties and American-style collars and presented a brisk clean-cut first impression. Dr. Merck offered his visitors golden Rhine wine from nearby Nierstein, served in tall, long-stemmed, green-tinted goblets, accompanied by small anise cakes. He offered polite small talk, during which a clerk closed an iron door leading from Dr. Merck's office to what was obviously the manufacturing department. He did not offer to show Dr. Squibb through the works.

"Although my father asked to be shown through the laboratories," Mary Squibb wrote years later, "we were only conducted into two rooms, which were little more than store rooms, with no active work going on in them. Father could not speak or understand German, but I could. I heard orders being given that certain rooms were to be closed until further orders.

"After we left the factory and were being driven back to the hotel, I said to father: 'Aren't you sorry you showed him everything in your laboratory and gave him all that information?'

"He replied: 'No, daughter. That's not the right spirit to have about information that belongs to the world. If thee feels that way, thee is just like Dr. Merck. He has probably set up an ether apparatus like ours and didn't want me to see it. I hope he is making better ether with it than he has heretofore.' "

Dr. Squibb did not learn the real reason for his host's queer behavior until the following year. Merck was preparing to invade the United States, to become a serious competitor of Squibb on his home grounds. In 1887 a blackbearded, beetle-browed young man Dr. Squibb had met in Dr. Merck's office in Darmstadt—Theodore Weicker, an assistant who had been with the firm since he was sixteen —came to New York to open an American branch of Merck & Company in Wall Street.

Dr. Squibb returned to the United States in the Cunarder *Servia* late in March 1886.

seventeen

CASCARA SAGRADA

I

WHILE DR. SQUIBB WAS IN Europe, his enemies, his competitors, and some of his friends were congratulating themselves that his honest-but-acid tongue had been temporarily stilled, and that his much-too-prickly *Ephemeris* was perhaps gone forever. In any event, they had a long breathing spell during which to dig pits and set snares should Old Prickly decide to return to the barricades after all. They were laying for him, although he did not realize it for some time.

Everything seemed happily quiet and normal enough when Dr. Squibb returned. He was even a little surprised to find everything at the laboratory running just about as well as when he had left for Europe. Things were running so well, in fact, that he decided to reduce working hours again. Saturday would be a half-holiday for two thirds of his staff. The other third would remain—in rotation—until three o'clock to clean up. But the laboratories would close down at noon, a radical step in labor-management relations in 1886.

Dr. Squibb was delighted with the flowers he found on

his desk, and with the resolutions of welcome from all the employees at both Doughty Street and Gold Street. He loved being stopped in the street—"sometimes twice in one block" —to be asked by friends how long he had been back. And he seriously set about picking up his personal responsibilities.

He had to persuade his old friend and dentist Dr. Gunning that he was not dying, for instance. "Two long visits to Dr. Gunning," he noted on May 8, not six weeks after his return, "to try to put some moral stiffening into him and persuade him he is not as sick as he thinks."

He was not as optimistic about Lucy Minor, whose physician he believed was not giving her proper attention.

"And two similar visits to Lucy Minor," he wrote in the same entry, "who really is quite sick, and to Dr. Emmett on her behalf . . ."

He also found it difficult to resume his daily routine in his private gymnasium, particularly as his varicose veins were bothering him again. His left leg was especially painful.

He still shuttled back and forth between Brooklyn and New York to get his many gifts through customs—a case of Geneva clocks for Ed (they had been badly smashed by stevedores somewhere along the line) and paintings for his various friends and relatives. He soon got his experimental work back on the rails in the laboratory—cocaine, opium extract, and camphor—and had to gird his loins to get the houses for his two sons ready for occupancy.

One of the drawbacks in the two new Columbia Heights construction projects were changes which had been made during his absence. He was particularly upset by Charles's "fastidious tastes." But he hurried around to get new mortgages to finish the work. When Union Trust, the Atlantic Savings Bank, and the Brooklyn Savings Bank turned him down, he finally found money at the South Brooklyn Savings Bank—$30,000 on the two new houses.

He dropped in at the theater again his first night, to compare the New York D'Oyly Carte company with the

Gilbert and Sullivan he had seen in London. He thought George Thorne as Ko-ko quite as good as the London performer.

On October 28, 1886, he went to Bedloe's Island to watch President Grover Cleveland dedicate the Statue of Liberty Enlightening the World. He had a "ticket and card, which some one had sent me, probably the Committee, as I had subscribed $100.00 to the pedestal. . . . The sight of the men-of-war and the great number of boats, from the ramparts, was very fine indeed, and had it been a fair day the sight would have been much better. The first part of the speaking was entirely drowned by the whistles, but later the President and Mr. Depew were well heard though somewhat disturbed by the whistles."

Dr. Squibb then got to work to start his *Ephemeris* going again. It was the end of the year before he resumed publication after a lapse of more than a year. Gone was the old bimonthly regularity, but the new *Ephemeris* was much fatter than the old. Volume III, No. 1—the January 1887 issue —was 56 pages thick. Volume III, No. 2—the October number—was 98 pages long. Both numbers seemed in the usual Squibb vein—informative, scientifically meticulous, with the usual free-swinging at Dr. Squibb's *bête noire:* proprietary medicines.

The table of contents looked innocent enough: Medicine and Pharmacy Abroad, The Relations of Physicians to Their Medical Supplies (a paper read before Dr. Squibb's pet organization, the New York State Medical Association, at its third annual convention in New York, November 16, 1886), Hydrochlorate of Cocaine, Notes of Veratrum Viride, Powdered Extracts, Fluid Extracts by Repercolation, Cascara Sagrada, and The Fluid Extract of Buckthorn. Vol. III, Nos. 1 and 2, however, caused a greater scandal than all the rest of *An Ephemeris* put together.

The first two years of *An Ephemeris* had been something of a sensation in the professions of medicine and pharmacy.

The publication had provided a running critique of the current Pharmacopoeia by a man who could both write and compound a prescription. It contained useful practical information for both druggist and doctor. It made honest appraisal of new remedies and apparatus. And it lambasted unmercifully all patent medicines and pharmacists' labels which did not accurately describe the contents of the bottle.

Dr. Squibb's hobby of assaying not only patent medicines but the products of his competitors, and of shouting from the housetops whenever he found a fly in the ointment, delighted a great majority of his readers. It also annoyed not only his sworn enemies in the Proprietary Association but manufacturers whose flies he had spotted. And Dr. Squibb's phobia against the advertising of medicines was regarded with a jaundiced eye by some medical and trade journals whose life blood was advertising income. So there had been undisguised joy in some quarters when he went off to Europe and abandoned his *Ephemeris*.

When he returned and decided to resume publication, his enemies were lying in ambush, waiting for him to make his first misstep. Among them was a relative newcomer to the pharmaceutical field, a Detroit house called Parke, Davis & Company. The firm had its inception in 1866, when Henry C. Parke bought into Duffield & Conant, Detroit druggists. A year later Mr. Parke hired a clerk named George E. Davis. The association grew into Parke, Davis & Company in 1875.

In the beginning Parke, Davis specialized in alkaloids, but the firm was soon sending out teams of explorers looking for new botanicals and new sources of old botanicals. In 1877 a Parke, Davis team found a West Coast source of cascara sagrada, a mild laxative, and as Mr. Davis was a salesman at heart, he did not hesitate to plug the product. Unlike Dr. Squibb, he believed in advertising. And when *An Ephemeris* reappeared, Parke, Davis had its own mouthpiece, *The American Lancet*.

Volume III, No. 1, of *An Ephemeris* did little more than

raise the hackles of Dr. Squibb's enemies with his paper on the "Relations of Physicians to Their Medical Supplies," which opened with this passage:

"There are a large number of physicians who, for both therapeutics and materia medica, depend largely,—if not mainly,—upon the traveling salesmen and their pamphlets and lists, and on the advertising pages of the medical journals. . . . With others smarter, more ingenious and more plausible than they, to think for them, and then to apply vigorous mercantile principles to their wants thus suggested for them, they have . . . as they argue, more time to think of and study out their cases. To this class the ready-made prescriptions in the form of beautifully colored and coated pills, or palatable solutions or mixtures, do not appeal simply as gratifying various degrees of laziness, or indisposition to think for themselves, but they present themselves as true labor-saving devices . . . giving time for the higher and more scientific reaches of the profession. . . . For example, the fashionable 'nervous prostration' being observed, what can be more simple or more easy than to order Smith's 'coated pills of Valerian, Quinine, Iron and Zinc, No. 1,' to be taken three times a day, and a draught of Jones' Effervescent Salts of Bromide of Potassium, Caffeine and Cocaine in solution at bed time. . . .'"

The *American Lancet* made note of this quotation and filed it for future use. The Squibb crack about "the advertising pages of medical journals," however, immediately got under the skin of the *Philadelphia Medical and Surgical Reporter*, which did not spurn advertising.

The *Medical and Surgical Reporter*, in its issue of April 23, 1887, found Dr. Squibb's remarks "as deliberate an insult to the intelligence of the profession as we remember to have read. False in spirit and in letter, and for Dr. Squibb, who has amassed his large fortune by the favor of the profession, to turn upon them, is not creditable to him in his latter years.

"Is he losing the market for his products that he turns thus bitter? Does he forget that to travel about to medical society meetings and read papers about the drugs he has for sale is just as much advertising as to take a page in the *Record* or the *Reporter?* Dr. Squibb has received a great deal of gratuitous advertising in medical journals; he has been smart enough to get to the windward of a good many medical editors; let him not display his ingratitude for what the medical press and the medical profession have done for him."

It was the following number of *An Ephemeris,* however, that really opened the floodgates of abuse upon Dr. Squibb.

In his issue for October 1887, he printed what appeared to be an innocent discussion of the comparative merits of two species of buckthorn used as aperients. Under the heading "Cascara Sagrada," Dr. Squibb wrote:

"Rhamnus Purshiana is a sub-variety of the Buckthorn family of small trees and shrubs, which grow in most of the temperate climates. This sub-variety grows abundantly in California and Oregon, and the bark under the name of Chittem bark or cascara sagrada has long been used as a purgative and the name cascara sagrada has more recently been usefully contracted to cascara. Some years ago it was taken up and pushed as a novelty, and by vigorous advertising, as a panacea for numerous ills, it has come into very common use, in the form of several pharmaceutical preparations.

"There seems to be no doubt that the bark of the branches and a well-made fluid extract, and extract of this bark, are all effective simple aperients, not very disagreeable in taste or effect, easy of management, and not very liable to lose their effects by continuous use. And . . . the dose may be adjusted in each individual case to any degree of activity or mildness without leaving a persistent reaction.

"These peculiar characteristics have long been known as belonging peculiarly to the bark of Rhamnus Frangula, and the use of this both in Europe and this country long antedated the use of cascara sagrada. And this longer and better known variety of the Buckthorn family was admitted to the present revision of the Pharmacopoeia, because it was supposed to be the better medicinal agent of the two. Its supposed advantages over cascara is that while having all the advantages of cascara, it is milder, more pleasant, more manageable in effect and more agreeable in taste, and less likely to disturb stomach and intestines which are sensitive or irritable. When properly used both are simple, mild aperients, but the buckthorn the more simple and agreeable of the two. . . ."

Although to many readers this seemed nothing more than a mild plug by Dr. Squibb for his own product, to Parke, Davis & Company it was an outrageous, unjustified, malicious, lying attack upon their own pet cascara, and the *American Lancet* rushed into the fray. In its issue for November 1887, under the title "The Mask Torn Off," the publication accused Dr. Squibb of implying that cascara sagrada "was unscientifically advertised as a cure-all. Is this the case? A careful examination of the advertising pages of the medical journals of this country, through the medium of which this remedy has been brought to the attention of the medical profession, will disclose the plain unvarnished fact that in every advertisement of this product it is uniformly and persistently advertised, not as a panacea, but as a tonic laxative in chronic constipation, and for the relief of those ills immediately dependent upon chronic constipation. The statement of Dr. Squibb, therefore, is an untruth."

The chief reason Dr. Squibb "enjoys the enviable position he has long held," declared the *American Lancet,* "is because he had succeeded in creating the impression that his work as a manufacturing pharmacist is disinterested, uncontaminated by any suspicion of mercenary intent, and for the benefit of medicine and pharmacy rather than Dr. Squibb.

"A further reason, perhaps, exists in the fact that certain preparations bearing his label, chloroform, ether, etc., for example, were always found reliable. That these are reliable preparations is beyond a doubt. That there are others equally so in the market is also emphatically true. In some cases these much lauded products are in all probability simply those bought in the market from sources open to all manufacturers, and purified by Dr. Squibb.

"Now how did our philanthropic pharmacist, having established a reputation for his products for superiority, which was not based on any greater skill or knowledge on his part than that possessed by other manufacturers, show his disinterestedness? Any examination of his price list and those of other manufacturers will answer this question and prove that this unmercenary (?) scientist, with an eye single to the elevation of pharmacy, set a price on his products out of proportion to the cost at which articles of equal or superior purity and excellence could be manufactured and sold at a reasonable profit."

The *American Lancet* then accused Dr. Squibb of inconsistency and dog-in-the-manger tactics because he had first disparaged both cocaine and cascara sagrada in his *Ephemeris* and later added both to his own list at prices far below market, in order to steal customers from the pioneer manufacturers of these two products.

"Judge him," concluded the *American Lancet* ". . . by what he is personally, and what he has done for medicine and the materia medica, as other men are judged, and he will soon, we believe, himself hasten his departure into that oblivion which alone can be a fitting termination for a career favored by great opportunities, but blasted by petty spite, by unscientific methods, and by that childish inconsistency indicative of faculties lapsing into innocuous desuetude."

Once the *American Lancet* article was circulated, other professional journals (particularly those carrying advertising) rushed in with their own overripe tomatoes. Dr. J. V. Shoemaker, editor of the *Medical Register* of Philadelphia, found it "a matter of sincere regret to those who have long known and respected Dr. Squibb as a pharmacist and physician, that he should have laid himself open to attack by an ill-natured article in the *Ephemeris*, which has brought down upon him an avalanche of criticism." However regretful, Dr. Shoemaker, in his issue of November 26, 1887, concludes that "Dr. Squibb is not a reliable authority in pharmaceutical science, inasmuch as he does not seem able to separate the interest of trade from those of gross misrepresentation, either from ignorance or sordidness, both of which are equally culpable in a man of his position."

Daniel's *Texas Medical Journal* declared that Dr. Squibb's *Ephemeris* pieces were either "the offspring of envy" or "the garrulousness of old age."

The *Western Druggist* also hinted that the doctor might be getting senile. "Dr. E. R. Squibb has done much for pharmacy and medicine in America, but like other men of genius, advancing years find him betraying weaknesses calculated to mar the symmetry of his career. An aggressive egotism has always been more or less perceptible in his writings and this has apparently developed into a belief that nobody is competent to discover, study, or manufacture anything medical or pharmaceutical, until the great oracle has spoken and sanctioned the proceeding. Offenders against this edict must expect no mercy. Yet, despite his threatenings, cocaine, cascara sagrada, and other additions to the materia medica have had the temerity to stay and flourish. . . . Dr. Squibb is a unique figure in American pharmacy; the history of few men would so fully portray the development, progress, and distinction of the art and its related sciences in this country; but this is the greater reason that his distorting prejudices should be conquered before his reputation for scientific exactitude is irreparably injured."

The vituperation continued for over a year. Few trade papers could resist taking pot shots at the aging lion. Most challenged his right to criticize advertisers when he himself engaged in free self-advertising by his contributions to professional journals. Some jumped on him for adding cascara to his list (at cut rates) after having "condemned" it.

And Parke, Davis & Company returned to the fray in January 1889, circulating a reprint of the *American Lancet* attack together with a new one-page flier headed "Philanthropic? Mercenary?" which referred to Dr. Squibb only as "a Brooklyn manufacturer" but which took him to task for first depressing the cascara market to 85 cents, then raising it to $2 although the wholesale price of cascara-sagrada bark had increased only 30 cents a pound.

Someone sent Dr. Squibb a copy of the "Mask Torn Off" reprint, inscribed in a bold hand, "About time, too," and the doctor pasted it into his journal. He was badly hurt by the cruel and personal character of the attacks on him, even though he had never given quarter when he took the offensive himself. On January 26, 1889, he wrote:

"Parke Davis & Co. have started again this week with their scurrilous attacks on me. Republished the editorial from their Lancet of Nov 1887, and adding another circular to it, are now sending it all over the country. . . . Don't think I should feel it so much if it were not so untrue and unjust. Makes me want to get out and run away, even if all my mountains are only mole hills."

II

THERE SEEMED LITTLE JUSTIFICATION for impugning Dr. Squibb's motives; no man was ever more generous in sharing with the world what others might call "trade secrets."

To call Dr. Squibb "mercenary" was certainly untrue. Though he kept his accounts to the penny, no man could be more scrupulously honest and no manufacturer ever paid closer heed to the consumers' interests.

There was truth, however, in one point many of his critics had seized upon: Dr. Squibb was getting old.

In 1889 Dr. Squibb was seventy. More and more of his friends and neighbors were leaving him behind. The Reverend Henry Ward Beecher, long his neighbor on Columbia Street, was dead. Dr. Joseph C. Hutchison had died of Bright's disease complicated by pneumonia. Dr. Dodge and Dr. McClellan were both dead. Lucy Minor had died of "cardiac asthma."

Dr. Squibb's sight was failing, and he wore a patch over his left eye a good deal of the time. The hand which faithfully wrote entries in his journal every Saturday was becoming cramped and angular. And he was developing a hernia.

"For some time past," he wrote, "have had an increasing intestinal protrusion into the right inguinal canal, and have had to keep it up some days with my hand in the pocket of that side when walking, and have delayed getting a truss. Showed it to Dr. [J. D.] Rushmore on Thursday and he advised a Pomeroy Truss. Yesterday went over and had one fitted, and have had a good deal of discomfort from it ever since. In a few days, however, will get accustomed to it, and I hope to be able to continue my habits of exercise and bath."

He was certainly continuing his habits of work and extracurricular activity. He was executor for Lucy Minor's estate. He broke in a new laboratory assistant, a Miss Mary Lovejoy, with assays of jalap, glycerine, and cocaine. He himself worked on opium, hydrogen peroxide, and Saigon Cassia. He still indulged his great passion for the theater, seeing Chauncey Olcott in *The Old Homestead* (permanent attraction at the Brooklyn Academy of Music); De Wolfe Hopper in Franz von Suppe's *Clover* at Palmer's Theater; Edwin Booth and Mme. Modjeska in *Macbeth* and *The Merchant of Venice* at the Brooklyn Academy; Trixie Friganza (as a herald) in Henry E. Dixey's production of Audran's *La Mascotte* at Palmer's; and John Drew in *The Masked Ball* at the Standard. He also had the curious experience of hearing *Il Trovatore* in German, which provoked the comment:

323

"Disgusted with the Germanizing that it had undergone. That French-German war seems to have damaged everything that had any grace or refinement to damage. Set back everything like refined taste a great many years, and France and Italy are too weak to recover them."

He also continued to write and publish the *Ephemeris*, Parke, Davis & Company to the contrary notwithstanding. Moreover, he was still not pulling any punches. The April 1890 number had one of his characteristic old-time fire-and-brimstone forays against adulteration, called "Boston Opium Again."

It seems that a combine of domestic and foreign swindlers was bringing in perfectly legal natural opium (which could be admitted only if it contained the legal 9-per-cent minimum of morphine). The importers then proceeded to process the import to order as "standardized opium," containing any morphine percentage ordered and priced accordingly. However, Dr. Squibb recorded "cases of this opium that were ordered to contain 8 per cent. of morphine, which were found on assay to contain only about 6 per cent., and there is now really no limit, and no way of valuing this handsome opium short of an actual assay." Dr. Squibb suggested that opium be bought and sold per unit of morphine in order to foil the merchants of "cut" produce.

"The National Wholesale Drug Association have condemned the adulteration specifically, and by resolution decided to obstruct and oppose it," he concluded, raising his voice a little for the benefit of his critics. "But this was a National Association. The individuals composing the association are the principal dealers in the adulterated drug, defending themselves on the ground that they must keep it because their neighbors do, and because there is an active demand for it by jobbers and retail dealers."

Dr. Squibb resisted the obvious temptation to add: And let the little dogs bark.

eighteen

"... AND SONS"

I

As he advanced into his eighth decade, Dr. Squibb came to the reluctant conclusion that he had better resign himself to the idea that no man is indispensable. And when physical signs reminded him that he was not immortal either, he began straightening up his affairs. He would do it personally, so that no one could misinterpret his wishes after he had passed on. Once he had disposed of responsibility and property, perhaps he could relax and enjoy the twilight of his life—if his health would allow it. But his health was deteriorating.

On March 1, 1890, Dr. Squibb wrote: "Consulted Dr. Rushmore early in the week, and last week and this have been examining my urine and still continue it daily now. Dr. Bierwirth is also examining it, looking for something to account for the giddiness and head discomfort that for nearly three weeks now has given me discomfort and uneasiness, and unfitted me for everything. There seems to be deficient elimination of urea."

The following week he added: "With the exception of Monday, and a couple of hours each morning, have by Dr.

325

Rushmore's advice staid at home all week and read novels to avoid detail work, and with a fairly good result, as my urea excretion has increased somewhat, and head generally a little better."

As a result of the series of urinalyses, his son Charles recalled later, "he was advised by his physician friends to put his house in order, for in his condition . . . they could see only twelve more months of life for him, one kidney gone and the other acting very badly."

Dr. Squibb thereupon drew up what Charles called "an impossible will" and convoked a family conference to explain its terms. The solemn conclave was becoming positively funereal when Charles incongruously injected a cheery note of hope and optimism.

"Mr. Johnson," said Charles, with the breezy, irreverent air which had long been the despair of his father, "whatever happened to that Army doctor you once said was the only man in the country who really understood the human kidney?"

Dr. Metcalfe, it seems, was in Georgia.

"Let's go see him," said Charles.

So Dr. Squibb and his son Charles—"Mr. Johnson" and "John"—took the train for Thomasville, Georgia. There, between long horseback rides through the fragrant pine woods, Dr. Squibb went through another series of tests and observations by his old friend Dr. Metcalfe, who told him to stop worrying about his kidneys. The one he had left was working well enough to last at least ten years—if he would go abroad for a year or so.

Returning to Brooklyn, Dr. Squibb booked passage on the Cunarder *Servia* sailing for Queenstown on April 19, 1890. He also got himself into another complicated situation at home. To his surprise, Caroline decided to go to Europe with him. What's more, she proposed to take a few of her friends along. Dr. Squibb, on the other hand, wanted to take along his assistant, Miss Lovejoy, "an entirely congenial person . . . as she is like a daughter to me. . . . John and Mary approved highly of my taking Miss Lovejoy, but Caroline, Ed and Charles objected on the ground of raising a scandal."

The dilemma was solved by Caroline's deciding to stay home after all, while Dr. Squibb's daughter-in-law Graves went along to chaperone Miss Lovejoy, accompanied by the two Squibb grandchildren, little Caroline and George, and their nurse, Katie O'Neil.

Caroline had become much more independent since entering her sixth decade. Her epileptoid attacks had apparently disappeared after she had passed the climacteric, although she remained high-strung and easily upset, particularly by Dr. Squibb. Dr. Squibb made no mention of it in his journals, but there seems to have been a tacit agreement that an occasional separation—even the long trips he made to Europe—were good for both of them. When he was in Brooklyn, their home life went on as usual, and she shared his lectures, visits to art exhibits, and an occasional concert or night at the theater. Summers, however, Caroline spent alone as she had always done, or with friends or, occasionally, her children. Dr. Squibb would usually take a week off to get her settled at the start of vacations, several summers by boat from Boston to Campobello Island off the Maine-New Brunswick coastal border, later at Unadilla and Mohawk in upstate New York. Very often they visited their grandchildren separately.

When Dr. Squibb went to Europe in 1890 with Graves, two grandchildren, the nurse, and Miss Lovejoy, Caroline visited friends in the Middle West and in California.

II

AFTER THE YEAR and a half abroad prescribed by Dr. Metcalfe, Dr. Squibb and his party returned to New York in the

Etruria a few days before Christmas, 1891. His health was not greatly improved.

"Eyes had become so bad that I could neither read nor write, but improved from the time I left Liverpool," he wrote, "and now, Saturday, Jany. 30th, 1892, they are so much better that I can write this note with difficulty and discomfort, but cannot read yet. Have not read a page in more than four months, nor written as much as this note since reaching home, and now cannot see to write longer."

He was back at the laboratory within a week, however, working on experiments for urea determination that took him nearly two months. Mary Macauley, his old secretary, had learned stenography and typing and was a great help in putting his urea paper together.

He was busy indulging his old passion for opera and the theater. He heard the De Reszkes and Emma Eames in *Romeo et Juliette,* saw John Drew and Ada Rehan in Daly's *Love in Tandem,* and heard Paderewski at the Brooklyn Academy.

But he was convinced at last that he was getting a little too old to resume active management of his business. The January 1892 semiannual price list—356 items, aside from 42 reagents and a score of miscellaneous items such as bandages —had two claims to distinction. It was the first to list quantities in terms of the metric system. And it was the last to bear the imprint of Edward R. Squibb, M.D.

The midyear list for 1892 bore the inscription:

Manufactured by

E. R. Squibb & Sons

III

The flier which announced the new firm name was dated January 11, 1892. In it, Edward R. Squibb, the undersigned, "begs to announce to those who are interested that on January 1st, 1892, he admitted to co-partnership with him his two sons, Edward H. Squibb and Charles F. Squibb, who have for some years been associated with him in subordinate capacities.

"They, having adopted the established policy of his business, and having gained the needful experience, are justly entitled to the position they now assume, and are earnestly recommended to the favorable consideration of those who for so many years have given their confidence and support to this laboratory."

Although the partnership was dated from the first of the year, Dr. Squibb had not satisfactorily worked out all the practical details until more than a year later.

Charles Squibb said, "My father believed that my brother and I could not manage the business." Dr. Squibb did, however, have great confidence in the technical skill and *esprit de corps* of the organization he had built up and trained. John Dunn was both reliable and imaginative as head chemist. Edward H. Squibb was showing a greater sense of responsibility. He had been soundly grounded in the business and indoctrinated in the Squibb principles. He tried hard to think like his father. With his close-cropped gray beard and his spreading bald spot, he even began to resemble his father physically.

Charles Squibb, too, was making himself useful at last. He was still full of ideas his father considered wild and radical, but he had taken a real interest in the acetic-acid works. He also had a great knack of getting along with people, both inside and outside the organization. He had taken over the job of showing visitors through the laboratories, and of attending conventions.

Another factor in Dr. Squibb's decisions was a man Charles had induced him—reluctantly—to bring into the firm as a financial adviser, William H. Spackman. Dr. Squibb, Charles reported, "was afraid that, being a warm friend of mine, [Spackman] was a sport or something. So he was, the best amateur billiardist in the Century Club, high gun in straight whist and chess, good at tennis and any other old game, but there was nobody at the Bowery Savings Bank, Fifth Avenue Bank, or in the railroads with which he was connected, who commanded higher respect for financial ability and knowledge of political economy. . . . The Big Boss eventually had the highest regard for him and trusted him fully."

The Big Boss did not, however, accept his son's plan for final disposition of the business. "I urged him to incorporate," Charles remembered, "placing the stock among friends of his choice and protecting my mother and sister by stock interest, but he could not approve of this. . . . He did not like combinations or corporations where responsibility was so divided as to be practically lost. I have heard him say, 'Individuality with proper support is the foundation of good business.' "

The first step of Dr. Squibb's own plan was to buy out the other stockholders in the National Chemical Wood Treatment Co., so that the acetic-acid works might become part of his estate to be divided. Charles was made manager of the plant.

Dr. Squibb then held a long series of conferences with a lawyer named William M. Ingraham and devised a complicated system of distributing his estate during his lifetime. He valued his total estate at $485,000. Of this, $194,000 represented the equity in $369,000 worth of real estate—the Doughty Street laboratory and property, the Gold Street factory, and the three houses on Columbia Heights—encumbered by $175,000 in first mortgages held by the South Brooklyn Savings Bank, the Dime Savings Bank, and the Dr. Minor estate. Machinery, stock, and fixtures of the laboratories and acid factory he valued at $278,600, and furnishings of the three houses at $12,500. There was no value placed upon good will.

He conveyed the three houses to his wife and two sons. Edward and Charles were also given title jointly to the business property and to the Greenwood Cemetery plot.

The business properties were then encumbered with second mortgages in favor of his family, in order to ensure each of the three children a weekly income of $125 for life, Caroline Squibb $188 a week for life, and Dr. Squibb a weekly salary allowance of $100 a week for life, "and at his death to cease and revert undivided to the business of E. R. S. and Sons."

The details of the plan were worked out by December of 1892, and by February 24, 1893, Mr. Ingraham had prepared the proper conveyances, deeds, bonds, mortgages and bills of sale to carry it out. Dr. Squibb then gave a copy of the plan to each of his three children and his wife, with the explanation:

"The principal reason for this distribution of my estate at this time are,—

"First, that I have now retired from active business on the ground of age and infirmities, and that therefore I do not think it equitable that my wife and daughter should share in any present or prospective profits or risks of my sons from a business in which I am no longer actively engaged; or, in other words, share in earnings or losses which would not be mine to divide; and

"Secondly, that being still in possession of a fairly sound judgment I can execute my own will in better accord with my own sense of justice and equity than executors could do after my death."

IV

ALTHOUGH DR. SQUIBB was "now retired," he still went to the laboratory every day. He was doing a long series of experiments on hydrogen peroxide, trying to meet the Army's demand for a product suitable for "extemporaneous use." His eyes had been improving steadily during the year, so much so, in fact, that he did not say no when Dr. Rice asked him to read proof on the revised Pharmacopoeia.

"A large part of the week," he wrote in March 1893, "has been given to the U. S. P. proof reading, the galleys coming by mail faster than I could read them, and they are now piled up on my desk."

He also kept his hand in with pieces for *An Ephemeris*. Dr. E. H. Squibb now signed articles in the *Ephemeris* as "junior editor." The senior editor, however, turned in a review of "Chloroform in 1893" and a 36-page paper on his experience with hydrogen-peroxide manufacture. Nevertheless, some of the fire had gone out of the periodical.

Dr. Squibb's critical thunder still appeared in his private journal, though. Toward the end of the year he wrote: "Wednesday went with Caroline and Margie to see [Henry] Irving's Merchant of Venice. He rants much more than when I last saw him in this character, excepting the court scene where he does not rant at all and where his acting is excellent and quite in keeping with the excellent acting of Ellen Terry as Portia."

All the children came to dinner at 152 Columbia Heights one day that week. It was Caroline's sixtieth birthday.

nineteen

PHYSICIAN, HEAL
THYSELF

I

AFTER HE "RETIRED FROM ACTIVE BUSINESS," Dr. Squibb
seemed to be busier than he had been for years. Curiously, his occupations paralleled those of his youth. The
wheel had turned full cycle. He was advising the government again on tariff matters. He was once more working for
the Navy. And he was deeply involved with ether, which he
tried on himself for the first time.

Toward the end of 1894, Dr. Squibb was experimenting
with a continuous process for the production of acetone
when the Commissioner of Internal Revenue asked his advice on a subject that had been coming up regularly ever
since the Civil War: proposed legislation to exempt from
tariff "alcohol used in the arts and for medicinal and other
like compounds." Dr. Squibb responded with long, pontifi-
cal letters to the Commissioner, and, to make sure his opinions were not misinterpreted, went to Washington to explain
them in person.

333

On his return he entertained a colleague he had met in Europe—Dr. Friedrich August Flückinger of the Kaiser Wilhelm University of Strasbourg. One of the less erudite wonders of the United States which Dr. Squibb showed to his Alsatian friend was an exhibition of "Edison's Kinetoscope, the most wonderful of all the wonders of photography, and the most ingenious," according to the Squibb journal.

The exhibition was advertised as a "faithful reproduction of a genuine prize fight fought to a finish by professional pugilists." It was "6 slashing rounds" of the fight of June 14, 1894, between "Mike Leonard, the champion 130-pound lightweight of the world, and Jack Cushing, the champion Brooklyn lightweight, for a purse of $500. . . . Both men were out for blood and fought viciously through six rounds when a clean knockout blow ended the contest." The film was shown continuously from 8 A.M. to 7 P.M. at 83 Nassau Street, Manhattan. "Admission, five cents for each round." Anyone was allowed to leave after the first round, if he had had his five cents' worth. If he wanted to see the remainder of "one of the fiercest [battles] ever staged in this country," he could pay an extra quarter.

Dr. Flückinger had scarcely sailed for home when Martha Dodgson came for her ever appreciated annual visit. And Dr. Flückinger had been home in Switzerland only a few months before Dr. Squibb had news of his death. "He seems to have had a rapid malignant tumor of the liver, so impacted that the operation for removal was unsuccessful."

Not long afterward Dr. Squibb recorded that "Dr. Hall died after a very long fight for life, on Thursday night about 11.30." (Dr. Hall was Dr. Squibb's favorite pastor—rector of Brooklyn's Holy Trinity.)

"A good deal troubled this week by uncomfortable spells of intermittent heart action—the spells seeming to be on the increase of late."

During 1896 the doctor suffered again from his varicose veins, from a rheumatic attack in one shoulder, and from an annoying ulceration of the scar tissue on the back of his left hand, which had been so badly burned in the Furman Street ether fire, nearly forty years earlier.

The hand bothered him. He had to dress it daily. He tried various unguents of his own manufacture and found them ineffective. He tried carrying his arm in a sling. No improvement. The suppuration was offensive and interfered with his sleep. He consulted Dr. Rushmore.

Dr. Rushmore began a microscopic examination and took urine samples. He delivered the section to a Dr. Wright, who "pronounced it to be a scirrhus sore, though there is no pain nor hardness. Upon this Dr. R. wanted more counsel, and on Thursday I went to see Dr. Markoe who thought it not scirrhus but more like epithelioma and wanted the tissue to be all destroyed by terchloride of antimony, but thought a more thorough histological examination needed, recommending Dr. T. Mitchel Pruden. Then went to Dr. R. F. Wier who pronounced the sore a typical epithelioma and recommended that it be cut out very thoroughly and healed by granulation. He also wanted a more thorough examination and gave me a note to Dr. Pruden.

"Found Dr. P. at the Pathological Laboratory of the College of Phys. and Surgeons and he directed the kind and size of section he wanted. On Friday morning Dr. R. cut out this section and later I took it over to Dr. P. to be examined and reported next week. It seems plain that the hand is to come off, and the sooner the better."

There was no doubt in Dr. Squibb's mind about what the pathologist's diagnosis would be, and accordingly he made his plans in advance. He handed over the household marketing to Caroline for the first time in their forty-four years of marriage. He wrote his son-in-law, Dr. John Munro, asking him to come down from Boston for the final consultation. He planned the amputation the way he thought his old professors Mütter and Pancoast would have done it, with improvements by Dr. Squibb. He decided exactly where the incision would be made. And he was going to take his own medicine, for once. He would take his own ether, and, what's more, he would administer it to himself as long as he was conscious.

The operation took place on November 19, 1896. Exactly one month later Dr. Squibb resumed writing in his journal and described the details:

"Dr. Pruden's examination of the section from my hand was promptly done, and the report upon it was received on Tuesday the 17th [of November]. Dr. Rushmore received the report and coming on the same day we decided that he should amputate the hand just above the wrist joint and through both bones on Thursday the 19th at 2:30 P.M., he to make all the arrangements for Dr. Baldwin to give the ether, and for a trained nurse, and to ask Drs. Lloyd and Bierwirth to be present.

"I wrote at once to Dr. Munro asking him to come on if not too inconvenient. On Thursday the 19th John came and entirely concurred in the operation. Remained till it was all over and returned home that evening. The nurse, Miss Helen E. Heubach, a graduate of the Brooklyn Training School, was next to come, and at the hour appointed Doctors Rushmore, Lloyd, Bierwirth and Baldwin.

"When all was ready, I in a sitting position on the bed smelled the ether vapor from 50 cc. of ether in a wide-mouth 500 cc. flask, as long as I could hold the flask, then gave the flask to Dr. R. and laid down, but don't know where or how Dr. B. applied his ether mask.

"The next thing I knew was that the operation was over and the wound closed and dressed. Had felt nothing and to my own senses was not confused or dazed, and in half an hour more they were all gone.

"By Dr. R.'s direction the nurse had given me at 2 P.M. 20 ℳ of Comp. Sol. of Opium and $\frac{1}{20}$ grain of sulph. of atropin, and I had taken no dinner. Had a quiet afternoon and night with a fair amount of sleep and quite without pain or nausea or any disagreeable effects either from the operation or from the ether,—the latter probably due to not being saturated as I had taken about 43 cc. by smelling from the flask, and about 70 cc. from Dr. B.'s mask. All present agreed that both anaesthesia and operation were very successful, and there was no increase of temperature or pulse rate on Friday or since that time, but always some disturbance of head and tachycardia. Only in bed on Friday and part of Saturday.

"On the night of Monday the 4th day, I must have hurt the stump in some way as the dressings were wet with florid blood in the morning. On removing the dressings the line of primary union was complete except the lower end where the fresh blood came from. This point, not larger than a pea, was daily washed with dilute solution of crude carbolic acid made alkaline, and dressed with sterilized paraffin. From 3 cc. of excretion a day to a few drops of pus required some ten or 12 days time. Then a dry dressing of bismuth subiodide formed a scab and now it seems to be cicatrized under the scab. All tumefaction is gone and the only discomfort is and has been the sense of forcible contraction of the fingers and thumb of the hand that is gone.

"Nothing could have been more successful than the operation, and but for the slight accident the primary union would have been complete on the 4th day. After the 6th day I was out every day, and generally across the Bridge and back. Miss Heubach's nursing and companionship were quite as successful as the operation, and I shall miss her very much when she leaves on Monday."

There were many messages and tokens of sympathy, "among the most acceptable . . . a very large bouquet of very fine flowers" on Thanksgiving Day with a card reading: "To Dr. E. R. Squibb with congratulations of your children at the Laboratory who are truly thankful."

There were also flowers from the Reverend Dr. S. D. McConnell, who had succeeded to the late Dr. Hall's pulpit at Holy Trinity.

337

II

DR. SQUIBB HAD Mary Fogarty sew him a little black jersey bag with a drawstring—he designed it himself—which she would draw on over the bandages of his stump each morning, after she had put the studs and cuff links in his shirts (which she also made for him). The occasional glimpse of black in his sleeve, he thought, would be less conspicuous.

By Christmas he was back at his routine, taking his daily walk across the Brooklyn Bridge to Manhattan and back. Policemen on duty along the span saluted the reappearance of the familiar white beard, the high-cut vest and the derby hat as the doctor passed.

He also went to the laboratory daily, just as though he had not turned over the business to his sons. When a friend sent over a young Russian named Michel Rogovin, a Ph.D. from Zurich Polytechnic with four languages, a wife, two children and no job, Dr. Squibb interviewed the man personally and "rather liked his appearance. He said he could live on 8$ a week and be very thankful for that, so offered him temporary occupation at 10$ a week until he could find a place . . . and set him at the specific gravities."

And when on the day after Christmas, 1896, his old boss, the United States Navy, inquired if the Squibb laboratories could furnish 100,000 pounds of ether for the manufacture of smokeless powder during the ensuing year, Dr. Squibb again took personal charge. He conferred with the naval chemist from the Newport Torpedo Station, worked out specifications, computed prices, and agreed to undertake the job—if the Bureau of Ordnance would furnish the alcohol.

While his junior partners did not object to Dr. Squibb's acting as though he were still running the show, his heart and vascular system did. He had frequent attacks of rapid and irregular pulse. He had precordial pains. He had dizzy spells which came upon him unexpectedly, sometimes forcing him to sit down on the stairs. And he was sleeping badly —rare for Dr. Squibb.

He consulted Drs. Rushmore and Delafield. They prescribed ten grains of potassium iodide three times a day and recommended that he go abroad again for a while. He told them that "this was impractical just now."

When he had finished preliminary details for the big Navy order, however, including arrangements for the Navy to furnish the metal containers for the ether, he booked passage to Europe on the new Cunarder *Pennsylvania*. His niece Helen Fellows accompanied him when they sailed May 29, 1897. They took a side trip on the S.S. *Augusta Victoria* from Hamburg to Spitzbergen to see the midnight sun.

He and Helen came home on the *Lucania* from Liverpool, arriving in time for Christmas. Dr. Squibb brought thermometers, barometers and hygrometers as gifts for his male grandchildren ("to try to cultivate habits of observation and accuracy in observing"), and copies of famous paintings or photographs of churches for his girl descendants. His children had been fairly prolific. Edward and Graves had produced three grandchildren for him, Mary and John four, and Charles and Margie six.

He came home with his health much improved, but he was not very happy with what his son Charles was doing to himself and to the business. He found that Charles had sold his Brooklyn house to his brother Ed and had taken his large and growing family to Bernardsville, New Jersey, to live permanently. After all, Dr. Squibb had built those houses to be homes for his sons, not parcels of real estate to be bought and sold.

What's more, Charles's pet plan, the Manhattan office and showroom, had expanded to dimensions that were beyond reason. For years Charles had been arguing that E. R. Squibb & Sons should have better buyer contacts than the horse and wagon that had been shuttling between the laboratories, the post office, and the express depots. Not that he thought Duryea's new horseless carriage would make the horse and buggy obsolete. It was just that customers liked to see what they were buying, these days, and many of them would not take the trouble to come all the way to Brooklyn to look.

Although he had "retired," Dr. Squibb still insisted that the Squibb name and the Squibb catalogue should be enough guarantee to any buyer. What good would it do him to look? The quality of a preparation was not visual; it depended upon careful tests—and the honesty and skill of the manufacturer. However, Charles had inherited his father's stubbornness. He had opened a branch in downtown Manhattan, at Ann and Williams streets, with space in the stock room for a full line of Squibb goods which would be replenished daily. When Dr. Squibb left for Europe there was only George Wells, an old Doughty Street hand, behind the counter, and one man in the stock room. When Dr. Squibb returned from Europe there were thirteen employees in the Manhattan office.

Since the new office seemed to be prospering, Dr. Squibb could hardly protest too loudly. He did, however, protest the breakdown in friendly relations with the Internal Revenue Service.

The Internal Revenue Service had suddenly discovered that the Squibb laboratories had been making absolute alcohol since the Civil War and therefore should be classified as rectifiers and pay 40 years' back taxes. Dr. Squibb was outraged. He immediately jumped on a train and went to Washington to protest.

Arriving at night, he was bothered by the heat and mosquitoes to an extent he would not have admitted in his younger days. Next morning he went around to the Treasury to tell the Internal Revenue people how ridiculous they were to class medicinal absolute alcohol with whisky. The tax ruling against E. R. Squibb & Sons was rescinded.

Then, in his eightieth year, proud to be working again for the employers of his youth, Dr. Squibb went around to the

Navy Department to call on Captain O'Neil of Naval Ordnance, "and talked ether making with the Captain and his chemists."

And, since this might be his last visit to the nation's capital, he also paid courtesy calls on the Surgeon Generals of both Army and Navy, partly to tell them what he thought of the Spanish-American War, which was then three months old: "a most unjust, unnecessary, and inhuman war on our part, and as irrational as it is unjust, and a shameful abuse of superior strength over a smaller and weaker nation."

Home again, he wrote a letter to the Dupont people on the subject of ether and smokeless powder. He was ready to supply their needs. It didn't occur to him that he was being influenced by his son Charles's philosophy of salesmanship. Charles was often on the road these days—Omaha or New Orleans or Boston—talking to jobbers and drug wholesalers. He went to conventions, too.

"At the conventions," Charles recalled, "I didn't care to listen to papers, or vote in the elections or stand by exhibits. I spent my time in the evening in some saloon with the representatives of the big houses on business in general, and was often able to give them good pointers on their own products as well as hold our own ground."

Dr. Squibb did quite a bit of traveling himself after his return from Washington. He made a regular triangular circuit to see all his grandchildren in turn—Bernardsville, New Jersey, Lexington, Massachusetts, and Harwich Port on Cape Cod, where Ed and Graves spent the summer.

He also made a trip to Darby to see Martha Dodgson one day, since she had been ailing and did not make her usual annual visit to Brooklyn.

III

DR. SQUIBB'S HEART was not behaving well that winter of 1898–99. His pulse rate sometimes went up to 180, and he had more and more frequent dizzy spells. One morning he fainted while at breakfast and fell to the floor. He was taking his iodide of potassium fairly regularly.

He was also going to his laboratory with great regularity. An irregular heart and the lack of one hand did not put a stop to his experimentation. He was busy with a new assay process for cinchona, with devising a new syphon extraction apparatus, and with finding a way to make a fluidextract of nux vomica using acetic acid instead of alcohol as a menstruum, which would avoid the formation of an emulsion.

The results of this work he summarized in a paper which he read in person before the American Chemical Society, and in papers for the *American Journal of Pharmacy* and for his own *An Ephemeris,* which he was keeping very much alive.

Aunt Mary King, Caroline's sister, caused a crisis that winter. In February 1899 Dr. Squibb wrote: "Had an anxious week, all of us, in regard to Aunt Mary King, who had not been seen or heard from since Friday evening of last week, her house being shut up tight and no answer to the door bell. She had either gone away somewhere and concealed her whereabouts, or was concealed in the house, and if in the house she was either ill or dead."

With Caroline's brother, William Cook, Dr. Squibb broke into Mrs. King's house "and found her ill and in a wretched condition. William Cook got a carriage and I brought her to our house."

The next week he was "still worried about Aunt Mary King's condition. She is quite incoherent and has not improved during the week. Three sharp convulsions on Monday. Caroline and I took her keys and she and I went into her house this afternoon. Found it in a very bad condition, piled up with bundles and dirt, indicating she has been insane for years."

The discovery "demoralized Caroline badly and she has demoralized the servants so that it has been a heavy week all around. . . . I persuaded her to go down to Mr. LeRoy's

Pine Tree Inn, and Bab took her down there on Wednesday under a promise to stay there till the Mrs. King episode is over. This makes it much easier for me."

Dr. Squibb had a council of war with the rest of the available Cooks—brothers Sam and William and sister Sally Fellows—and they decided to send Mrs. King to Dr. Harrison's sanitarium at Breezehurst, if Dr. Lloyd could persuade her to go. Caroline returned ahead of time, while the process of persuasion was going on, "and last night she again failed to sleep and had nausea this morning." However, by the end of March Dr. Squibb and Caroline took Mary King to Breezehurst, "where she was received very kindly and tactfully by Dr. Harrison, and was put into her nice large cheerful room where we left her,—I," concluded Dr. Squibb wistfully, "wishing it was me that was left."

Next week he took his New Jersey grandchildren to the Central Park Menagerie and noted that his heart was less troublesome.

twenty

NIGHTFALL

I

HIS EIGHTIETH BIRTHDAY found Dr. Squibb in only fair health. He was complaining a good deal about "light-headedness, especially in the mornings . . . and mental depression." When he felt too miserable to work, he managed "to get through the time and discomfort by reading Trollope's novels."

The week after his birthday, he wrote (July 8, 1889): "Got rid of some enforcement of idleness this week by occupying two or three hours a day on my new assay process for Belladonna root, and by having a good many birthday letters to write as responses to the children.

"Think the light-headed confusion is somewhat less, but it is still troublesome, especially in the mornings. Drs. Rushmore and Lloyd both advise me to continue potassium iodide 3 to 5 grs. twice a day. . . . Caroline went to Squirrel Inn, Catskills, on Wednesday morning."

Gone was the cavalier attitude toward iodides of Dr. Squibb's youth when, during his rubbing up at Jefferson, he had complained about Dr. Mitchell's lectures: "and very tired I am getting of his arsenic, ointment of three, and iodide of potassium."

He had "received from Caspari, secretary of the American Pharmaceutical Association, a beautifully engrossed copy of Resolutions passed, congratulating me on my 80th birthday." He had the resolutions framed, to hang beside the honorary degree of Master of Pharmacy which the Philadelphia College of Pharmacy had conferred upon him in 1894.

When he felt up to it, he continued his experiments on belladonna and worked on a paper describing them when he had finished. After Thanksgiving he "started on a parallel percolation of buckthorn for the next paper."

For Christmas, he had "Donald, Ned [Mary's boys], and Robinson [Charles's boy] come to carry out my desire and plan to have the three older grandsons with me for the holiday week, and George [Ed's boy] joining them, we have had a week together, I getting acquainted with them and they with each other by going to several places of amusement . . . a good wholesome week."

At midweek, while Graves gave a children's party for the younger boys, Dr. Squibb took Donald and Robinson along with Caroline and Bab to a matinee of John Drew in a Charles Frohman production of *The Tyranny of Tears,* by Haddon Chambers.

Dr. Squibb was pretty miserable through most of the winter and spring. Some weeks he was "hardly up to reading a good novel. The influence of the iodide is very conflicting. In 10-grain doses it stops the tachycardia but gives a curious depressing malaise that is most uncomfortable. Two bad nights this week, Tuesday and Thursday, each controlled by a 10-grain dose but both followed by great depression."

He tried "Dr. Segur's prescription of 1 ℆ of F. E. Digitalis 4 times a day for 5 days but without perceptible heart benefit and have now discontinued it."

On good days, however, he would take his usual walk

across Brooklyn Bridge and back. He was also working on Cascara, and on a paper on specific gravities.

II

ON HIS EIGHTY-FIRST BIRTHDAY Dr. Squibb received an engrossed set of congratulatory resolutions from the College of Pharmacy of the City of New York, a faculty he had served without pay during its struggling early days.

He also received copies of Volume VI, No. 2, of his *Ephemeris,* dated July 1900. The issue was written entirely by himself between spells of tachycardia and depression during the past year. Its contents—published simultaneously in the *American Journal of Pharmacy,* Volume 72, No. 7— were devoted to one paper entitled "On Acetic Acid as a substitute for Ethyl Alcohol in Extracting the Active Principles of some Officinal Drugs (Fourth Paper)," with the subhead "The Officinal Varieties of Rhamnus of the U. S. P.— Rhamnus Frangula and Rhamnus Purshiana (Buckthorn and Cascara Sagrada)."

It is curious that Dr. Squibb's last contribution to his *Ephemeris* should be in effect a continuation of the comparison between the two varieties of Rhamnus which set off the cascara-sagrada battle of 1887. Or perhaps it is not curious, for Dr. Squibb did not give up easily. He still classed buckthorn as "milder and more gentle" than cascara. He pointed out again that buckthorn "has steadily increased in appreciation and use . . . without special advertising or effort and against an active competition with Rhamnus Purshiana which has had much special advertising and effort."

With the July 1900 issue, *An Ephemeris* reached page 2551—and the end of Dr. Squibb's editorship.

That summer Dr. Squibb and Mary Fogarty made the usual rounds of the grandchildren—three weeks at Bernardsville, three at Buzzard's Bay, four at Gloucester (Ed and

Graves having adandoned Cape Cod that year). Returning just before Labor Day, he noted that if there was "any perceptible change in condition, it is for the better, on the whole, but now coming back from so cool a place as Gloucester into this city heat is unfavorable. Ed, Graves, Mary and John all advised me against coming home during the heat, but I overruled them by believing the heat was over."

He resumed his work on specific gravity, however, although complaining that "the depressing influence of the heat has made it a pretty miserable week. Very little tachycardia but much head swimming and general discomfort, mental depression, and a bad book."

Despite the bad book, Dr. Squibb continued, later that September, with "the usual amount of novel reading to try to get mental extrovertion."

On September 29, he noted that he had been working on a specific-gravity paper for Dr. Charles Rice, chairman of the Committee of Revision of the U. S. Pharmacopoeia.

On October 6 he wrote: "A little work on s.g. for the committee of Revision, but a very uncomfortable week. Two doses of iodide and scarcely any tachycardia, but much confusion of head and general discomfort made worse by warm, sultry weather."

The first line of the entry was written in the familiar even, carefully formed hand. The other lines became spidery and uncertain.

The next Saturday, however, he was back with his regular weekly entry:

Saturday afternoon, Oct. 13, 1900.

Still a little work on s.g. for the U. S. P. Committee, though a very uncomfortable week of demoralization. The chief and most active discomfort is shortness of breath on any considerable exertion. Iodide twice.

It was a typical entry, typical of a man who believed in both precept and example, typical of the doctrine Dr.

Squibb was trying to teach his grandchildren: accuracy of observation. It was also typical of the trained, thorough physician—detailed enumeration of symptoms, accurate record of treatment.

These were the last of the more than a million words that made up the amazing journals of Edward Robinson Squibb, M.D.

The following Saturday Dr. Squibb was too depressed to make his weekly entry. It was the last Saturday of his life.

On Thursday, October 25, 1900, he again complained of shortness of breath and rapid heart thumping. Late in the afternoon he told Caroline he was going upstairs to lie down for an hour before tea.

When he did not come down at teatime—he who had made a fetish of punctuality at all meals—Caroline went up to see if he had fallen asleep. He was not asleep. He was having difficulty breathing. He smiled, patted her hand, and said: "I'll be right down, Mother."

Caroline sent Mary Fogarty for Dr. Rushmore.

An hour later Dr. Squibb was dead—of what he would surely have diagnosed as cardiac dyspnea due to occlusion of the coronary artery.

III

THERE WAS GENUINE MOURNING for Dr. Squibb. His employees bore him true affection. So did the hundreds of people, big and little, in all walks of life, for whom he had done small favors or held out a helping hand in time of dire distress. His professional associates, even those with whom he had violently disagreed, could hardly remain unmoved by the passing of a man of great strength and great integrity. His death marked the end of an era.

The tears shed were real and unashamed. The hats doffed were in deep respect. There was some disappointment among the staff, however, in the way Charles Squibb handled the funeral arrangements.

"On the day of the funeral I ordered the coffin closed," Charles recalled. "I would have no undertaker manipulating his scarred face. And it was a long while before I heard the last of the regrets that C. F. would not give us a last look at the Big Boss.

"There were many uniforms among the crowds at the house, for he always took care of the Police and Fire Departments. All his personal effects were distributed and everything was treasured, down to the last collar button and pair of socks."

There was a crowd, too, at the red Gothic church of the Holy Trinity at Montague and Clinton streets, which the Quaker doctor had at last called his spiritual home after a long voyage of religious exploration. The Reverend Dr. S. D. McConnell, whom Dr. Squibb had admired for his vigorous, forthright sermons and whom Caroline Squibb considered "too blunt," read the Episcopal service and delivered a simple but touching eulogy.

And on a chill October afternoon, the last October of the century, Dr. Squibb was buried beside his infant son George in the spot he had chosen for himself in Greenwood Cemetery.

IV

OF ALL THE THOUSANDS of eulogistic words printed in many languages in the obituary columns of many lands, Dr. Squibb would have liked best two tributes paid by his colleagues.

One was by Joseph P. Remington, the Squibb apprentice who rose to be one of the leading figures in American pharmacy and who was to succeed to the chairmanship of the U. S. Pharmacopoeia upon the death of Dr. Rice, just a year after the passing of Dr. Squibb.

"His standards of purity for pharmaceutical products were the highest attainable," said Professor Remington in his memorial address on Dr. Squibb. "He was honest, not from policy, but because it hurt him sorely to be otherwise, and surrounded as he was by those who sought temporary advantage by questionable business practices, trickery, or even doubtful methods, his life work was carried on in the face of active warfare. It would be impossible for anyone to meet him and then forget him; he stamped his personality indelibly on one's memory. He was a leader among leaders.

"He might wound the feelings of some by his frank, outspoken condemnation of what he believed to be wrong, but it was the sin and not the sinner that he denounced. It would be impossible for him to yield to any course of doubtful morality. He often stood alone and would make no effort to win others to his views of truth when they were founded on principle and on the rock of truth itself. In non-essentials he would often yield because he knew the great principles for which he contended would be all the stronger if he did not degenerate into a mere pessimist or chronic objector. He loved to quote, when standing alone, bereft of the support of his friends on some important question, the famous words of the orator, 'God and one are a majority.' "

And the minutes of the Committee on Revision of the U. S. Pharmacopoeia 1900-1910 contained the following:

"Dr. Squibb had the unique distinction of possessing a sound knowledge of medicine, an innate fondness for chemical research, an extraordinary grasp of pharmacy, and the scientist's ideal—love of truth. . . .

"He could always be found . . . opposing any course which tended to weaken the cause of righteousness or ethics. There was no hesitation, vacillation or compromise. . . . He never expected from others a rule of conduct he could not follow himself. He disliked praise and flattery, for he was always conscious that he fell far short of the ideal upon which his eyes were fixed. He believed no man should be praised for simply doing his duty. . . .

"It made no difference to him whether he accepted membership in the Revision Committee, or had declined it, the Chairman could call upon him, either for special research work or for an opinion on a general subject; he never refused freely to give time, labor or expense in perfecting the work, and when the Pharmacopoeia proofs were placed in his hands, he scanned every page, every letter, and every figure, and many an error was corrected before the last plates were cast. . . .

"Fullness of years was vouchsafed him, and although a sufferer during the latter part of his life, his most intimate friends heard no complaint; his sufferings were borne with the courage of a Stoic and the patience of a Christian.

"Thus has passed away from this life Edward Robinson Squibb. Pharmacy has lost a Nestor, medicine a leader, and the world the noblest work of God—an honest man."

EPILOGUE

I

D R. SQUIBB WOULD HAVE reacted variously to the post-humous courses of his several works. He would have been deeply gratified by the ultimate triumph of his crusade for a Federal food-and-drug law. He would have been pleased, too, that his tradition of purity and uniformity was being carried on by the firm bearing his name. He would have been amazed by the size, shape, and scope of the firm, while of course disapproving of its modern merchandising techniques.

With the death of the founder, the firm of E. R. Squibb & Sons was like a ship with two captains. Completely different in temperament, Charles and Edward could reach no agreement on a common course, and the ship veered and yawed wildly.

Charles wanted to go modern at once. He wanted to give a 25-per-cent discount to jobbers and 15 per cent to retailers, on top of 5 per cent for cash. He wanted to organize a sales force to break Powers & Weightman's age-old grip on the South and invade the Middle West to fight Parke, Davis on their home grounds. He wanted to defy another parental taboo and try a little advertising.

Edward, on the other hand, was as conservative as his father had been and even more cautious. He saw no reason to abandon the policies which had made Squibb known throughout the world. And he had been thoroughly indoctrinated with his father's horror of advertising and aggressive salesmanship.

Charles wanted to expand into all sorts of related sidelines. He wanted to distill commercial alcohol on a big scale. He wanted to move the ether plant to New Jersey, reducing insurance rates on the Brooklyn laboratories. He wanted to put on a big campaign to sell Acetum Opii Compound, "The Big Boss's Diarrhoea Mixture," and Compound Alum Powder direct to the consumer.

Edward insisted on following in his father's footsteps. He wanted E. R. Squibb & Sons to remain what it had always been: manufacturing pharmacists to the medical profession.

Charles won the first round. A few months after the death of Dr. E. R. Squibb, who hated corporations, the firm was incorporated under New Jersey law. On May 29, 1901, Dr. Edward H. Squibb became president of the corporation, Charles F. Squibb vice-president, and William G. Rothe, the Squibb bookkeeper of 1868, secretary-treasurer. Other directors were Mary King Squibb Munro, John Dunn, the chief chemist who had risen from a $12-a-week lab assistant since 1866, and a man named Frederick J. Faulks.

The board of directors was little help in resolving the fundamental differences between the two Squibb sons. Mrs. Munro sided now with one brother, now with the other. She had a greater personal liking for Charles, but her worship of her father was such that she was more often inclined to back Edward's orthodoxy. Old Rothe was even more conservative than Edward. John Dunn was more often on Charles's side.

On one point the brothers did agree: Divided leadership and indecision were doing the firm no good. Edward also reluctantly agreed with Charles that expansion was imperative to keep the firm abreast of twentieth-century trends—which meant more capital, and probably selling control. Three years later this was done, and the business passed into other hands.

Charles played no continuing part in the new corporation; as he reported years later: "I was too radical or conservative or wild or something for the new regime, which insisted that I retire."

After an unsuccessful fling with a co-operative distillery in New Jersey, Charles went to France. He had a small business in Paris which required his presence for a week out of every month. The rest of the time he lived in an old farmhouse in the South of France at Fontcouverte-Bellegarde, in the Tarn, not far from the birthplace of Toulouse-Lautrec.

Charles never saw the towers, battlements, and beehive communities that bore the name of E. R. Squibb & Sons in Brooklyn, Manhattan, and New Jersey. After the Germans overran France in 1940, he decided he was too old to pull up roots again and he refused repatriation.

He died before his compatriots swarmed over the beaches of Normandy to liberate France, each carrying in his kit a Squibb "syrette," a sterilized hypodermic holding one dose of morphine for battlefield emergencies.

After the war Charles's body was brought back to Brooklyn to be buried in the family plot in Greenwood Cemetery.

Dr. Edward H. Squibb remained a member of the board until his death in 1929. His sister Mary King Squibb Munro outlived him by some ten years.

Their mother, Caroline Squibb, and Mary Fogarty, who had been nurse to all the Squibb children, continued living in the house on Brooklyn Heights until Caroline died at the age of 72 the year E. R. Squibb & Sons was sold to outside interests. Mary Fogarty survived for another dozen years. "Dr. Ed" kept the old house open for her for a while, then provided an apartment in which she went to live with her two nieces.

Two of the Squibb houses on Brooklyn Heights were torn down when excavation was begun for the I.R.T. subway to Manhattan shortly after Caroline's death. The third house still stands. It is occupied today by Jehovah's Witnesses.

II

DR. EDWARD ROBINSON SQUIBB died in the last months of the nineteenth century. With Dr. Squibb and the century there died a way of life, a state of mind, a philosophy, a trend.

The nineteenth century was the age of the individual. Dr. Squibb was high priest of the cult of the individual. So insistent was he on trumpeting the worth of the individual, the character of the individual, the morality of the individual, that he was at times a nuisance to his family and friends. "Manly" was one of his favorite words. A man was the cornerstone of society. "Individuality," as he told one of his sons, "is the foundation of good business."

Of Dr. Squibb's business in Dr. Squibb's century, certainly.

But not as American business was developing in the twentieth century, not even "individuality" as distinct and forceful as that of Dr. Squibb, who was so pronounced an individual that his critics looked upon him as a crotchety old egocentric.

American life was getting too complicated for a one-man show, even the amazing one-man show that Dr. Squibb had been running for fifty years. The new century demanded a highly organized team—the soulless corporation—rather than the gifted individual. Small firms combined into big businesses, and big businesses, for better or for worse, merged into complex bureaucratic giants.

The firm of E. R. Squibb & Sons followed the new pattern of growth, expansion, and absorption of smaller companies with collateral interests. Branch offices and manufacturing laboratories were established throughout the world. The organization whose founder would never employ a salesman had a thousand men in the field at mid-century.

Then within a few years a series of mergers made E. R. Squibb & Sons a part of a huge chemical corporation which in 1957 employed 40,000 people and earned three quarters of a billion dollars.

Old Dr. Squibb, whose total sales for 1859 came to slightly

more than five thousand dollars, must have turned over in his grave.

III

Dr. Squibb has left his name to many things, material and abstract, one of which might serve him as a memorial today. There is the Manhattan skyscraper he never saw, the complex of factories and laboratories he never imagined, the world-girdling monster of a firm he would never recognize. There is also the Squibb Institute for Medical Research, which certainly perpetuates his scientific ideals and might well be his monument.

The most appropriate memorial to the character and ideals of Edward Robinson Squibb, however, does not even bear his name, although it most certainly bears the strong imprint of his principles and personality. The Federal Pure Food and Drug Act of 1906, with its subsequent amendments to safeguard life and health in the nation by outlawing false and extravagant claims, forbidding adulteration, setting up the U. S. Pharmacopoeia as legal standard, and requiring non-officinal preparations to list ingredients on the label, is the posthumous triumph of Dr. Squibb's crusade.

Dr. Harvey W. Wiley, chief chemist of the U. S. Department of Agriculture, picked up the torch from Dr. Squibb several years before the end of the nineteenth century, probably in 1893, when Dr. Wiley was elected president of the American Chemical Society. In that year Dr. Squibb read a paper on absolute alcohol before the society and afterward held long and earnest conversation with Dr. Wiley on the subject of the legislation that he had been seeking for so many years.

Dr. Squibb had been dead six years when the Pure Food and Drug Act was finally passed. Although Dr. Wiley was the father of the law, Dr. Squibb was certainly the grandfather. The law codifies the principles for which Dr. Squibb had been fighting all his life. It is a monument of which he would have been proud.

Index

About the Author

LAWRENCE G. BLOCHMAN *worked on newspapers in San Diego, Tokyo, Hong Kong, Calcutta and Paris before he became an independent writer. Except for a tour of duty during the war as chief of the Radio Program Bureau of the Office of War Information, he has been writing novels, articles, short stories, motion pictures, and television scripts since 1927. He has been president of the Mystery Writers of America and vice-president of the Overseas Press Club.*

The best-known detective in his fiction, Dr. Daniel Webster Coffee, is a medical pathologist, who was introduced to readers in one book—Diagnosis: Homicide—by the late Dr. Thomas A. Gonzales, chief medical examiner for the city of New York. During Mr. Blochman's long and deep concern with the world of Dr. Squibb, he has spoken before the New York Society for Industrial Medicine and the Armed Forces Institute of Pathology.